**BEEF
PRODUCTION**

SECOND EDITION **BEEF**

PRENTICE-HALL, INC.

Englewood Cliffs, N. J.

PRODUCTION

RONALD V. DIGGINS

Vocational Agriculture Instructor
Eagle Grove, Iowa

CLARENCE E. BUNDY

Professor of Agricultural Education
Iowa State University

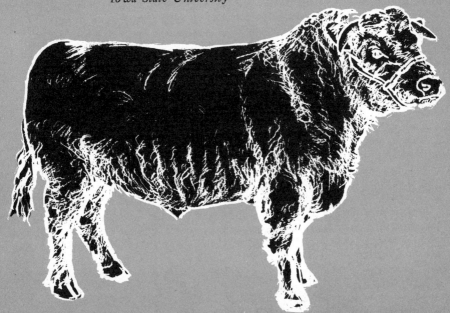

PRENTICE-HALL VOCATIONAL AGRICULTURE SERIES

Beef Production, *Ronald V. Diggins and Clarence E. Bundy*
Crop Production, *Richard J. Delorit and Henry L. Ahlgren*
Dairy Production, *Ronald V. Diggins and Clarence E. Bundy*
Exploring Agriculture, *Everett F. Evans and Roy L. Donahue*
Fruit Growing, *G W. Schneider and C. C. Scarborough*
Judging Livestock, Dairy Cattle, Poultry, and Crops, *H. G. Youtz and A. C. Carlson*
Leadership Training and Parliamentary Procedure for FFA, *Jarrell D. Gray and J. R. Jackson*
Livestock and Poultry Production, *Clarence E. Bundy and Ronald V. Diggins*
Modern Farm Buildings, *Wallace Ashby, J. Robert Dodge, and C. K. Shedd*
Poultry Production, *Clarence E. Bundy and Ronald V. Diggins*
Profitable Farm Management, *James E. Hamilton and W. R. Bryant*
Profitable Farm Marketing, *Obed L. Snowden and Alvin W. Donahoo*
Profitable Southern Crops, *E. V. Walton and O. M. Holt*
The Range and Pasture Book, *Roy L. Donahue, Everett F. Evans, and L. I. Jones*
Records for Farm Management, *John A. Hopkins and Deane A. Turner*
Sheep Production, *Ronald V. Diggins and Clarence E. Bundy*
Soil—Use and Improvement, *J. H. Stallings*
Swine Production, *Clarence E. Bundy and Ronald V. Diggins*
Using Electricity on the Farm, *J. Roland Hamilton*
Your Future in Poultry Farming, *John W. Goodman and David C. Tudor*

BEEF PRODUCTION (second edition)
Ronald V. Diggins and Clarence E. Bundy

LIBRARY OF CONGRESS CATALOG CARD NO.: 62-10554

Printed in the United States of America
07305–E

PREFACE

The livestock industry is making rapid changes. New developments in feeding, breeding, management, and marketing made it necessary to revise *Beef Production* and bring it up to date.

Beef Production, Second Edition, has been written in the same simple style that was so well received by the readers of the Diggins and Bundy livestock series, which includes *Livestock and Poultry Production, Swine Production, Dairy Production, Sheep Production,* and *Poultry Production.* Technical or nonessential material has been eliminated, so that only the information essential for practical beef production is treated. At the end of each chapter we have listed an easy-to-read, attractive group of reference books that will facilitate finding the answers to practical beef production problems. We have included many up-to-date and carefully selected illustrations and charts.

Research material from many agriculture experiment stations and suggestions from numerous vocational agriculture instructors have been most helpful to us. Practical beef cattlemen, beef cattle breeders, college authorities, and packers were interviewed, and their contributions were of great value.

We are indebted to the secretaries of the beef cattle breed associations; the National Research Council; Strohmeyer and Carpenter; *Successful Farming; Wallaces' Farmer and Iowa Homestead; Capper's Farmer; The Farm Journal-Country Gentleman;* the United States Department of Agriculture; Iowa State University; a large number of equipment manufacturers who have provided illustrative materials and research information; and to the Morrison Publishing Company, Professor Leonard W. Schruben of Kansas State University, and the Doane Agricultural Service, Incorporated, for special permission to reproduce copyrighted materials.

We are grateful for special materials and suggestions provided by Dr. Louis L. Madsen, head of the cattle research section of the animal and poultry husbandry research branch of the United States Department of Agriculture. We appreciate the cooperation of J. R. Pichard of Livestock Conservation, Incorporated; Professor Reuben Albaught of the University of California; Professor Shawnee Brown, Director of Extension, Oklahoma State University; Dr. Wise Burroughs of Iowa State University; Dr. W. M. Beesen, Purdue University; Shubel D. Owen, Associate Professor at North Dakota Agricultural College and Assistant State Supervisor of Agricultural Education; and Justin Thebiay, Eagle Grove, Iowa.

Ronald V. Diggins
Clarence E. Bundy

CONTENTS

BEEF
PRODUCTION

Opportunities in Beef Cattle Production

"We're having steak for dinner!" This cry seldom has to be repeated to bring an American family to the dinner table. Beef is one of the more important meats in the American diet. It is high in nutritional value, and many people consider it first in flavor. The fact that we consumed an average of 81.0 pounds of beef and 5.8 pounds of veal per person in 1960 is evidence of the importance of beef in our eating habits. Our total consumption per person of all red meats averaged 158.5 pounds. Thus over half of the meat we ate consisted of beef and veal. January of 1960 saw a record number of over 91.5 million head of cattle on American farms. Although this represented a record number of cattle, it is not a record number per person, averaging less than 60 head per hundred persons. In the year 1900 we had 79 head of cattle per hundred persons.

With our ever expanding population, there will be an even greater demand for beef in the future than there has been in the past. However, beef producers must keep in mind that the demand for beef can be maintained only if the price of the dressed product is in line with the consumer's ability to buy. When prices of beef are too high the consumer looks for less expensive products to buy, and the producer loses part of his market. Cattlemen must meet the challenge of producing at a profit more beef per acre of farm and grass land, and they must furnish beef to the consumer at a price he can afford to pay. Only those cattlemen who are skilled in beef cattle husbandry can expect to maintain a profitable enterprise over a long period of time. However, opportunities in beef production are numerous. Almost any young man with a love for livestock, an eagerness to learn, and a willingness to work can find a life of satisfaction in some phase of the beef production industry.

TABLE 1

CIVILIAN CONSUMPTION OF MEAT, NOT INCLUDING POULTRY, PER CAPITA,
IN THE UNITED STATES

(ALL FIGURES IN POUNDS)

Year	Beef	Veal	Lamb Mutton	Pork except Lard	Total Meats
1933	51.2	7.7	6.7	69.6	134.6
1934	64.9	9.7	6.4	65.0	146.0
1935	53.0	8.0	6.8	48.1	115.9
1936	57.8	8.3	6.6	54.8	127.5
1937	54.8	8.6	6.6	55.4	125.4
1938	54.0	7.6	6.9	57.8	126.3
1939	54.5	7.5	6.6	64.3	132.8
1940	54.2	7.3	6.5	72.4	140.4
1941	60.0	7.5	6.7	67.4	141.6
1942	60.4	8.1	7.1	62.8	138.4
1943	52.5	8.1	6.4	77.9	144.9
1944	54.9	12.2	6.6	78.5	152.2
1945	58.6	11.7	7.2	65.7	143.2
1946	60.8	9.8	6.6	74.9	152.1
1947	68.6	10.7	5.2	68.6	153.1
1948	62.6	9.4	5.0	66.8	143.4
1949	63.0	8.8	4.0	66.8	142.6
1950	62.5	7.9	3.9	68.1	142.4
1951	55.2	6.6	3.4	70.6	135.8
1952	61.2	7.1	4.1	71.6	144.0
1953	76.6	9.5	4.6	62.9	153.6
1954	79.3	9.9	4.5	60.0	153.7
1955	82.0	9.4	4.6	66.8	162.8
1956	85.4	9.5	4.4	67.4	166.7
1957	84.6	8.8	4.2	61.5	159.1
1958	80.5	6.7	4.1	60.7	152.0
1959	81.0	5.8	4.5	67.0	158.5

Source: *Livestock and Meat Situation*, U.S. Department of Agriculture.

FIGURE 1. *A good herd of cattle combined with the knowledge and skill required for success in the cattle business offers a satisfaction that cannot be evaluated entirely in terms of dollars and cents. (Courtesy American Aberdeen-Angus Breeders Association.)*

Although beef cattle are produced in every state in the union there are four rather well-defined beef producing sections in the United States. The methods of production differ in each of these areas. The kind and amount of feed available, land, and climate account for the differences in production practices.

The Western Range. This region consists primarily of all the land lying west of the one-hundreth meridian. If we were to draw an irregular line on the map of the United States starting from the lower tip of Texas up, or north, entering North Dakota about one-third the distance from the eastern border and crossing the state diagonally to the northwest corner, we would have roughly outlined the western range. Much of the land lying west of this line is semiarid, and grass is the principal crop that is raised for livestock feed.

Most of the western range is devoted to the production of feeder cattle which are sold and shipped into the grain producing areas for fattening. The common practice is to maintain a cow herd that is bred to drop calves in late winter or spring and then to sell them as calves, yearlings, or as two-year olds for further feeding and fattening.

The western range may be further divided into the Great Plains region, the Rocky Mountain region, the Pacific Coast region, and the American Desert region.

The Great Plains Region. This region represents an area ranging from 300 to 400 miles west from the eastern boundary of the western range and extends the full distance from north to south through the United States. It includes parts of the following states: Texas, New Mexico, Oklahoma, Kansas, Colorado, Nebraska, Wyoming, South Dakota, Montana, and North Dakota.

The Rocky Mountain Region. As the name indicates, this section is mountainous and comprises parts of Colorado, Utah, Idaho, Wyoming, Montana, Nevada, Washington, and Oregon.

The Pacific Coast Region. This region is represented by an area extending inland between 200 and 400 miles from the West Coast, starting at the Canadian border and running south through about two-thirds of California.

The American Desert Region. This area is semiarid to arid and is located in the southwestern United States. Parts of Nevada, California, Arizona, New Mexico, and western Texas comprise the region.

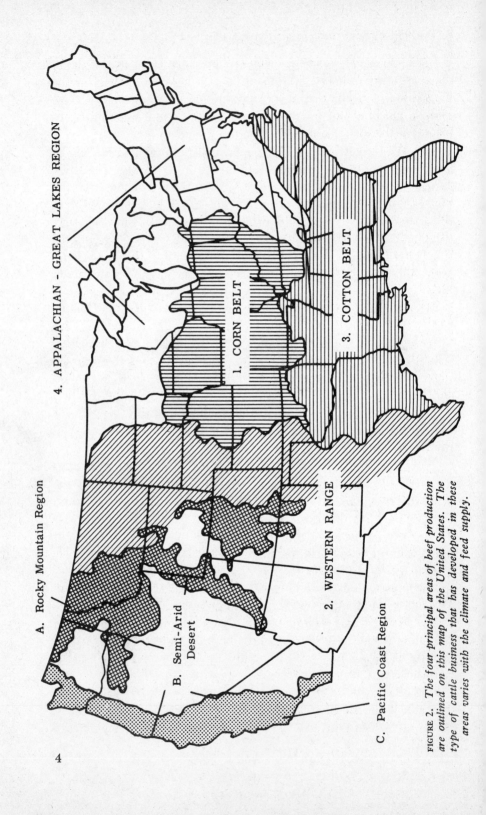

4

FIGURE 2. *The four principal areas of beef production are outlined on this map of the United States. The type of cattle business that has developed in these areas varies with the climate and feed supply.*

4. APPALACHIAN - GREAT LAKES REGION

1. CORN BELT

3. COTTON BELT

A. Rocky Mountain Region

B. Semi-Arid Desert

2. WESTERN RANGE

C. Pacific Coast Region

FIGURE 3. *This scene depicts the short grass or semi-arid range sections of the United States. Although the grass is short, it is low in moisture content and highly nutritious. Note the excellent condition of these cows and calves.* (*Courtesy American Hereford Association.*)

The Corn Belt. The corn belt is devoted largely to the production of corn and other grain crops. The soil is fertile, and rainfall is abundant. Although many cow herds are maintained for the production of calves, the region is noted chiefly as a cattle fattening area. Thousands of head of cattle are purchased annually from the western range by corn belt farmers and fattened for market. The region includes eastern Nebraska, southeastern South Dakota, southern Minnesota, northern Missouri, Iowa, most of Illinois, Indiana, and Ohio.

The Appalachian and Great Lakes Regions. These regions are characterized by a rolling topography, rivers, streams, and woodlands. Dairying and the production of dual-purpose cattle are more extensive in these areas than is the production of beef cattle. However, beef production has been on the increase in these regions since the mid-1930's. Because much of the land is more capable of producing grass than cultivated crops, further increase of cow herds may be expected. Owing to the abundant grass of relatively high feeding value, the production of calves is especially well suited to these areas.

The Cotton Belt. The development of cattle breeds particularly adapted to southern conditions and an awakened interest in soil conservation by southern farmers has resulted in a sudden upsurge of beef production in the cotton belt. Formerly, cattle were confined largely to nontillable land. Now they are an important source of

5

FIGURE 4. *A large cattle fattening setup. Note the grain storage in the background. (Courtesy American Hereford Association.)*

income on many farms and plantations that were formerly devoted almost entirely to the production of cotton, tobacco, or other cultivated crops.

A very extensive program of beef cattle improvement for southern farms has been developed and carried out by agricultural experiment stations, farmers, and ranchers. It was learned by experimental methods that Brahman cattle would thrive under conditions where the European breeds had not succeeded too well. These cattle and new breeds developed by crossing Brahmans on Angus, Shorthorns, and Herefords (which are described later in this book) have done much for the cattle industry in the cotton belt. This region can be expected to become more important as a cattle producing area in the future.

FIGURE 5. *A fine purebred herd of Angus on a Massachusetts farm. (Courtesy American Aberdeen-Angus Breeders Association.)*

TABLE 2

NUMBER OF CATTLE BY STATES

All Cattle and Calves			Beef Cows Two Years and Over			
1961 Rank	State	1961 No.	1960 No.	1961 Rank	State	1961 No.	1960 No.

(000's Omitted)

1961 Rank	State	1961 No.	1960 No.	1961 Rank	State	1961 No.	1960 No.
1	Texas	9,379	9,106	1	Texas	4,374	4,206
2	Iowa	6,460	6,660	2	Nebraska	1,519	1,499
3	Nebraska	5,175	5,072	3	Oklahoma	1,490	1,390
4	Kansas	4,473	4,429	4	South Dakota	1,288	1,250
5	Wisconsin	4,296	4,253	5	Kansas	1,245	1,195
6	California	4,203	4,121	6	Missouri	1,169	1,135
7	Missouri	4,099	3,980	7	Montana	1,116	1,114
8	Minnesota	4,054	3,975	8	Iowa	1,008	993
9	Illinois	3,901	3,981	9	California	851	853
10	Oklahoma	3,513	3,378	10	Louisiana	834	804
11	South Dakota	3,327	3,262	11	Mississippi	810	808
12	Ohio	2,272	2,250	12	Colorado	784	761
13	Colorado	2,240	2,267	13	Florida	699	741
14	New York	2,152	2,131	14	Illinois	681	668
15	Montana	2,133	2,245	15	North Dakota	680	648
16	Kentucky	2,115	2,053	16	Alabama	669	669
17	Mississippi	2,107	2,107	17	New Mexico	631	625
18	Indiana	2,103	2,062	18	Arkansas	574	554
19	Pennsylvania	1,951	1,913	19	Wyoming	556	550
20	North Dakota	1,916	1,758	20	Kentucky	556	515
21	Tennessee	1,914	1,858	21	Oregon	555	553
22	Louisiana	1,818	1,765	22	Tennessee	526	492
23	Michigan	1,701	1,701	23	Georgia	508	508
24	Alabama	1,656	1,656	24	Idaho	385	385
25	Florida	1,596	1,629	25	Virginia	384	371
26	Georgia	1,438	1,424	26	Minnesota	352	334
27	Oregon	1,435	1,421	27	Indiana	350	347
28	Virginia	1,408	1,394	28	Arizona	321	343
29	Idaho	1,401	1,415	29	Washington	289	283
30	Arkansas	1,388	1,374	30	Ohio	268	260
31	New Mexico	1,174	1,198	31	Nevada	265	264
32	Washington	1,174	1,162	32	Utah	262	252
33	Wyoming	1,116	1,175	33	North Carolina	200	202
34	Arizona	1,014	1,019	34	South Carolina	177	177
35	North Carolina	898	907	35	West Virginia	161	152
36	Utah	726	719	36	Wisconsin	123	123
37	South Carolina	542	537	37	Michigan	113	109
38	West Virginia	540	540	38	Pennsylvania	94	90
39	Nevada	516	549	39	Maryland	49	49
40	Maryland	508	493	40	New York	40	43
41	Vermont	431	427	41	Maine	9	8
42	Maine	200	194	42	Delaware	4	5
43	New Jersey	198	200	43	New Jersey	4	4
44	Connecticut	153	150	44	Connecticut	3	3
45	Massachusetts	153	151	45	Massachusetts	3	3
46	New Hampshire	99	98	46	Vermont	3	3
47	Delaware	53	56	47	New Hampshire	2	2
48	Rhode Island	20	21	48	Rhode Island	–	–
		97,139	96,236			26,984	26,344

FIGURE 6. *These excellent Angus are proof of the ability of West Virginia to produce the best in beef cattle. (Courtesy American Aberdeen-Angus Breeders Association.)*

CLASSES OF BEEF CATTLE PRODUCERS

The three main divisions of the beef cattle production industry are (1) the production of feeder cattle, (2) the production of fat or slaughter cattle, and (3) the production of purebred beef cattle. It is also possible under certain conditions to develop a program combining two or more of these phases of the beef industry.

The Production of Feeder Cattle. The production of feeders is carried on primarily by producers located on lands that are generally not suitable for heavy crop production other than grass. The semiarid to arid western and southwestern United States and the mountainous or hilly lands are important feeder cattle-producing areas.

These farmers and ranchers maintain herds of cows to produce calves. The calves are usually dropped in the spring, and run with the cows on the pasture or range during the grass season. In the fall the calves are weaned from their mothers and sometimes sold as feeder calves for fattening to someone in the grain area. They may be carried through the winter on hay, pastured the next summer, and sold as yearlings to be fattened for slaughter.

It is not necessary to have grain for feed in feeder cattle production. The cow herd may be successfully maintained on pasture in season and on hay during the winter. Such a program, therefore, is well adapted to land not suitable for rotation crops. Lands that are rolling and subject to erosion when cultivated—that is, areas too

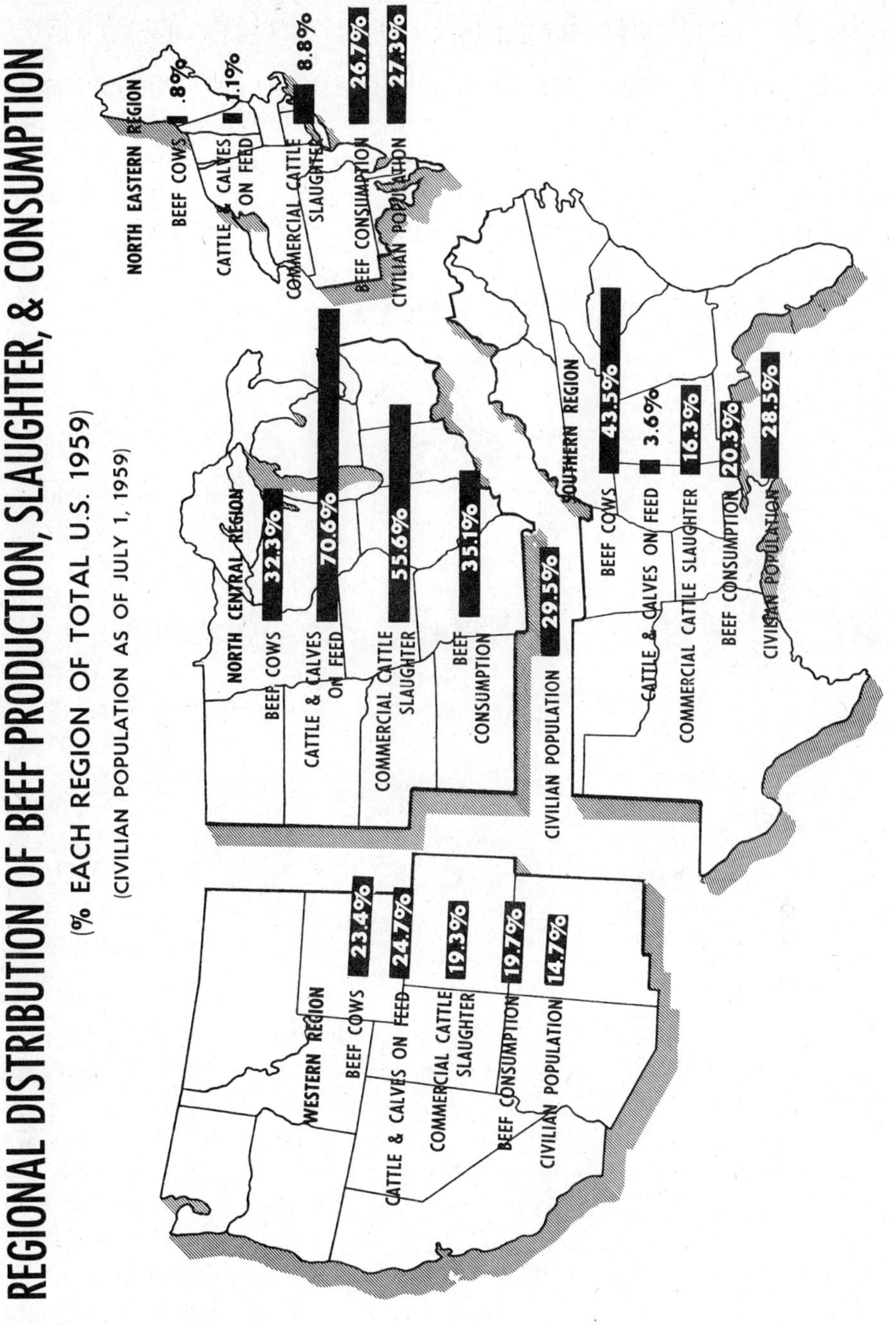

REGIONAL DISTRIBUTION OF BEEF PRODUCTION, SLAUGHTER, & CONSUMPTION

(% EACH REGION OF TOTAL U.S. 1959)

(CIVILIAN POPULATION AS OF JULY 1, 1959)

NORTH EASTERN REGION
- BEEF COWS .8%
- CATTLE & CALVES ON FEED 1.1%
- COMMERCIAL CATTLE SLAUGHTER 8.8%
- BEEF CONSUMPTION 26.7%
- CIVILIAN POPULATION 27.3%

NORTH CENTRAL REGION
- BEEF COWS 32.3%
- CATTLE & CALVES ON FEED 70.6%
- COMMERCIAL CATTLE SLAUGHTER 55.6%
- BEEF CONSUMPTION 35.1%
- CIVILIAN POPULATION 29.5%

SOUTHERN REGION
- BEEF COWS 43.5%
- CATTLE & CALVES ON FEED 3.6%
- COMMERCIAL CATTLE SLAUGHTER 16.3%
- BEEF CONSUMPTION 20.3%
- CIVILIAN POPULATION 28.5%

WESTERN REGION
- BEEF COWS 23.4%
- CATTLE & CALVES ON FEED 24.7%
- COMMERCIAL CATTLE SLAUGHTER 19.3%
- BEEF CONSUMPTION 19.7%
- CIVILIAN POPULATION 14.7%

FIGURE 7A. *This chart shows the percentage of distribution of cattle in the United States by regions; the percentage of beef consumed and slaughtered in the region; and the percentage of population in each region. (Courtesy Swift and Company.)*

9

dry for crops other than grass, as well as timber or wet bottom land—
may be profitably utilized as grazing areas for cows and feeder cattle. Since cattle can grow and produce on rations containing
mostly roughages, it is possible to develop a profitable business on
what may otherwise be waste land.

FARM INCOME—1959

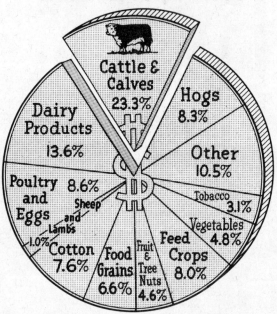

FIGURE 7B. *The largest
single source of farm in-
come in 1959 was from
the sale of cattle for
meat. (Courtesy Swift
and Company.)*

The western rancher is probably the most typical of the producers of feeder cattle. Thousands of acres of semiarid lands are
producing high quality feeders. Although most of these cattle are
shipped into the corn belt for fattening, the better grass areas are
able to send some grass-fat cattle directly to the packers for
slaughter. It is also true that the corn belt proper has much hilly
land that can produce grass which may eventually be marketed as
beef. Land not capable of raising high yields of grain, fiber, or oil
seed crops can often be converted to grass, which will make more
profit for the owner.

Many young farmers with capital too limited to purchase high-
priced crop land may find opportunities in the purchase of low-
priced grass land, which can be used in the production of feeder

cattle. Successful feeder cattle production depends largely upon having a good supply of cheap forage crops available.

Production of Fat or Slaughter Cattle. Farmers who make a business of buying feeder cattle and fattening them for market are called *cattle feeders*. Most cattle feeders buy range cattle in the fall. The fall corresponds to the end of the grass season on much of the range and the harvest of grain crops in the cattle fattening sections. The rancher generally wants to sell his feeders before snow covers the grass, and the cattle feeder is interested in buying when he knows about how much grain he has produced for feed.

Since grain is usually essential in finishing high quality beef, most cattle feeders are located in a feed grain area.

FIGURE 8. *Grass is the most important crop in much of the great plains and mountainous sections of western United States. Cattle are especially well adapted for converting grass to meat. (Courtesy American Hereford Association.)*

Profits from fattening cattle come from two sources: (1) the selling price over purchase price, which is known as margin, and (2) the value of the increased weight over the cost of gain. If a feeder buys cattle weighing 700 pounds at $18 per hundredweight and sells them after fattening for $20 per hundredweight, he has made a margin of $2 on each 100 pounds of original weight, or a

FIGURE 9. *Western cattle that have been finished to grade choice or prime in a midwestern cornbelt feed lot. (Courtesy of Harry Groves.)*

total margin of $14 per head. If the cost of feed and other expenses of the feeding operation amounts to $17 per 100 pounds of gain, then the feeder has made a profit of $3 per 100 pounds of gain. If he increases the weight of these cattle to 1,100 pounds, which represents a gain of 400 pounds per animal, his profit on the gain is $12. His marginal profit is $14, giving a total profit of $26 per head.

The principal reasons cattle feeders have for buying and fattening cattle are (1) to receive a higher price for their grain by selling it in the form of beef and (2) to increase soil fertility by spreading the manure on the land.   If the manure is properly handled, a large part of the plant food removed by the crops may be returned to the soil.   Farms that have had a cattle feeding program over a period of years are generally high in fertility.

The Purebred Beef Cattle Industry.   The breeder of purebreds produces high quality bulls and cows to improve the breed and to provide bulls for use by producers of feeder cattle.   He maintains a pedigreed herd of breeding stock.   He sells to feeder cattle producers and to other breeders.   Quality purebred animals usually bring premium prices.   Commercial cattlemen turn to the breeder for bulls, and occasionally for females, for use in improving their herds.   The breeder of purebreds can rightfully claim most of the credit for the improvement of the beef cattle breeds.   More skill, knowledge, and patience are probably required for success in the purebred business than in any other phase of beef production.   The breeder of purebreds must know the type of cattle that are in demand.   He must keep in mind the kind that will make the most

FIGURE 10. *Purebred Angus cows and calves. Most of these calves will be sold for breeding purposes to improve both purebred and grade herds. (Courtesy American Aberdeen-Angus Breeders Association.)*

money for the producer and the feeder, and the type that will cut a carcass to suit the consumer. Producers and feeders desire rapid-growing and fattening cattle, whereas consumers want a tender, flavorous kind of beef with uniform distribution of fat. The breeder must understand all these problems in order to select and mate animals that will produce the desired kind of meat and will gain rapidly and economically. The breeder should have abundant knowledge of cattle nutrition, because proper feeding is important in developing breeding animals.

More capital is needed per animal for purebred production than for any other phase of the beef cattle business. Foundation stock is usually high in price, and equipment needs per animal are greater than for feeder or slaughter cattle production. Improvement is slow, and it may be many years before a herd of quality and quantity of animals is ready for sale. Although it is not essential, experience in growing and fattening commercial cattle may be helpful before attempting to develop a purebred herd.

Large amounts of grain are not essential in purebred production. Bulls and females that are being fitted for the shows probably need grain in order to produce the finish necessary to bring out the type and quality of the animals. Animals carrying a good finish are usually more attractive to prospective buyers; therefore, some fattening grains may be desirable.

Combining Two or More Enterprises. Under certain circumstances two or more beef enterprises may be combined profitably. An example might be the program on a half-section farm with 160 acres of land capable of producing good grass, but too hilly for rotation cropping; the other quarter-section may be level, fertile land suited for cultivated crops. If the fertility of the tillable land is to remain high, from 20 to 40 acres will probably be seeded in rotation to a legume and grass crop and 20 to 40 acres to oats, leaving from 80 to 120 acres for corn. A herd of stock cows may be kept to consume the pasture and part of the hay, but there may not be enough corn to feed out the entire calf crop. Some of the calves may be sold as feeders and the remainder placed in the feed lot and fattened. Many such programs have been successfully developed on Midwest farms. A purebred herd may be developed in combination with a fattening or range program. Many times commercial cattle programs can be depended upon to furnish a living and to provide capital until the purebred herd is established.

PLANNING THE BEEF PRODUCTION PROGRAM

Before entering any phase of the beef cattle industry, one must be quite certain that he likes and possesses the fundamental knowledge of beef cattle necessary for success. With this assurance he must decide upon the phase of the industry best suited to his conditions. Although there are many factors to consider, the four most important are (1) kind and amount of feed usually available, (2) the kind and amount of buildings and equipment available, (3) the amount of capital he has to work with, and (4) the markets available for his product.

Adjusting the Cattle Program to Available Feeds. There is a beef program adapted to nearly every set of conditions that may be found on any farm or ranch. Beef cattle programs are probably more flexible than any other type of livestock enterprise. Any individual living on the land who is interested in beef production and willing to study the problems involved in beef production can develop a program suitable to his conditions.

The kind, amount, and cost of feed is the first consideration in planning the beef program. Farms that are best adapted to the production of grass, hay, and other types of forage crops are generally suited to a beef program that involves the raising of calves and yearlings to be sold as feeder cattle. Cow herds may be kept and the calves sold for fattening purposes. This type of beef production is typical of the western range, where grass is cheap and grain high in price. Farmers located on land well adapted to grain production will usually find that buying feeders and fattening them for slaughter is a more profitable enterprise for them than raising feeders. For example, a good Midwest corn belt farm will produce a gross income of from $60 to $150 per acre of corn. Whereas a crop rotation program, including some legumes and grasses, is essential for maintaining soil fertility, it is seldom profitable to convert enough acres to grass for the production of the required number of cattle to consume the available corn. Therefore, many corn belt farmers find that they can buy feeder cattle from the grass land farmer cheaper than they can raise them. On many farms only part of the land is suitable for grain production. Farmers living on these farms often maintain a breeding herd to utilize the grass and then fatten out the calves they raise on corn produced on the better land.

Since it is usually necessary to have a crop rotation that includes legumes and grasses to maintain soil fertility, most farmers living on these areas have some hay and pasture to be utilized. Sometimes the equipment is inadequate for maintaining a breeding herd. These farmers often buy 400- to 500-pound calves in the fall, winter them primarily on hay or grass silage, and turn them on pasture in the summer. The following fall they are put in the dry lot and fattened for market. Since gains of at least one pound per day can be expected from these cattle fed on hay and pasture, they will weigh from 800 to 900 pounds when they go into the feed lot. The farmer will have produced from 400 to 500 pounds of beef per animal, primarily from grasses. Such a program enables him to utilize available rough feed profitably. With this type of program the farmer has two bunches of cattle on the farm most of the year. One is in the fattening yard and the other is either on hay feeding or pasture.

Another type of cattle feeding program adapted to many grain producing farms consists of buying feeder cattle in the fall and wintering them on hay, silage, or both, with enough grain to produce one and one-half pounds of grain per day. The cattle are turned out on pasture during the summer, with a full feed of grain, and sold at the end of the pasture season. This program does not usually produce as high a quality of beef as is produced in dry lot, but it does permit the utilization of grass, which, since less grain is required, cheapens the ration. Although cattle fattened in this way seldom bring as high a price as cattle of equal quality fattened on dry feeds, they may be just as profitable through cheaper production cost.

Farmers producing feed grains are at present faced with mounting surpluses, especially that of corn. Considerable pressure from the government is being exerted to enforce acreage control of surplus crops. This will undoubtedly result in the conversion of more acres to forage crops. Many cattle feeders will have to adjust their feeding operations toward greater utilization of hay and pasture crops.

Adjusting the Cattle Program to Available Buildings and Equipment. Buildings and equipment must be considered in any plan for a cattle program. The kind and amount of equipment necessary depends upon the climatic conditions and the type of program planned for.

In the northern areas, if breeding herds are to be kept and early calving is desired, then warm barns where cows may calve are necessary. Unless such buildings are available, calving will have to be delayed until warm weather.

Cattle feeders need adequate lots and strong fences for retaining the cattle. They also need plenty of feed bunks; hayrack and feed storage facilities, such as grain bins, hay barns, and silos; and means for moving the feed to the cattle. Labor is expensive and sometimes difficult to get. Therefore, equipment that will permit the efficient use of labor is important. Cattle utilize great quantities of water. One must consider the available water supply when planning the cattle program.

Adjusting the Cattle Program to Available Capital. It takes capital to handle cattle, but some programs require more than others and involve greater risks. One who has very limited capital and cannot afford to take much of a risk probably will find the cow and calf program safer. He can start with a few cows and a good bull, retain his best heifers in the herd for breeding, and eventually develop a good-sized herd of quality cattle without any great outlay of capital in any one year. Such a program is slow, but reasonably safe. If he finds that buying feeders and fattening them on homegrown grains best fits his farm, then light cattle will cost less per head than heavy animals. He will need to feed them longer, but the capital outlay for cattle will be less.

One with adequate capital will have more choice, and may concern himself more with the best possibilities for profit. He may vary his program from year to year, depending upon market conditions, economic outlook, and so forth.

Adjusting the Cattle Program to Market Conditions. The principal reason for developing any type of cattle program is to make a profit. The market for the beef produced is important, because it determines the price the producer will receive for his product.

Markets tend to develop in areas according to the predominate kinds of animals they produce. In the range section, where a large percentage of the cattle are sold as feeders, auction companies and central feeder cattle markets (such as those at Denver, Colorado, and Omaha, Nebraska) have developed. In the corn belt the predominant markets are for slaughter or fat cattle. Chicago and many other cities in the area have packing plants. Cattle are either sold directly to the plants or to commission firms, which in turn sell to the packers.   Very few fat cattle are sold in auction sales like those found throughout the West.

The closer one is located to an available market the greater his net sale price will be, because he will have less shipping expenses and shrinkage on his animals.

SUMMARY

Since the population of the United States is continuously increasing, there will be ready consumers for the beef produced.   However, beef prices will have to be in line with the consumers' ability to buy.   Producers will need to improve their methods to gain more efficiency in production, which will permit them to sell beef at competitive prices and still make a profit.

The important beef producing areas of the United States consist of the western range, the corn belt, the Appalachian and Great Lakes regions, and the cotton belt.

The corn belt is important as a cattle fattening area, whereas the other areas are devoted largely to the production of feeder cattle. The western range constitutes by far the largest cattle section and produces a large share of the cattle that are fed out in the corn belt feed yards.   The development of breeds and strains of cattle adapted to the South has done much to increase cattle numbers in the cotton belt.

The three main divisions of the beef cattle industry are (1) feeder cattle production, (2) fat or slaughter cattle production, and (3) the purebred industry.   Feeder cattle production consists of maintaining a cow herd and raising calves.   This program is adapted to farms or ranches where grass is an important crop.   The calves are usually sold as feeder cattle to be fattened for market.   Fattening cattle requires grains and is more common in the corn belt and in the other grain producing areas.   The cattle feeder depends upon margin (the selling price over purchase price) and the value of the increased weight over cost of gain for his profits.

The purebred beef cattle industry consists of breeders who maintain purebred animals for the improvement of the respective breeds. Their profit comes from the sale of breeding stock.   More knowledge and skill is required and more capital needed per animal in the purebred business than is necessary in the production of fat or feeder cattle.

Under some conditions the combining of two or more beef cattle enterprises may prove profitable. Many cattle feeders produce their own cattle.

In planning the cattle program one should carefully consider his feed supply, buildings, equipment, available capital, and market outlet.

QUESTIONS

1. What are the prospects for continued demand for beef?
2. What responsibility does the producer have in keeping the demand high for beef?
3. Discuss the main beef cattle producing areas of the United States.
4. Describe the main classes of beef cattle producers in the United States.
5. How do the various types of cattle producers plan to make their profits?
6. What is meant by the term *margin* as it applies to beef cattle?
7. What is meant by cost of gain?
8. Show by example how a cattle feeder may make a profit.
9. What skills and knowledge are required for success in the purebred beef cattle business?
10. Under what conditions may it be profitable to combine two or more enterprises? Give examples.
11. What are the important considerations in planning the beef cattle program? Why?

REFERENCES

Bundy, C. E., and R. V. Diggins, *Livestock and Poultry Production* (Second Edition), Prentice-Hall, Inc., Englewood Cliffs, N.J., 1960.

Ensminger, M. E., *Beef Cattle Husbandry,* The Interstate Printers and Publishers, Danville, Illinois, 1951.

Snapp, Roscoe R., and A. L. Neuman, *Beef Cattle* (Fifth Edition), John Wiley and Sons, Inc., New York, 1960.

Williams, D. W., *Beef Cattle Production in the South,* The Interstate Printers and Publishers, Danville, Illinois, 1950.

Breeds and Breed Selection

Upon entering the beef cattle business one must decide which breed of cattle to produce. Breed is an important consideration for the person producing purebred animals or feeder cattle. The cattle feeder is usually less concerned about breed because his animals go directly to the packer for slaughter, and he is then in the market for another bunch of feeder cattle. Anyone producing young animals for either breeding purposes or the feed lot may be considered a breeder. However, the term *breeder* generally applies to one who produces improved purebred animals for breeding purposes.

DEVELOPMENT OF BEEF CATTLE BREEDS

Most of the early developmental work on beef cattle breeds was started in the eighteenth century by British breeders. The most prominent early British breeders were Robert Bakewell, the Collings brothers, Richard Tompkins, Amos Cruickshank, and Hugh Watson. These men were largely responsible for the establishment of breeds and the improvement of beef cattle, recognized the value of growth ability and carcass quality, and placed considerable emphasis on these characteristics in their cattle breeding work. Unfortunately these important characteristics were not considered necessary among many later breeders. However, with the research information now available, modern breeders have developed an appreciation of the breeding practices and objectives of the early breeders of beef cattle.

During the latter part of the eighteenth century, British cattle breeds were imported into the United States, and until about 1900 were the only important breeds used in the improvement of cattle in this country. Since 1900 importation of cattle from India and

France has been made for the purpose of developing breeds that could be adapted to certain sections of the United States.

SELECTING THE BREED

The breeder has many decisions to make before he selects a breed of cattle. It generally takes a long time to establish a herd of high quality animals. To change breeds, once a start has been made, means a delay in reaching his goal.

Careful consideration should be given the following before a start is made on a cattle breeding program of either purebred or grade animals: (1) personal likes, (2) availability of breeding stock, (3) outlet for surplus animals, and (4) environmental conditions under which the animals will be raised.

Personal Likes. Most cattle breeders develop a liking for certain breeds of livestock. Such characteristics as color, form, and general appearance have a personal appeal. One who likes the compact Black Angus may find it difficult to develop the same interest in Brahman cattle, which are so important in the cattle improvement program in some of the southern areas of the United States. Dollar value alone should not determine which breed of cattle one selects: personal satisfaction and pleasure derived from the work is part of a satisfactory vocation. Unless other conditions make it inadvisable to select a breed of personal choice, one should give that factor due consideration before making a start in breeding cattle.

Availability of Breeding Stock. The cattle breeder must be continually on the lookout for animals he can bring into his herd for the purpose of improving his own cattle. Other breeders of the same breed are his main source of supply. If they are few and far between in his particular area, the cattle breeder will have to travel over long distances for replacing animals at greater cost.

Outlet for Surplus Animals. The breeder of purebreds depends upon the other breeders and grade breeders for the sale of bulls and surplus females. The number of breeders, particularly owners of grade herds, in his area contributes much to his sales. Although breeders buy from one another, the grade-herd owner is the largest buyer. If there are more breeders of any one breed than the demand will justify, then all will likely have difficulty in selling all their surplus breeding stock. It is important that one considers the demand before selecting a breed. Unless there is a good market available for breeding stock, prices will be low and profits small. An Angus breeder in the center of a Hereford or Shorthorn area may have to ship his animals over long distances for a market outlet, and it is unlikely that he will find a good market for many of his animals. Buyers will have to travel further to inspect his offerings, thereby increasing the cost to the purchaser and decreasing the profits to the owner.

Grade-herd producers generally find cattle feeders their best market outlet. Although cattle feeders are less concerned than cattle breeders about breed, certain areas tend to show partiality for certain breeds. If the producer of commercial cattle has a good market in a certain locality, he will be wise to give consideration to the breed most popular among feeders in the area.

Environmental Conditions. Weather, grazing, disease, and insect conditions are important factors in selecting a breed of cattle. The Brahman cattle, for example, are able to make good use of poor forage; are not particularly bothered by flies, ticks, or mosquitoes; and are resistant to Texas fever, all of which makes them and their crosses especially valuable in certain southern areas. The Hereford is noted for hardiness and foraging ability where certain diseases and insects are not prevalent. The Shorthorn and Angus have special merits under certain circumstances. Cattle best adapted to the conditions under which they will be raised should therefore be considered by the prospective producer.

PUREBRED BEEF CATTLE DEFINED

A purebred breed is a group of animals that have a common origin. They possess certain, well-fixed characteristics, such as color, markings, horns, or polled character, that they are able to transmit to their offspring. A record of their ancestry, known as a *pedigree*, has been kept. Most purebred breeds have an association whose membership is made up of breeders interested in that particular breed. The association policies are determined by a board of directors elected by the membership and a hired or elected secretary. The association determines the standards to be maintained for the breed they represent. They also are responsible for keeping the records, especially the pedigrees, and promoting the breed. Many breed associations sponsor a breed paper for the purpose of keeping their members and other interested persons informed of new developments. Breed associations are financed through paid memberships, recording fees (fees paid by breeders for pedigrees), and advertising in the breed papers.

BREEDS OF BEEF CATTLE DEVELOPED IN EUROPE

Aberdeen-Angus. *Origin.* The Aberdeen-Angus is one of the most popular breeds of beef cattle in the United States. According to the best historical evidence available, the Aberdeen-Angus cattle originated in northern Scotland in an area not noted for its soil fertility and under cool, damp climatic conditions. The land is rolling and more adaptable to cattle production than other livestock enterprises.

Introduction into the United States. The first importations of these Scottish cattle to play an important part in the United States were made in 1873 by George Grant, a native of Scotland then living in Victoria, Kansas. He imported three bulls to use on his native cows. The first breeding herd, including animals of both sexes, to be brought to the North American continent was imported into Canada, in 1876, by Professor Brown of Ontario College of Agriculture. Many more importations were made during the latter part of the nineteenth century, and have continued up to the present time. However, as the breed became well established in America, importations gradually declined. Today most of the great sires of the breed in the United States were produced in this country.

Characteristics. The Aberdeen-Angus cattle are black—white is not permitted except to a moderate extent on the underline behind the navel. The breed is polled (no horns), which has contributed to Angus popularity among many breeders. The polled characteristic in Angus cattle is so well established that when Angus are cross-bred with horned breeds most of the first cross offspring are polled. Angus cattle have shown more resistance to certain eye diseases, particularly cancer eye and pinkeye, than have some of the other breeds. Calves from Angus cows are usually smaller at birth than are the calves from other breeds, but the weaning weights are equal to or greater than that of other breeds. The smaller calves at birth cut down calving difficulties, and there are fewer cow and calf losses at this time.

The body form of Angus cattle is smooth, broad, low-set, blocky, compact, and well muscled. No other breed has gained a better reputation as a show ring winner in the fat steer and carcass classes than has the Angus.

Red Angus. *Origin.* Occasionally a red animal crops out from a herd of black Angus, even though both parents were black. This is because many black Angus carry a red gene. (See Chapter 12.) The gene is a simple recessive. When two animals carrying the red gene are mated, on the average one in four resulting offspring will be red. When two Red Angus are mated, the offspring will always be red. Red Angus have existed for years, but it is only recently that

FIGURE 11. *The type of Angus bull that will improve almost any herd. (Courtesy Aberdeen-Angus Breeders Association.)*

FIGURE 12. *An ideal type Angus female. (Courtesy American Aberdeen-Angus Breeders Association.)*

FIGURE 13. *This Aberdeen-Angus herd against the snowy background forms a nice picture.* (*Courtesy American Aberdeen-Angus Breeders Association.*)

a group of breeders has been organized for the purpose of breeding Red Angus in the United States. The Red Angus breeders have adapted high standards for registration. Each animal must be inspected by a committee and approved before registration.

Characteristics. The general characteristics are similar to the black Aberdeen-Angus, since they have the same ancestry except for color. The Red Angus have a deep red color that is especially attractive. Like the blacks, they are low-set, wide, deep and exhibit excellent beef qualities.

Galloway. *Origin.* The Galloway cattle are native to Scotland. The breed was developed in southwest Scotland in a district in-

FIGURE 14. *A beautiful Red Angus bull.* (*Courtesy* Capper's Farmer.)

cluding the counties of Kirkcudbright and Wigtown.   This breed is probably one of the oldest of the British breeds.

Introduction into the United States.   They were probably introduced into the United States about 1860.   For a period following their introduction, they became popular through the north central states.   However, probably due to the slower development of the Galloway, the breed has steadily declined in the United States.

Characteristics.   Galloways are good rustlers and extremely hardy, which allows them to stand cold weather conditions.   They

FIGURE 15. *A Galloway bull. (Abernathy Photo.)*

FIGURE 16. *A Galloway heifer. (Abernathy Photo.)*

are the smallest of the beef breeds, black in color with long curly hair. The breed is polled, has short legs, and is blocky and compact in type.

Hereford. *Origin.* Hereford cattle are native to England. They originated in the county of Hereford, which lies in the fertile valley between the Severn River and the eastern boundary of Wales. The fine quality of the pasture and the climatic conditions caused this area to be especially adapted to the development and production of beef cattle.

Introduction into the United States. The first breeding herd of Herefords to play an important part in establishing the breed (1840)

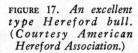

FIGURE 17. *An excellent type Hereford bull. (Courtesy American Hereford Association.)*

FIGURE 18. *An ideal type Hereford female. (Courtesy American Hereford Association.)*

in the United States was that of William H. Sotham and Erastus Corning of Albany, New York. There is, however, a record as early as 1817 of Hereford importations into this country. The Hereford breed multiplied rapidly in the United States, so that today there are more Herefords than any other breed in this country. The breed is popular from coast to coast and constitutes by far the largest percentage of the cattle found on the western range.

FIGURE 19. *This Hereford herd is a common sight throughout the range country. (Courtesy American Hereford Association.)*

Characteristics. Hereford cattle are easily distinguished by their red-colored bodies and white faces. The accepted color is a rich red with a white face. The white is found on the flank, underline, breast, crest, tail switch, and below the hock and knees on both fore and hind legs. They are often referred to as "white-faced cattle."

In form, Hereford cattle are low-set, muscular, compact, broad, and smooth. They are well developed in the regions of valuable cuts—the back, loin, and hindquarters or round.

The Hereford breed is well known for its vigor and foraging ability. These characteristics have made them popular with ranchers of the West and Southwest.

Polled Herefords. *Origin.* In 1900, Warren Gammon of Iowa wrote to nearly every breeder of Herefords in the United States asking if they had any cattle that did not develop horns. He succeeded in securing 13 head of purebred Herefords that were polled.   From this small beginning the Polled Hereford breed was established.

The breed has become very popular among breeders who desire the Hereford form but dislike the horns.   Many commercial or grade Hereford breeders buy polled bulls.   When polled bulls are used on horned cows a large percentage of the calf crop will be polled.   Polled Herefords that originated from registered Hereford stock may be registered in both breed associations.

Characteristics.   In form and characteristics the Polled Hereford closely resembles its ancestors, the Herefords, but the main distinguishing difference is the absence of horns.

FIGURE 20. *A Polled Hereford bull of excellent type. (Courtesy* Polled Hereford World.)

FIGURE 21. *A Polled Hereford female that would improve most herds. (Courtesy* Polled Hereford World.)

FIGURE 22. *Polled Hereford herd.* (*Courtesy American Polled Hereford Association.*)

Shorthorns. *Origin.* The Shorthorns originated in northeastern England in an area that includes the counties of Durham, Northcumberland, and York. The region is located in the Tees River Valley. This valley has excellent pastures conducive to beef production. The breed was given the name because early English breeders succeeded in shortening the horns of the long-horned cattle by a breeding process.

Introduction into the United States. The breed, introduced in 1783 by Miller and Gough of Virginia, was the first to be established in America. These cattle gained rapidly in popularity, and are found throughout the United States today. They represent one of the three most popular breeds, along with the Angus and Herefords, in this country.

Characteristics. In form, the Shorthorn is the largest of the British breeds of beef cattle. They are rectangular and compact. They range in color from red to white to all combinations of these colors, such as spotted or roan. The Shorthorn is the best milking breed of beef cattle, and many farmers who desire a good beef animal plus one that will give enough milk for home use have been attracted to the Shorthorn breed. Shorthorns are well liked by many commercial cattlemen to cross on other breeds for the production of feeder cattle.

FIGURE 23. *A fine example of a Shorthorn bull. (Courtesy American Shorthorn Breeders Association.)*

FIGURE 24. *This Shorthorn cow would make a good addition to any Shorthorn herd. (Courtesy American Shorthorn Breeders Association.)*

FIGURE 25. *The ideal in beef type is portrayed by this champion Shorthorn fat steer. (Courtesy American Shorthorn Breeders Association.)*

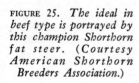

Polled Shorthorn. *Origin.* The Polled Shorthorns were developed by a cross and from naturally polled Shorthorns found in the breed. Most of the earlier animals were developed by crossing, and were eligible to be registered only as Polled Shorthorns. Most present-day Polled Shorthorns are descendants of purebred Shorthorn cattle and are eligible for registration in the American Shorthorn Breeders Association herd books.

The Polled Shorthorn was developed in Ohio, Indiana, Illinois, and Minnesota, in the period from 1870 to 1890.

Characteristics. In form and color the Polled Shorthorns are similar to the Shorthorn except for the polled characteristic.

FIGURE 26. *The absence of horns combined with excellent beef qualities have made the Polled Shorthorn popular among many cattlemen. (Courtesy American Shorthorn Breeders Association.)*

FIGURE 27. *The kind of Polled Shorthorn cow any breeder would like to own. (Courtesy American Shorthorn Breeders Association.)*

FIGURE 28. *This fullblood Charolais herd sire in pasture condition shows those characteristics desired by Charolais breeders. His stout thick neck, masculine head, and rugged, well-muscled body are typical of a good Charolais bull. (Courtesy Litton Charolais Ranch.)*

FIGURE 29. *This three-year-old Charolais cow in pasture condition is a good example of the type desired by most Charolais breeders. Charolais cows at maturity will weigh from 1700 to 1800 pounds. (Courtesy Litton Charolais Ranch.)*

Charolais. *Origin.* The Charolais originated in France, and is one of the most important breeds of French cattle.

Introduction into the United States. Only a small number of Charolais cattle have been imported into the United States. Most of the animals of this breed that have been brought into this country have gone to Texas, Louisiana, and Florida where they have been used for crossing purposes, especially with Brahmans.

Characteristics. Charolais are light, creamy-colored and are one of the largest of all beef breeds. They are quite compact in body form but lack the smoothness of the British breeds.

Scotch Highland. *Origin.* The Scotch Highland breed of beef cattle was developed in the Hebrides, a group of islands near the west coast of Scotland. They are one of the oldest European breeds of beef cattle. It is reputed that they were recorded as a definite breed as early as the twelfth century.

Introduction into the United States. The breed has not been popular in the United States, although a few have been imported from time to time. The American Scotch Highland Breeders Association was formed in 1948.

Characteristics. Scotch Highland cattle are small but exceedingly hardy. Because of their native vigorous climatic conditions and scant feed supplies, they have developed exceptional foraging and mothering ability. They have a long, coarse, outer hair coat and a soft, thick undercoat, which gives them natural body protection against severe weather conditions. Acceptable colors are black, brindle, red, light red, yellow, dun, and silver. They have straight lines, are blocky and compact in body form, and produce excellent carcasses.

They have recently found favor among some ranchers in the northern plains for crossing on other breeds to produce animals more capable of withstanding the long hard winters.

FIGURE 30. *A Silver Highland Herd owned by Ray Carr, Valentine, Nebraska.*
(*Courtesy* Capper's Farmer.)

A typical group of excellent Brahman cattle owned by Paul Cornelius, Coleville, California. (*Courtesy* Western Livestock Journal.)

BREEDS OF BEEF CATTLE DEVELOPED IN INDIA

Brahman. *Origin.* Several breeds of cattle exist in India. Most of them have been named after the Indian province in which they were developed. In Europe and South America they are known as Zebu and are called Brahman in the United States. They are the oldest existing breed of domestic cattle.

Introduction into the United States. The first cattle of this breed to play a part in the development of Brahman cattle in this country were two bulls given, in 1854, to Richard Barrow of Louisiana. These bulls were a gift of the British Crown in recognition of Mr. Barrow's services in teaching sugar cane and cotton raising to a British representative. Although Brahman cattle had reached this country in 1849, it is believed that the purebred animals were wiped out by the War Between the States. The use of Brahman cattle for purebreeding and crossbreeding in the United States was given considerable emphasis when two Texas ranchers, J. M. Frost and Albert Montgomery, bought some crossbreds from Mr. Barrow and later imported two bulls from India.

In recent years, considerable interest has been shown in the development of Brahman cattle in the South. A number of Brahman crossbred feeder cattle have reached Midwest feed lots and have given good results as fattening cattle.

Characteristics. Brahman cattle are characterized by a large hump over the shoulders and loose skin in the area of the dewlap. They have drooping ears, and instead of the "moo" of other cattle they produce a sound resembling a grunt. The most prevalent color is some shade of grey, although red is very acceptable.

In form, the Brahman cattle are more upstanding, are less compact, and lack the smoothness of the other breeds.

Brahman cattle are resistant to Texas fever, can stand heat well, and are bothered little by flies, ticks, and mosquitoes. They are able to produce beef when grazing on poor quality forage on which many other breeds would fail. These characteristics have made Brahman and crossbred strains, developed by using Brahman on other breeds, very popular in areas of the southern part of the United States. The crossbred calves have produced gains and carcass quality equal to any of the other breeds. Like the Angus, they show resistance to cancer eye and pinkeye.

FIGURE 32. *A Brahman bull. A breed that has done much for the improvement of cattle in the South. (Courtesy American Brahman Breeders Association.)*

FIGURE 33. *A Brahman female. (Courtesy American Brahman Breeders Association.)*

FIGURE 34. *Yearling Brangus heifers. These cattle represent a breed resulting from combining Angus and Brahman breeding. An example of how the infusion of Brahman breeding with that of the European breeds has resulted in cattle that are especially adapted to the conditions in parts of southern United States.* (*Courtesy American Brangus Breeders Association.*)

BREEDS OF BEEF CATTLE DEVELOPED IN THE UNITED STATES

Several breeds of beef cattle have been developed in the United States. All of these breeds were developed by using Brahman crosses on European breeds. The objectives were to combine the Brahman ability to graze poor quality forage and their resistance to insects and heat with the smoother more compact qualities of the European breeds.

The need for beef cattle that could withstand the hot, humid climate and the pests and diseases prevalent to many sections of the South was the primary factor in creating an interest among southern farmers, ranchers, and experiment stations toward the development of new breeds. These breeds have played an important part in changing much of southern agriculture from a one-crop system to a cropping and livestock program. The results have been improved soil fertility, converting the forage of untillable land into beef, and greater income to the farmers and ranchers.

Santa Gertrudis. *Origin.* The Santa Gertrudis breed of beef cattle was developed on the King Ranch in southeast Texas. The breed gets its name from the Santa Gertrudis division of the famed King Ranch.

The breed was developed by crossing Brahman beef-type bulls on beef-type shorthorns. The bull, Monkey, is credited with being the foundation sire of the breed. His sons and grandsons were used in herds with the result that only bulls that descended from Monkey were found in purebred Santa Gertrudis herds. After thirty years of selection and inbreeding the offspring of Monkey, they were recognized by the United States Department of Agriculture as a breed in 1940.

Characteristics. The Santa Gertrudis is approximately three-eighths Brahman and five-eighths Shorthorn. It is a large beef animal, with its mature cows attaining weights of 1,600 pounds and mature bulls 2,000 pounds on pasture. It is solid, cherry-red in color, and horned. The ears are somewhat pendulant. It is smoother and more compact than the Brahman, but it retains the loose hide and underline skin folds characteristic of their Brahman ancestry.

The breed is especially adapted to subtropical climates and semi-arid grazing conditions. They are noted for their ability to make large gains on grass, to rustle for a living on areas of sparse forage, and to tolerate heat and insects.

FIGURE 35. *Santa Gertrudis bull. (Courtesy American Santa Gertrudis Breeders International.)*

FIGURE 36. *A champion Santa Gertrudis two-year old heifer. (Courtesy American Santa Gertrudis Breeders International.)*

Brangus. *Origin.* Brangus is a breed of cattle developed by blending Brahman blood with that of the Aberdeen-Angus. The term *Brangus* refers to animals that have three-eighths Brahman and five-eighths Aberdeen-Angus breeding. The breed had its beginning in Craig County, Oklahoma, in 1942, when Raymond Pope

FIGURE 37. *A champion Brangus bull. (Courtesy American Brangus Breeders Association.)*

FIGURE 38. *A three-and-a-half-year old Brangus cow weighing 1,867 pounds. (Courtesy American Brangus Breeders Association.)*

and Frank Buttram mated 900 Brahman cows to Aberdeen-Angus bulls. Later the procedure was reversed due to a shortage of good Brahman cows. With this beginning, along with selection and inbreeding, the breed was established in 1949.

According to the rules of the American Brangus Breeders' Association, one may become a member of the Brangus Breeders by following one of two procedures.   (1) The first method is to enroll as foundation animals approved purebred Brahman and purebred Angus animals, and then make the crosses necessary to produce the three-eighths and five-eighths blood percentage.   The intermediate foundation crosses are known as quarter-bloods, half-bloods, and three-quarter-bloods.   The number indicated in the name denotes the amount of Brahman blood.   All foundation stock is enrolled, and only the three-eighths and five-eighths animals may be registered as purebred Brangus.   To produce a Brangus, an animal possessing one-quarter Brahman and three-quarters Angus may be mated to one that is one-half Brahman and one-half Angus, or by mating a three-quarters Brahman and one-quarter Angus to a purebred Angus.   (2) The second method is to secure purebred Brangus animals registered in the American Brangus Breeders' Association.

Characteristics.   The tolerance of the Brahman to heat, insects, and poor grazing conditions has been successfully blended with the winter hardiness and excellent beef qualities of the Angus to produce a fast gaining good quality beef animal adapted to a wide variety of climatic conditions.

Brangus are black, hornless, somewhat less compact than the Angus, but much smoother and more compact than the Brahman. The breed has shown up very well in feed lot tests with other breeds.

FIGURE 39. *A Brangus cow and her calf. (Courtesy American Brangus Breeders Association.)*

Beefmaster. *Origin.* The Beefmaster breed of beef cattle had its beginning on the ranch of E. C. Lasater at Falfurrias, Texas. Mr. Lasater was interested in developing a breed of beef cattle capable of withstanding the hot, humid climate, the pests, and the diseases of his area. He wished to eliminate pinkeye and cancer eye, which had been troublesome problems in his herd.

In 1908 he bought five Brahman bulls and crossed them on his Hereford cows. Mr. Lasater died in 1930 and his son Tom carried out and further developed the breeding program started by his father. Tom added Shorthorn blood to his breeding program and arrived at a blend of Brahman, Shorthorn, and Hereford breeding that resulted in the breed now known as Beefmaster. Whereas no accurate measure of blood percentage exists in the breed, it is estimated that it consists of approximately 50 per cent Brahman, with the balance being Hereford and Shorthorn. Tom Lasater has

FIGURE 40. *A Beefmaster bull. (Stewarts Photo. Courtesy Lasater Ranch.)*

FIGURE 41. *A three-year-old Beefmaster cow. (Stewarts Photo. Courtesy Lasater Ranch.)*

stressed disposition, fertility, weight, conformation, thriftiness, and milk production in his breeding program.

Characteristics. Beefmasters have no specific color. They may be dun, brown, reddish brown, red, and red with white extensions and spots. They are large and horned and make rapid growth rates. The breed can withstand a wide variety of climatic conditions and are good rustlers. Although they do not have the smoothness and compactness of the British breeds, they produce a very good carcass.

Charbray. *Origin.* The Charbray was developed from a cross of Charolais and Brahman. The animals must have at least one-eighth and not more than one-quarter Brahman blood, and the re-

FIGURE 42. *A Charbray bull calf. (Courtesy American Charbray Breeders Association.)*

FIGURE 43. *A Charbray cow. (Courtesy American Charbray Breeders Association.)*

mainder Charolais, in order to qualify for registration in the American Charbray Breeders Association.

Characteristics. Charbray calves are born a light tan color that usually bleaches into a cream-white in a few weeks. The Brahman hump is bred out, but a slight hint of Brahman dewlap remains. Charbray have horns and are very large cattle. Mature cows may reach a weight of 1,700 to 2,200 pounds and mature bulls from 2,500 to 3,200 pounds. Charbray are vigorous, fast growers, and good grazers. They produce an excellent carcass and dress out well; the meat is tender and high in flavor.

FIGURE 44. *Braford cow.* (*Courtesy Galen M. Savage.*)

Braford. *Origin.* Braford cattle were developed from a Brahman-Hereford cross. They have not been recognized as a breed, but have found favor among some southern ranchers.

Characteristics. Brafords may be red or red with white faces, brindle, or dark brown. They are reported to be good growers, resistant to many diseases and well adapted to the Gulf Coast area.

Crossbred Cattle. For commercial cattle, crossbreeding has shown some definite advantages over purebreeding or straightbreeding. Experiments conducted by the University of Illinois on Hereford-Angus crossbreds showed fewer losses of crossbred calves at birth, or as young calves, than those of the purebreds of the corresponding breeds. The crossbred calves outgained the purebred calves from birth to weaning. In the feed lot test, the crossbred

FIGURE 45. *This steer weighed 1705 pounds at 21½ months. His dam was a purebred Hereford cow and his sire a purebred Charolais bull. Although there is not much demand for such heavy beef in the market place, this steer is an example of outstanding growth and fattening ability. (Courtesy Litton Charolais Ranch.)*

calves made more efficient gains than did the Angus, but the purebred Herefords were more efficient than the crossbreds. Crossbreds from Angus cows sired by a Hereford bull yielded the highest grading carcasses.

Brahman crosses on Hereford, Shorthorn, Angus, and Charolais cattle improved the carcass quality over the purebred Brahman,

FIGURE 46. *A Hereford cow and her crossbred Angus calf. Note the size of this calf. (Courtesy Geo. A. Hormel and Company.)*

while retaining much of the heat and insect pest resistance of the Brahman. The crossbred Brahman has shown more ability to graze and produce beef on low quality forage than the European breeds.

Experimental work of the United States Department of Agriculture has shown that a rotation system of crossing three breeds results in somewhat heavier calves at weaning time and faster feed lot gains.

The use of a naturally polled breed, such as the Angus, when crossed with a horned breed, results in the first-cross calves being polled. This saves the time and cost of the dehorning operation.

Highland cattle, when crossed on Herefords, reputedly produce fast gaining animals with greater foraging ability and more resistance to cold stormy weather than the purebred Hereford.

For a period of six years Geo. A. Hormel & Company of Austin, Minnesota, kept a breeding herd consisting of Shorthorn, Angus, and Hereford cows. A crossbreeding program using different crosses was carried out to determine the gaining ability and economy of gain of the different crosses. The following table shows the growth results from 1951 through 1954.

TABLE 3

COMPARISONS OF GAINS, KILLING WEIGHTS, AND WEANING WEIGHTS OF CROSSBRED CATTLE IN THE HORMEL TEST

Crosses	Average Daily Gain	Average Killing Weight	Average Killing Age	Average Weaning Weight of All Crosses
1951-52 Calf Crop				
Angus-Hereford	1.70	781	424	
Hereford-Shorthorn .	1.74	808	429	
Shorthorn-Angus	1.73	806	433	
				318
1952-53 Calf Crop				
Angus-Hereford	1.78	864	451	
Hereford-Shorthorn .	1.76	856	453	
Shorthorn-Angus	1.78	863	451	
				360
1953-54 Calf Crop				
Angus-Hereford	1.82	884	452	
Hereford-Shorthorn .	1.84	891	452	
Shorthorn-Angus	1.97	947	451	
				426

NOTE: Weaning weights on all calves during each of the three years were taken on December 20. The killing date for the respective years 1952-54 were August 19, September 26, and August 22.

There are also disadvantages to be considered when crossing cattle. Crossbreds usually are of mixed color and lack the uniformity in type of the straightbred cattle. Uniformity in color, type, and size adds to the appearance of a group, and uniform cattle generally sell better, especially if sold as feeders.

FIGURE 47. *A Highland-Hereford crossbred cow and her calf sired by a Hereford bull. This cross produces excellent beef animals that are especially hardy.* (*Courtesy* Capper's Farmer.)

SUMMARY

A cattle breeder is one who produces animals either for breeding purposes or the feed lot. However, the term "breeder" generally refers to one who tries to improve the breed and produces purebred animals primarily for breeding purposes.

British breeders are credited with most of the early developmental work on beef cattle breeds and for establishing a breeding pattern which is still followed today.

The prospective breeder must consider personal likes, availability of breeding stock, outlet for surplus animals, and environmental conditions when selecting a breed.

A purebred breed is a group of animals that have a common ancestry and possess certain well fixed characteristics. They must be registered with a breed association, which provides what is known as a pedigree. The breed association is made up of cattle breeders interested *in the same breed*, keeps the breed records, and promotes the breed.

The most important breeds of cattle in the United States are three British breeds: the Aberdeen-Angus, Hereford, and Shorthorn. The Angus is black and polled. The Herefords consist of two varieties, the horned (generally called Herefords) and the Polled Herefords, which are a hornless variety of the Hereford. The Herefords are red with white faces, white underlining, and white feet. The Shorthorn is also divided into two classes: the Shorthorn and the Polled Shorthorn. They range from red to white, including spotted and roan. The British breeds are low-set, compact, and well muscled, and they produce excellent carcasses.

Other European breeds found in the United States include the Galloway, a British breed, and the Charolais, a French breed. The Galloway has lost much of its earlier popularity in the United States, whereas the Charolais has been used primarily for crossing on Brahman and other breeds by some southern farmers and ranchers.

There are several strains or breeds of Brahman cattle in their native India, but all are called Brahman in the United States. The breed differs considerably from the European cattle, because it is more upstanding, less compact, and has drooping ears. It is resistant to many insects and diseases affecting European breeds and can graze and produce on forage too scant for the survival of many other breeds. It has found particular favor among southern cattlemen in crosses on European cattle and for the development of new breeds particularly adapted to conditions of heat, insects, disease, and less favorable grazing conditions.

The Brangus, Charbray, Beefmaster, Santa Gertrudis, and Braford are all breeds that were developed in the United States, particularly in the South, by blending Brahman blood with Angus, Charolais, Hereford, and Shorthorn cattle. These breeds are credited by their supporters with having exceptional vigor, more size, fast growing ability, and a tolerance of insects, diseases, and extremes in climatic conditions. They are good rustlers and can forage over areas of scant vegetation and survive.

Crossbred cattle have shown some advantages in gaining ability over straightbred cattle. Crossbreds have also proved superior under certain climatic conditions to the straightbred cattle. Lack of uniformity is probably the greatest disadvantage of crossbred cattle.

QUESTIONS

1. Define the term "cattle breeder."
2. Where and when was most of the early beef cattle breed developmental work carried out?
3. List the important decisions a prospective cattle breeder must make.
4. Define the term "purebred breed."
5. What is a breed association and what are the functions of a breed association?
6. Describe the European breeds of beef cattle found in the United States.
7. What are the three most popular breeds of cattle in the United States?
8. How does the Brahman differ from the European breeds of beef cattle?
9. List the breeds of beef cattle developed in the United States.
10. How were the breeds listed in question 9 developed?
11. What are the characteristics of the breeds developed from Brahman crosses on European breeds?
12. What are some of the advantages and disadvantages of crossbred cattle?

REFERENCES

Clark, R. T., *Beef Cattle Breeds for Beef and for Beef and Milk*, Farmers' Bulletin No. 1779 (Revised), 1954, U. S. Department of Agriculture, Washington, D. C.

Williams, D. W., *Beef Cattle Production in the South*, The Interstate Printers and Publishers, Danville, Illinois, 1950.

3

Selecting and Establishing the Breeding Herd

Before attempting to start a breeding herd of beef cattle, either grade or purebreds, one should carefully consider the conditions existing on his farm and in his community.

CONDITIONS TO CONSIDER BEFORE STARTING A COW HERD

Available Feed. The breeding herd will consist largely of cows and young growing stock. Since roughages (hay, silage, and pasture) are the most economical feeds for the breeding herd, it is important that a sufficient supply of these feeds be available. Many herd owners successfully maintain a breeding herd without using any grain whatsoever. Unless cheap roughages are available, including ample amounts of pasture, it is questionable whether the establishing of a cow herd would be economically sound. Farms that have large areas suited primarily for permanent pasture or make it necessary to maintain a large acreage of grasses and legumes to keep up the soil fertility are usually adapted to the raising of cattle.

FIGURE 48. *Land suited primarily for the production of grass may be profitable when the grass is converted to beef, as is being done on this New York farm. (Courtesy American Aberdeen-Angus Breeders Association.)*

Normally, farmers living on farms that consist mostly of level crop land and are suitable for heavy grain production have not found profitable the maintaining of a large breeding herd for the production of commercial cattle. However, with the introduction of acreage allotments as a prerequisite to price supports for grains, farmers may have to grow more grasses and legumes on their farms. Grass crops will need to be utilized by livestock if they are to return a profit. Many grain farmers may find that a cow herd can cause this rough feed to make a profit for them.

Demand for Feeding and Breeding Stock. The calves produced from a breeding herd are the principal source of income from the enterprise. The commercial cattle producer must either have sufficient grains and facilities for feeding out his calves or a good market for feeder cattle. Producers of commercial feeder cattle, located in areas where such an enterprise is the chief source of income, generally have good marketing facilities. Auction sales and large terminal cattle markets catering to the sale of feeders have sprung up in these areas, so buyers tend to travel to these areas to buy their feeder cattle. One who produces a few cattle in an area not known as a cattle country and where few cattle feeders exist may find his marketing expenses too high, and prices received too low, to make a profit.

The purebred breeder must rely upon other purebred breeders and more particularly upon commercial herd owners for the sale of breeding animals. If there are very few cow herd owners in his area the probabilities are that the demand for breeding stock will not be enough to make it a profitable enterprise.

Capital Available. The establishment of a good breeding herd is a long-time proposition. This is especially true of a purebred herd. Profits in the form of cash will not materialize to any great extent for several years. Therefore, it is necessary to have sufficient capital or other sources of income to carry on and pay the family expenses until there is a supply of surplus high quality animals for sale. In addition to having little income from the cattle herd the first few years, a sizable investment will be required to obtain good foundation stock. There is also the chance that one may start when cattle prices are high and find the prices low by the time surplus animals are ready for sale. However, it should be pointed out that once a breeding herd has been established to the extent that the bulk of the calf crop may be sold each year, there is little speculative risk such as that which the buyer and feeder of fattening cattle experiences.

The calf crop is quite reliable, and the herd owner is reasonably certain of an income each year. If he sells his animals for feeding or breeding purposes, he does not have a lot of high-priced grains tied up in them. If he is producing commercial cattle and also grain, he has a choice either to fatten out his calf crop or sell them as feeders.

When and How to Obtain Foundation Stock. The question when to buy is probably one that has seldom been correctly answered. Naturally the time to buy is when prices are at the low point. But when are they at a low point? Rather definite long-time trends in cattle numbers and corresponding prices have developed, but it is difficult to predict accurately when the exact low or high points will come in the cycle. Therefore, the cattleman should first consider whether his farm is adapted to raising cattle. Second, he should decide whether he has enough capital or income to tide him over until such time as he will have animals for sale. If the answer is Yes to both questions, he can at least buy a few heifer calves and a bull. This will give him a start. More animals may be added later, if conditions are favorable, and if not, he will have a nucleus from which to build by keeping his best heifer calves as additions to the herd. Where plenty of capital is available and the cattleman can afford the risk, he can get into the business more quickly by buying bred cows or heifers. However this latter practice cannot be recommended for the inexperienced cattleman.

SELECTION OF FOUNDATION BREEDING STOCK

When the breed has been decided upon, the problem of selecting individual animals for foundation stock must be considered. Good and inferior animals exist in all breeds. Regardless of the breed, certain general characteristics that contribute to beef production should be understood and used as a basis of selection. The breeder of purebreds will be concerned with breed characteristics which animals must have if they are to be eligible for registration.

The following are some features that would disqualify animals from being recorded as purebreds: Herefords having horns or horn spurs could not be recorded in the Polled Hereford herd book; an Angus having white marking anywhere except on the underline near the navel could not be registered as a purebred Angus. There are many other disqualifications, too numerous to mention in this book, with which a prospective breeder should become familiar. This information can be secured from the breed associations.

The producer of grade animals is usually less concerned about breed disqualifications, but, like the purebred breeder, should carefully consider those factors that contribute to economical beef production.

The building of a good herd of breeding cattle is a long-time proposition. Many breeders have spent a lifetime without ever having reached their goal. It is important that very careful consideration be given to the selection of foundation animals. It should be remembered that the cost of feeding and managing an inferior herd is equal to that of a good herd. Although the initial cost of superior foundation animals may be high, the long-time cost in relation to income from the herd will be less than that from inferior foundation stock. If the goal is the establishment of a high quality herd, it is better to buy a few good animals than a larger number of poor ones. This is especially true for the breeder of purebreds.

In selecting foundation stock the breeder should consider two sets of conditions: (1) those that he can see in sizing up the individual animal and (2) those wherein he must rely upon production records for his information.

Determining Desirable Body Conformation. One can judge desirable conformation by closely inspecting the animal in question. If possible, a similar inspection should be made of the sire, dam, sisters, brothers, and other closely related animals. By inspecting close relatives of the animal being considered for foundation stock, one can determine, to some extent, whether the line breeds true to type. It is not uncommon to find an attractive animal from a strain in which few good ones exist. Such an animal may be disappointing in the quality of his or her offspring. Since animals may inherit poor qualities from ancestors several generations back, it is important to observe as many representatives of the line as possible to determine to what extent undesirable qualities are cropping out.

Size for age. Fast growing animals are important to economical production. Undersized animals for their breed or age are not generally good foundation stock or good additions to the herd. Of course, when it can be accurately determined, the conditions under which the animal was raised should be considered. Young stock receiving grain along with good roughages may be expected to be larger than the same animals fed only on poor roughages.   Generally speaking, foundation animals should be at least average in size for their age and breed.

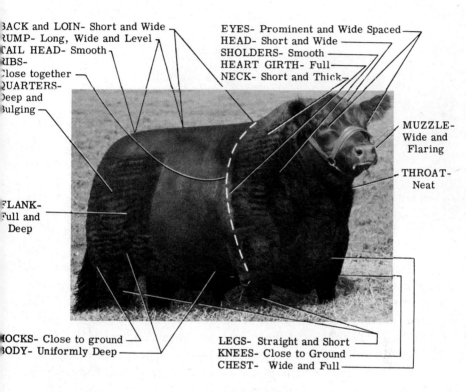

BACK and LOIN- Short and Wide
RUMP- Long, Wide and Level
TAIL HEAD- Smooth
RIBS-
Close together
QUARTERS-
Deep and
Bulging

EYES- Prominent and Wide Spaced
HEAD- Short and Wide
SHOLDERS- Smooth
HEART GIRTH- Full
NECK- Short and Thick

MUZZLE-
Wide and
Flaring

THROAT-
Neat

FLANK-
Full and
Deep

HOCKS- Close to ground
BODY- Uniformly Deep

LEGS- Straight and Short
KNEES- Close to Ground
CHEST- Wide and Full

FIGURE 49. *Before one can become a good judge of cattle, he must know the various parts that make up the conformation of the animal. (Courtesy American Aberdeen-Angus Breeders Association.)*

Observations from side view.   To size up properly the qualities of an individual animal, as a possible addition to the herd, one should take a position about ten feet from the animal to be judged.   In type it should be reasonably low-set, blocky, and compact.   Does the shoulder blend smoothly into the body?   Is the heart girth full? Is the neck short and thick?   Does the tailhead blend smoothly into the rump?   Is the rump long and level?   Does the animal have good depth with a well-sprung rib?   Is the top and underline straight?   Does the animal move freely and with style?   Are the legs straight and out on the corners?   Is the bone clean cut, dense,

and moderate in size?   If the answers to these questions are satisfactory, then the next move is directly behind the animal for further observations.

FIGURE 50. *From a side view this animal presents a nearly ideal type. (Courtesy American Shorthorn Breeders Association.)*

Observation from rear view.   The hindquarters should be wide,
plump, and well developed in proportion to the rest of the animal.
The thighs should be thick, carrying flesh down to the hocks.   The
twist should be deep, not cut up between the hind legs.   When
looking over the top of the animal, one should observe if it is broad
over the back, loin, and rump.   On cows or heifers of calving age
the udder should not be fleshy; it should extend well forward and
well up behind, with the teats squarely placed, well apart, and of
good size.   After making the preceding observations, one should
move to a position in front of the animal.

FIGURE 51. *Note the excellent development of the hind quarters, the great width over the back and loin, and the uniformity of this animal from end to end. (Courtesy American Shorthorn Breeders Association.)*

FIGURE 52. *The trained judge measures with his eye rather than a ruler or tape measure, but this expert is pointing out to the beginner the importance of length from hip bones to pin bones. (Courtesy American Shorthorn Breeders Association.)*

FIGURE 53 (*left*). *Here the trained judge points out the importance of having good width of hind quarters.* FIGURE 54 (*right*). *Good depth of the hind quarters means more beef. (Courtesy American Shorthorn Breeders Association.)*

 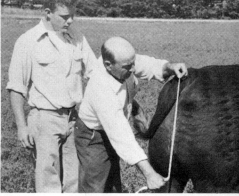

FIGURE 55 (*left*). *The round should carry down to the hock if a maximum amount of round steaks and roasts are to be obtained.* FIGURE 56 (*right*). *The loin provides the highest priced steaks; great width is important here. (Courtesy American Shorthorn Breeders Association.)*

Observation to be made from the front view. The desired head is broad, short, slightly dished, and clean cut. The eyes are full and expressive, with good width between them. The distance from the eyes to nostrils is of moderate length. The muzzle should be wide and flaring and the nostrils open. The shoulders should be smooth, compact, and broad on top. The brisket must be wide, moderately deep, free from flabby flesh and wrinkled skin, and not too prominent. The forelegs should be wide apart, allow-

FIGURE 57. *The head of the bull should show masculinity but be free of coarseness. This is an example of excellent breeding. (Courtesy American Shorthorn Breeders Association.)*

FIGURE 58. *The female head should be feminine and free from coarseness. Look for this kind of head on cows. (Courtesy American Brangus Breeders Association.)*

ing for good width on the chest floor.   Bulls should possess pronounced masculinity with a well-developed crest.   Females should show refinement and should give indication of being good producers.

FIGURE 59. *Note the width and fullness of the chest of this animal.* (*Courtesy American Shorthorn Breeders Association.*)

FIGURE 60. *This beginner is checking the depth of chest on a very desirable Shorthorn bull.* (*Courtesy American Shorthorn Breeders Association.*)

Handling qualities. As a final step in breeding stock selection step close to the animal, keeping the hand flat, and feel down over the back, loin, and ribs. This procedure will show the amount and uniformity of fleshing over the region of valuable cuts. Breeding cattle do not necessarily need exceptionally high condition, unless they are to compete for premiums in a show ring. However, the covering should be uniform and free from patches and lumps. Animals that carry good flesh, as compared to others being given the same feed and management, usually indicate easy keepers and are desirable breeding stock prospects. The hide should be pliable and of medium thickness, and the hair should be fine and soft.

Passing final judgment on breeding stock. There is no perfect animal. Leading judges who have judged and observed hundreds of shows all over the country will admit they have never yet found an animal beyond criticism. However, after carefully considering all the points listed here, if the animal has scored well compared to the average of the breed, then we may be sure the general type is satisfactory.

It is important to try to correct weaknesses that exist in the herd. For example, if one is buying a bull to breed cows that are rough in the tailhead, then he should select a bull that will help to correct this fault. Many times, to correct a herd fault, one may have to compromise on other characteristics in buying additions to the breeding herd. It is also important to evaluate properly good and bad points. For instance, if one animal is shallow in the hindquarters but is smooth in the tailhead, a second animal may be deep in the quarter but a little rough over the tailhead. If they were equal otherwise, certainly the shallow-quartered animal would be the least desirable of the two. An undersized bull indicating a slow rate of growth and maturity would be a poor choice. The cattleman can afford to overlook a number of other faults if he can get fast growing and maturing ability bred into his herd.

Most cattlemen will agree that type, development in the regions of the most valuable cuts, size for age, health, and vigor should receive the most emphasis when buying breeding stock for commercial herds. Breeders of purebreds will have to give special considerations to characteristics that may disqualify an animal for registration. The other factors mentioned should be considered, but they are secondary to those that are most important to economical beef production.

FIGURE 61 (*above*). *The hands may be used to help determine the fullness of the heart girth and spring of foreribs.* (*Courtesy American Shorthorn Breeders Association.*)

FIGURE 62 (*right above*). *Determining width and degree of natural fleshing.* (*Courtesy American Shorthorn Breeders Association.*)

FIGURE 63 (*right below*). *The hide should be thin and pliable and the hair soft.* (*Courtesy American Shorthorn Breeders Association.*)

FIGURE 64 (*below*). *The judge is checking the covering over the ribs.* (*Courtesy American Shorthorn Breeders Association.*)

Using the Score card. Score cards have been developed for the various breeds of beef cattle. Their purpose is to help direct the beginner's attention to each of the detailed parts of the animal and to indicate the relative importance of these parts. Each part of the animal is given a numerical value, which represents the value of that part in relation to the rest of the animal. The greater the numerical number the greater is the importance of that particular part of the body conformation. Many beginners in the cattle business tend to attach too much importance to minor faults and overlook major defects in conformation. A careful study of the score card will be of help in evaluating more correctly the good and bad points in conformation.

The following score cards are examples of the type of score card that has been developed for the various breeds. Although the point values given for different parts of the body vary with the different breeds, a study of the score cards will reveal that the recognized desirable body conformation for all breeds is about the same. Desirable individual breed characteristics, such as the horns, color, size, or the polled condition, vary considerably depending upon the breed. The breeder of purebreds must necessarily carefully consider breed characteristics when selecting his breeding stock. The grade herd owner, or one who practices crossbreeding, is primarily interested in that part of the body conformation that denotes good gaining ability and beef qualities. All the beef breeds have about the same standards of excellence in the production characteristics.

A GENERAL STANDARD OF EXCELLENCE ACCEPTABLE
FOR MOST BEEF BREEDS

Score Card for Breeding Beef Cattle *

Scale of Points	Standard
1. Weight and size, according to age	10
2. Form—deep, broad throughout, low-set, straight top and underline	25
3. Constitution—good depth and width of chest	15
4. Quality—smooth throughout; good handler as indicated by soft, loose, pliable skin covered with fine, glossy hair; bone, fine yet of sufficient substance and strength to carry the body	15
5. Condition—carrying natural flesh enough to indicate vigor; free from patchiness	10
6. Breed type and color—clean-cut head and neck with good form; color marking typical of breed	10
7. Sex character—strong, masculine head and neck in bull; more refinement throughout cow than in bull	10
8. Disposition—docile with quiet temperament	5
TOTAL	100

* SOURCE: Farmers' Bulletin 1068.

The general standard of excellence or a unified score card has been developed that is applicable to most breeds of beef cattle. The unified score card does not take into consideration those strict breed qualifications, such as color, horns, and the polled condition.

SHORTHORN BULL SCORE CARD

Ideals of Type and Breed Characteristics to Be Based on This Score Card

Based on Order of Observation		*Perfect Score*
1. General Appearance—balanced, well coupled, deep, top and underline straight, no holes or angles; when on parade ability to walk well, good carriage, size for age in evidence, moderate condition mature bull weight range 1,800-2,100 lbs. 24 months, 1,250-1,400 lbs.	13	13
2. Head—		
Forehead and poll	1	
Face—reasonably short, wide between eyes, bridge broad, well proportioned, general contour of face slightly concave and bell-shaped with evidence of strength	2	
Muzzle and Jaw—broad and bulged, nostrils wide and open, mouth large. Jaw strong, not undershot; nose waxy white .	2	
Eyes—full, bright, expressive yet mild	1	
Horns—well set on with flatness at base, gradually diminishing toward tips (roundness or extreme coarseness undesirable), moderate in length, curving inwards and slightly downward, at least three-quarter of horn waxy white in color	2	8
3. Front—		
Throat—clean without excessive skin development	1	
Neck—short and muscular, thick, spreading out to join shoulders smoothly, moderate crest, which increases with age	3	
Shoulders—smooth, moderately broad, well covered with flesh on top and on blades, joining neck and forerib without holes or slackness	4	
Chest and Brisket—chest deep and with plenty of width between forearms; brisket broad and well covered	4	12
4. Back—		
Ribs—well sprung from a straight backbone so that they are arched and deep; foreribs must fit neatly into shoulders; no slackness should appear in area of heart, girth, or crops	10	
Hips and Loin—broad and straight, hook bones not prominent and well covered. Loin broad and well covered	10	
Rump—long and straight from hooks to pins, broad and smooth, well filled in and molded neatly into the hindquarters	8	28
5. Rear—		
Hindquarters—deep and full, meated well down to hocks; thighs thick and broad, twist full and deep	8	

Based on Order of Observation

Perfect Score

Tail—neatly set in, coming out of body on a line with backbone 2   10

6. Feet—large and well formed, squarely placed. Legs—short and straight, squarely placed, hind legs inclined very slightly forward below hocks; hind legs should not show nearness; when walking, no straddling effects; forearm should be broad and muscular 8   8

7. Bone—leg bone sturdy, strong and of good quality 8   8

8. Fleshing—even, deep, firm but not hard, bumps and patchiness very undesirable 8   8

9. Hair—heavy and silky (coarse, faded, and black patches very undesirable) 2   2

10. Hide—mellow, flexible, and moderately thin 3   3

TOTAL 100

FIXED AND MINUS SCORES

Feet and Legs .... Inability to stand and walk correctly—deduct up to 50 per cent from the total score.

Bone .... An animal with exceedingly light bone and spindly legs—deduct up to 50 per cent from total score.

Wry Face .... Deduct 5 points from total score.

Wry Tail .... Deduct 5 points from total score.

Muzzle .... Completely smoky—deduct 1 point from total score.

Blindness .... In one eye—take 5 per cent from total score.

Black Hairs .... Around muzzle, mouth, or eyes—deduct 2 per cent from total score.

General .... Should any other abnormal defects appear sufficiently serious—deduct from 1 per cent to 2 per cent from the score.

COMPLETE DISQUALIFICATION

Black Coloring .... Black patches, or a patch the size of the adult hand or larger.

Jet Black Muzzle......

Testicles .... One testicle, or distinctly abnormal testicle or testicles.

Sharp Practice .... Animals showing signs of having been operated upon or tampered with for the purpose of correcting or concealing faults in conformation or with intent to deceive relative to animal's soundness.

Total Blindness .... With provision for reconsideration.

Marked Lameness ..... Apparently permanent.

SCORE CARD FOR HEREFORD BREEDING CATTLE

Points

GENERAL CONFORMATION AND TYPE

Beefy, compact, low-set and blocky—

Body—wide, compact with ribs close together and last rib close to hip. Loin deep, wide and thickly covered. Flanks deep. Top and underlines parallel 19

Points

Rump and Rear Quarters—rump long, wide, smooth, and well covered, carrying width in proportion to width of body and hips. Rear quarters deep, wide, muscular, meated close to hocks and bulging as viewed from the side. Twist deep and full   12

Shoulders—full, smooth, and well-covered. Top of shoulder slightly below vertebra. Shoulder slightly sloping to add style and height to head. Good width on top. Strong shoulder in bulls. Neat in females   6

Brisket—deep and wide but free from flabbiness   2

Tail—tailhead smooth and level with topline   1

THICKNESS OF FLESH

Deep, smooth and firm, yet springy to the touch. Uniform covering in all parts—not patchy   8

HEAD AND SEX CHARACTER

Forehead broad and prominent. Face short, muzzle full and flaring. Head wide. Eyes prominent, large and expressive. Horns of medium size, even-colored and coming from head at right angle, then curving downward and forward ....

Bulls masculine, and possessing vigor and strength. Females feminine, yet short and broad   8

Throat—neat without excessive flesh or fat underneath   2

Neck—short, thick, and blending smoothly into shoulder. Neck vein full and thick. Muscular neck and full crest in bulls, according to age   2

CONSTITUTION AND RUGGEDNESS

Chest full as denoted by well-sprung foreribs. Full back of shoulders. Deep foreflanks. Flaring muzzle. Thrifty appearance   10

QUALITY AND SMOOTHNESS

An over-all appearance of quality and smoothness in both makeup and fleshing. Fullness yet neatness in all parts. Hide of moderate thickness, mellow and pliable. Hair thick and silky. Bone heavy yet clean   7

SIZE

Age and condition to be considered   5

SUBSTANCE AND LEGS

Short, straight legs squarely placed and perpendicular both from side and end view. Forearm muscular. Bone heavy yet neat. Short joints from knees and hocks to ground   10

BALANCE AND SYMMETRY

A balance or blending of all parts. Top and underline parallel to ground level. Rump as long as body. Head and neck set on smoothly and with style. Body deeper than long. Appearance of a tight rather than loose frame   5

COLOR AND MARKINGS

Medium deep, rich red with white head, breast, belly, crest, switch, and ankles. Objections: White back of crops, high on flanks or too high on legs   3

TOTAL   100

STANDARD OF EXCELLENCE FOR ABERDEEN-ANGUS CATTLE

	Score	
	Bull	Cow

A. GENERAL APPEARANCE.

1. Color—black. White is objectionable, except on underline behind the navel, and there only to a moderate extent. A white scrotum in male is undesirable .... 1 | 1

2. Size—well developed according to age. Bulls 1,700 to 2,100 lbs. at maturity in good flesh. Cows 1,200 to 1,500 lbs. at maturity in good flesh .... 2 | 2

3. Form—broad, deep, low-set, compact, symmetrical, smooth. Top, bottom, and side show lines straight. Flanks full. Bull should possess pronounced masculinity. Females should show refinement and combine all female characteristics indicative of being a producer. Walk straight, active with quick step .. 10 | 10

4. Quality—hide, pliable, of medium thickness; mellow to the touch with a thick covering of fine soft hair; bone, clean cut and not too heavy; fleshing smooth .... 10 | 10

5. Condition of Flesh Covering—thick, firm, mellow, even, free from patches, lumps, rolls, and ties. Flank and root of tongue full; throat not too heavy .... 9 | 7
                                                                    32 | 30

B. HEAD AND NECK.

1. Head—forehead—broad, short, slightly dished, clean cut with well-defined poll, flatness being objectionable. Eyes mild, full and expressive, with good width between them. Distance from eyes to nostrils of moderate length. Nostrils wide and open. Ears of good medium size, well set, slightly erect and well covered with hair. Appearance of scurs of buttons disqualify for registration .... 7 | 7

2. Neck and Throat—neck short and thick, full neck vein, blending smoothly into the shoulders. Throat, clean cut without any development of loose flesh or surplus skin underneath ... 6 | 5
                                                                    13 | 12

C. FOREQUARTERS.

1. Shoulders—moderately oblique, smooth, well covered on blades and top, compact and broad on top. A narrow-pointed shoulder top or coarse open shoulder is objectionable .... 5 | 4

2. Brisket—not too prominent. Wide, moderately deep, free from flabby flesh or loose, wrinkled skin .... 2 | 1

3. Legs—short, straight and squarely placed. The forearms should show heavy muscular development, bones fine and dense joints. Clean cut and moderate size .... 1 | 1
                                                                    8 | 6

D. BODY.

1. Chest—wide on floor and deep, round and well-filled back of shoulders .... 4 | 4

2. Back—broad, level from shoulder to tailhead. Thickly covered with smooth natural flesh. Hooks moderate in width, well laid in .... 10 | 10

	Score	
	Bull	*Cow*

3. Ribs—well sprung from backbone; arched, with plenty of length to give depth to body. Neatly joined to the crops and loin, covered with smooth, thick, natural flesh well down on ribs. There should be no depression back of the shoulders .. | 8 | 8 |
| 4. Loin—broad, level, thick, full, smooth .... | 8 | 8 |
| | 30 | 30 |

E. HINDQUARTERS.

1. Hooks—level, smooth, well laid in and well covered with flesh, giving a symmetrical appearance .... | 2 | 2 |
2. Rump—long, wide, level; tailhead smooth with tail coming neatly out of the body on a line with the back and hanging at right angles to it .... | 6 | 6 |
3. Thighs—broad, deep, thick and full, carrying well down to the hock, with a well-rounded appearance .... | 6 | 6 |
4. Twist—deep and full .... | 2 | 2 |
5. Legs—short, slightly inclined forward below the hocks; muscular above the hocks; bone clean cut, dense and not too heavy .... | 1 | 1 |
6. Udder *—Not fleshy, coming well forward in line with the body and well up behind; teats squarely placed, well apart and of good size .... | — | 5 |
| | 17 | 22 |
| TOTAL .... | 100 | 100 |

STANDARD OF EXCELLENCE FOR AMERICAN BRAHMAN CATTLE

	Score	
	Bull	*Cow*

A. GENERAL APPEARANCE.

1. Color—solid or gradual blending of two colors. Unpigmented skin objectionable. Brindle is a disqualification. Muzzle and hoofs dark. A white nose, light-colored hoofs, or white switch undesirable .... | 1 | 1 |
2. Size and Weight—well developed according to age. Bulls 1,600 lbs. to 2,200 lbs. at maturity in good flesh., Cows 1,000 lbs. to 1,500 lbs. at maturity in good flesh .... | 8 | 8 |
3. Form—massive, broad, deep, medium low-set, moderately compact, symmetrical, smooth. Straight back with a slightly rounding rump. Any appreciable dropping off from hips to region of crops or hump undesirable. Bull should possess hump of ample size, located directly on top of shoulders, moderate in thickness, somewhat resembling a bean in shape and extending backwards. Females should show hump of moderate development more oval in shape than that of bull

---

* For heifers under calving age, give the five points allowed for udder in cow for feminine appearance that strongly indicates development into a productive matron, thus combining all the feminine characteristics.

NOTE: Score cards are useful to beginners in calling attention to the various parts of the animal, the relative value of each part, and the importance of breed characteristics. They are not practical for use in judging in the show ring. The judge must carry the ideal animal in his mind's eye and make his ratings on a comparative basis.

and located on top of shoulders. Bottom line straight except
for sheath in bull and navel in cow. Excessive development
of sheath or navel objectionable. Flanks full. Bull should
possess pronounced masculinity. Females should show all
characteristics of refinement and femininity which would indicate a good producer. Walk straight, strong and active 8   8

4. Quality—hide soft and pliable, of medium thickness, densely
covered with hair of medium texture, oily to the touch.
Well-developed dewlap with generous amount of soft pliable skin arranged in folds extending from lower jaw to
chest floor. Moderate development of loose skin under belly.
Bone ample in substance, clean cut and strong. Fleshing
smooth 5   5

5. Flesh Covering—thick, firm, mellow, and uniformly distributed 7   6
                                                       ——   ——
                                                       29   28

B. HEAD AND NECK.

1. Head—forehead broad, practically flat to moderately prominent, face short, slightly tapering toward nose; muzzle full,
nostrils wide and open; lips dark. Eyes mild and full with
good width between them. Distance from eyes to muzzle of
moderate length. Ears ample in length, moderate in width,
and characteristic of predominating strain. Horns wide apart
at the base, thick, varying in length and shape according to
predominating strain. Horns of cows should be thinner than
horns of bulls 7   7

2. Neck and Throat—neck short with full crest in bull; neat in
cows, blending smoothly into shoulders. Throat clean on
sides, but with development of loose skin underneath 2   2
                                                       ——   ——
                                                        9   9

C. FOREQUARTERS.

1. Shoulders—moderately oblique, smooth and well covered on
blades, broad on top and covered by hump 5   4

2. Brisket—not too prominent. Wide and moderately deep, covered with loose skin 1   1

3. Legs—moderately short, straight and squarely placed. The
forearms should show heavy muscular development; the bones
strong and clean with dense joints 3   2
                                                       ——   ——
                                                        9   7

D. BODY.

1. Chest—wide and deep, round and full back of shoulders.
Good width on chest floor and well filled in fore flank 6   6

2. Ribs—well sprung from backbone, arched, with ample length
to give depth to body. Symmetrically joined to loin and
crops, well covered with smooth, thick natural flesh. There
should be no appreciable depression behind the shoulders .. 7   7

3. Back—broad and level from hump to hooks; slightly rounding
from hooks to pin bones or tailhead. Well covered with
thick, smooth natural flesh. Hooks moderately wide and well
laid in. A sharp angle of back between and extending above
hooks objectionable 8   8

	Score	
	Bull	Cow

4. Loin—broad, thick, level, blending smoothly into back and rump 7   7

                                           28   28

E. HINDQUARTERS.

1. Rump—long wide, nearly level (slightly rounding toward tail-head) smoothly joined to loin. Tailhead smooth with tail coming neatly out of body on a line with or slightly below level of the back and hanging at right angles to it. (Steep slope objectionable.) 8   8
2. Hooks—slightly below level of back, medium in width well laid in and moderately covered with flesh 1   1
3. Thighs and Twist—broad, thick, full, and deep, extending well down to hocks. Twist deep and full 8   8
4. Legs—moderately short, straight, and squarely placed; perpendicular from rear view but slightly inclined forward below the hocks; muscular above hocks; bone with ample substance, clean and dense. Strong, short, moderately sloping pasterns. Toes uniform and ample in size 2   2
5. Tail—neatly attached to the body on a level with the topline or slightly below; long, whiplike, with dark switch 1   1
6. Udder—ample in capacity, extending well forward in line with belly and well up behind; not fleshy. Teats moderate in size, squarely placed, well apart .... —   4
7. Scrotum—the scrotum should contain two testicles of equal size; only one testicle showing is very objectionable 1   —

                                           21   24

F. DISPOSITION.

Alert but docile 4   4

TOTAL 100   100

Selection Based Upon Production Records. Research work in progress by the United States Department of Agriculture and several state experiment stations shows that there is little association between the body conformation of an animal and its ability to grow and fatten efficiently and rapidly. The correlation between external conformation and high carcass quality (quality based upon marbling, proportion of fat to lean, tenderness, and flavor) has been disappointing. Carcass shows held at a number of livestock fairs have revealed that expert live-animal judges have been unable to evaluate accurately the quality of carcass of the live animal. This does not mean that we will discard our present method of judging live animals, but it does show the necessity of determining which characteristics will indicate high dressed-carcass quality.

The most important factors in the production of beef are high rate of gain, efficiency of gain (the ability of an animal to produce a pound of gain on the least amount of feed), milking and mothering ability of the cows, high fertility record, and desirable carcass quality.

A combination of progeny testing, production records, and live-animal evaluation is necessary to build a high-quality beef cattle herd.

Determining inherited growth ability. The term "progeny testing" means the testing of the offspring from certain breeding animals. Since the bull contributes half the characteristics inherited by the calf crop, most progeny testing has been done on herd sires. The purpose is to determine the ability of a bull to produce fast- and efficient-growing calves that have desirable body conformation and carcass quality.

FIGURE 65. *This range bull may not be all that is desired in type and conformation, but his offspring have fast growing and fattening ability.* (*Courtesy Montana State College.*)

The birth weight of calves has been found to be a fairly accurate method of determining both their growth rate and the ability of a sire to transmit this desirable quality to his offspring. Selecting at least five calves at random from different cows all sired by the same bull, and recording their rate and efficiency of gain, will also give a fairly accurate record of the growth-transmitting ability of a sire. A combination of both birth weight and growth records on the progeny of a bull will give sufficient evidence to prove or disprove him as a good sire.   When sufficient evidence has been obtained as to the ability of a bull to sire fast-growing calves with desirable characteristics, he is known as a proven sire.   Such sires are few in number and very valuable as breeding animals.   The best guarantee that animals will transmit desirable qualities to future offspring is their past performance.   When the service of a proven sire cannot be secured, young animals sired by a proven bull are next best.

Progeny tests conducted by the United States Department of Agriculture and various state experiment stations show that certain blood lines or families within a breed have greater ability to produce desirable qualities than other families in the same breed.   The wise breeder will try to obtain breeding stock from tested blood lines.

Selection based on weaning weight.   The weaning weight of calves is a good indication of the milking ability of the dams.   If feeding and environmental conditions are uniform, calves that are the heaviest at weaning time indicate growth ability and good milking qualities of the mother.   Many beef cows fail to provide enough milk for the rapid growth of the calf.   It is also true that the ability of calves to make rapid gains and milk production of the cows are

FIGURE 66. *Regular weight check will determine growth rate of calves.* (*Courtesy* Farm Journal - Country Gentleman.)

inherited. It must be remembered that weaning weights have little comparative value unless the entire calf crop has been on the same feed and under the same management. Feed is an important factor in growth rate. Calves receiving liberal amounts of good forage and grain can be expected to gain more than those on poor rations.

The breeder who combines birth weight, feed lot tests, and weaning weights along with careful selection based on conformation will eventually build a herd of fast growing animals with desirable conformation and good milking cows.

FIGURE 67. *This calf was heavier than average at birth and its mother will produce sufficient milk for rapid growth.*

Fertility record of the cows. A 100 per cent calf crop is desirable, but seldom achieved. However, a cow herd that will produce a strong calf crop with only a few cows failing to breed indicates a high fertility rate bred into the herd. Since the profit lies in the calf crop, the fertility record of the herd and individuals in the herd is important in selection. Cows and bulls that are slow to breed and bulls that fail to settle most of the cows should be eliminated, and their offspring should not be kept as breeding animals.

Goals for Carcass Quality. Carcass quality can be determined accurately only by slaughtering the animal and studying the carcass. Bulls with a record of siring offspring that have high carcass quality as well as the previously mentioned qualities are highly regarded as sires. The following goals for carcass quality have been established:

1. Animals of 900 to 1100 pounds live weight, yielding dressed carcasses of 550 to 700 pounds.
2. Firm, white fat cover uniformly distributed no thicker at the twelfth rib than 1/10 inch per 100 pounds dressed carcass.
3. At least 48 per cent of carcass weight in hindquarters.
4. Bright-red, firm, finely textured ribeye having at the twelfth rib at least 2 square inches of lean area per 100 pounds of dressed carcass.
5. Yield of primal cuts per side no less than 22½ per cent for round, 17¾ per cent for loin, and 9¼ per cent for rib.
6. Finely dispersed, abundant marbling of ribeye.
7. Tenderness of no less than 6, based on a scoring of 1 as extremely tough to 8 as extremely tender.
8. Kidney and suet not exceeding 3 pounds per 100 pounds of carcass.
•9. Deep-red bone.

THE NATIONAL BEEF CATTLE BREEDING PROGRAM

The national beef cattle breeding program was created in 1947, and the projects were prepared in 1948. The program consists of a cooperative effort between the United States Department of Agriculture and several state experiment stations for the purpose of improving the breeds of cattle. Each of the several experiment stations were given certain research programs to carry out.

Objectives of the Program. In general, the program is designed to develop beef animals that will make rapid gains economically and produce the type of carcasses that are desired by the consumers. Some of the specific research projects being carried on by the co-operating states with assistance from the United States Department of Agriculture are the following: (1) testing sires and cows to discover family lines of fast gaining animals that will yield good meat carcasses; (2) making family and progeny tests of lines and crosses of these lines for rate and efficiency of gain and carcass quality (3) developing methods of estimating the breeding value of young bulls with respect to type, growth rate, and efficiency; (4) developing strains of beef cattle particularly suited to the southeastern, coastal plain, and southwestern regions; (5) determining the effect on performance of different systems of feeding and management; (6) studying the effect of varying feed intake in order to find lines of cattle best adapted to various environments, particularly where seasonal and climatic changes bring "ups and downs" in feed supplies; (7) developing inbred lines of beef cattle within established breeds; (8) comparing different conformation types and sizes of beef cattle under range and feed lot conditions; and (9) studying the heritability of weight, grade, rate, efficiency of feed lot gain, carcass grade and yield, type and conformation, and resistance to cancer eye.

How to Benefit from the National Beef Breeding Program. By using tested stock, cattlemen can make a very material increase in beef production. Steers sired by tested bulls may be expected to make an increased gain of 0.2 pounds per head per day. Feeders can afford to pay more for steers from tested herds, and many have shown a willingness to do so. Through the vocational agriculture instructor, the county extension director, or the state agricultural college, information may be obtained as to the nearest tested herds as to where breeding or feeding stocks are available.

DEFORMITIES AND ABNORMALITIES

There are several types of deformities that may occur in cattle. Most of them are rare and do not cause a large economic loss. However, dwarfism, or a condition that causes cows to produce midgets or dwarf offspring, has appeared so often in beef cattle herds throughout the United States that special consideration will be given the subject.

Dwarfs are usually compact and stocky, but very much undersized. They generally develop a large stomach and heavy shoulders, and later they may become sway-backed and develop crooked legs. Dwarfs represent almost 100 per cent loss economically.

Cause of Dwarfism. The condition leading to dwarfism is inherited. The parents may be perfectly normal but, when mated, may produce a dwarf. The problem is to determine which animals in the herd are dwarf carriers. When a bull, normal in appearance but a dwarf carrier, is mated to a similar cow, on the average one calf in four will be a dwarf. Of the remaining three calves, two will be carriers of the dwarf factor but will appear normal, and one will be free of the dwarf factor. As an example of how great the loss would be, let us suppose that in a herd of sixteen cows eight were dwarf carriers. If the eight dwarf-carrying cows were mated to a dwarf-carrying bull, one may expect two dwarf calves per year. Of the remaining six calves, four would carry the factor, and, if kept in the herd, might produce more dwarf calves. In addition, the nondwarf-carrying cows, if bred to the same bull,

FIGURE 68. *Dwarf calves. Note the sway back and large middles. These calves have reached their maximum size. (Courtesy U.S.D.A. Bureau Animal Industry.)*

would produce an average of four calves carrying the dwarf factor, although they would be normal in appearance. To produce dwarf calves both parents must be carriers of the factor.

Prevention of Dwarfism. To purge the herd of dwarfs is not simple. If a dwarf results from any mating, both parents carry the factor, and they should be eliminated. This does not tell us how many more cows may be carriers. The ratio of dwarf calves from parents that are carriers is one in four. This is only a ratio based on large numbers, and it is conceivable that a carrier cow mated to a carrier bull for ten years may never produce a dwarf.

After disposing of the carrier bull, one is confronted with the problem of securing a replacement that is not a carrier. If the prospective bull has been in service and has not sired any dwarfs, that is some indication that he may be free of the factor. If replacement animals are selected from a herd where the record has shown no dwarfism, there is some assurance that they do not carry the factor.

At present scientists are busy trying to perfect methods whereby dwarf carriers may be detected before going into service and contaminating cattle herds. Prospects of new discoveries in such detection methods as X rays and other devices are promising, but it is too early to reach any definite conclusions.

Other Types of Abnormalities. There are a number of other inherited abnormalities, but fortunately they do not occur often enough to be of any great economic importance. Some of the abnormalities are known as *lethals* (meaning that the calves will either be stillborn or die within a few days of birth), while others show up as defects in conformation or as sterility.

SUMMARY

Before attempting to establish a breeding herd (whether it is to be a purebred or commercial herd), one should consider the kind and amount of available feed, the demand for feeding or breeding stock, and the amount of capital available.

If the prospective cattleman has the capital and a farm adapted to raising cattle, he is reasonably safe in starting a herd at almost any time. Where capital is limited it is advisable to start with a few heifers and bull rather than to risk going into debt to buy a cow herd.

Foundation stock should be selected on the basis of conformation, progeny, and production records. Low-set, blocky, compact, uniformly covered animals, well developed in the hind and front quarters and carrying good depth of body and straight top and underlines, represent the desirable conformation. Animals sired by bulls with progeny records and out of good milking cows will improve the gaining ability of the herds into which they go.

The national beef cattle breeding program is a cooperative research effort between the United States Department of Agriculture and several state experiment stations to develop fast and efficient gaining cattle with desirable carcass quality. Cattlemen can profit from the research work by contacting agricultural teachers and agricultural colleges for information relative to the location of breeding stock.

Dwarfism is an inherited abnormality that has caused considerable economic loss in many herds. Dwarf calves result from mating two animals that carry the factor. The ratio of dwarfs from such matings is one in four. Of the remaining three, two will carry the factor and, if mated to a dwarf-carrying animal, will produce dwarf calves in the one-to-four ratio.

QUESTIONS

1. What are the conditions one should consider before starting a breeding herd of beef cattle? Explain.
2. Describe how you would proceed to obtain breeding stock.

3. Describe what you would look for in breeding stock.
4. How can the score card be used to help beginners?
5. What information will production records reveal?
6. What is the National Beef Cattle Breeding Program and what are its objectives?
7. How can the individual benefit from the National Beef Cattle Breeding Program?
8. List the goals established for carcass quality in slaughter cattle.
9. Discuss the cause and prevention of dwarfism.

REFERENCES

Baker, Marvel L., Leslie E. Johnson, and Russell L. Davis, *Beef Cattle Breeding Research at Fort Robinson*, Agricultural Experiment Station, Miscellaneous Publication 1, 1952, University of Nebraska, Lincoln, Nebraska.

Beef Cattle Feeding and Breeding Investigation, Kansas Agricultural Experiment Station, Reports 37, 38, 40, Kansas State College, Manhattan, Kansas.

Feeding and Breeding Tests, Progress Report, Oklahoma Agricultural Experiment Station, Miscellaneous Publications No. MP-27, Oklahoma A & M College, Stillwater, Oklahoma.

Feeding and Breeding Tests, Progress Report, Oklahoma Agricultural Experiment Station, Miscellaneous Publications No. MP-31, Oklahoma A & M College, Stillwater, Oklahoma.

Feeding and Breeding Test with Beef Cattle, Reprinted from Miscellaneous Publication No. MP-34, Oklahoma Agricultural Experiment Station, Feeder's Day Report, 1954, Oklahoma A & M College, Stillwater, Oklahoma.

Gregory, P. W., W. C. Rollins, and F. D. Carroll, *Heterozygous Expression of the Dwarf Gene in Beef Cattle*, Reprint from the *Southwestern Veterinarian*, Vol. 5, No. 4, Summer, 1952, pp. 345-49.

Iowa Beef Cattle Improvement Program, Agricultural Extension Service, A. H. 810, 1960, Iowa State University, Ames, Iowa.

Livestock Breeding Research at the U.S. Range Livestock Experiment Station, Agricultural Information Bulletin No. 18, U.S. Department of Agriculture, Washington, D.C.

Ralston, F. A., *Beef Production in Montana*, Agricultural Extension Bulletin 272, 1951, Montana State College, Bozeman, Montana.

Roubicek, C. B., N. W. Hilston, and S. S. Wheeler, *Progeny Studies with Hereford and Shorthorn Cattle*, Wyoming Agricultural Experiment Station Bulletin 307, 1951, University of Wyoming, Laramie, Wyoming.

4

Selection of Feeder Cattle

Feeder cattle are cattle that are unfinished or those that do not carry enough condition to make the slaughter grade they are capable of. Such cattle are usually purchased from the range by cattle feeders and put into the feed lot to be fattened. The cattle feeder is usually located in the corn belt or a grain producing area. He generally raises at least part of the feed, although many feeders buy large quantities of grain, and a few purchase all of their feed supplies. The feeder depends upon margin and value of the gain over feed costs and other expenses for his profits. (See Chapter 1.)

FIGURE 69. *Choice feeder cattle ready for shipment to a midwestern feed yard. (Courtesy American Hereford Association.)*

Feeder cattle vary considerably in age, weight, body conformation, ability to make rapid gains, and amount of condition they carry. Heifers and steers will vary in their performance in the feed lot. These large variations in feeder cattle create a number of problems for the purchaser of cattle for fattening. There will be price variations depending upon weight, quality, and sex, but the prices will not vary in the same proportion each year. Sometimes heavy cattle may be in demand, and at other times calves or light cattle will be more popular among feeders, with a resulting variation in price. Occasionally, lower-grade cattle will be selling several dollars below choice feeders, and at other times the spread may be narrow.

Certain weights and quality of cattle may be better adapted to the amount and kinds of feed available. Also, the future market outlook must be considered. The cattle feeders' problems are many, and only those with good judgment are likely to succeed financially over a long period.

CLASSES AND GRADES OF FEEDER CATTLE

Feeder cattle are classified and graded according to age, sex, weight, and conformation.

Age. For age, cattle are classified as calves, yearlings, two-year-olds, cows, bulls, and stags. All cattle are designated as calves until they are one year old. Between the ages of one year and two years they are classified as yearlings. Animals over a year, but less than eighteen months old, are sometimes referred to as *short-yearlings,* whereas the term *long-yearlings* is applied to animals over eighteen months, but under two years of age. Two-year-olds are cattle between the ages of two and three years. Cattle three or more years of age seldom enter the feeder trade, except for cows, bulls, and stags. Conditions under which cows, bulls, and stags may enter the feeder trade will be discussed later.

Sex. In sex, cattle are classified as steers, heifers, heiferettes, cows, bulls, and stags.

Steer. A steer is a male animal that was castrated at an early age, and before he reached sexual maturity.

Heifer. A heifer is a female animal that has not developed the mature form of the cow and has not had a calf. Usually females under three years of age are classed as heifers. Heiferettes is a term often used in the cattle trade. It refers to young cows, usually those that have not had more than one calf.

Cow. A cow is a mature female that has had one or more calves. A barren female (one that fails to "get with calf") that has reached maturity is also classed as a cow.

Bull. A bull is an uncastrated male of any age.

Stag. A stag is a male animal castrated after he has developed the physical characteristics of a mature bull.

Weight. Weight for steer and heifer groups of feeder cattle is classified as heavy, medium, and light. There is no weight classification for cows, bulls, and stags. The weight class that a steer or heifer falls in is determined by the age of the animal. For example, a steer calf to be classified as heavy would need to weigh from 450 to 500 pounds. A heavy yearling feeder steer would weigh from 700 to 800 pounds, whereas a heavy two-year-old feeder steer would weigh around 1,100 pounds. The amount of condition is important in determining the weight classification of feeder cattle. Some cattle have a frame large enough to classify as heavies, but owing to a short feed supply they may be thin and not classify heavier than medium or, in extreme cases, as lightweights. Heavy calves could be heavier than light yearlings. This is especially true if the yearlings are thin. Cattle have attained most of their growth by the time they are two and a half years old. Weight beyond 1,000 pounds is largely due to finish. Yearlings on good pasture could be as heavy as two-year-olds that have less abundant grazing conditions.

Grade. Steers and heifers are graded according to quality: fancy, choice, good, medium, common, and inferior. For cows, bulls, and stags the highest grade is choice, with a total of only five grades.

Fancy cattle. The term "fancy" is applied to only a small percentage of feeder steers and heifers. Those grading *fancy* show exceptional smoothness, and body conformation. Such cattle, especially the steers, are in demand by showmen who fatten them out for exhibition at the fat-cattle shows. They usually sell for too high a price to be profitable for commercial feeders.

Choice cattle. *Choice* is the highest practical grade of feeder cattle. They are superior in conformation, natural finish, and quality. They are blocky, compact, wide, and deep, and are straight in their top and underlines. Well developed in the quarters, they

FIGURE 70. *A fancy feeder calf. (U.S.D.A. Photo.)*

show evidence of having only high-grade or purebred ancestry of strictly beef cattle breeds. One who buys choice steers can expect them to finish into *high choice* or *prime* slaughter grades and bring the higher price paid for the top grade of fat cattle.

Good cattle. Cattle grading *good* must show evidence of having ancestry mostly from the beef breeds, but show less compactness and be more upstanding and not as smooth as the higher grades. They lack in the development of the more valuable cuts, such as the back, loin, and hindquarters. Feeder cattle grading *good* can be expected to finish into good to choice fat cattle.

Medium cattle. This grade of cattle are upstanding, and uneven in the top and underlines. The hip bones are prominent, and they

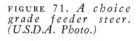

FIGURE 71. *A choice grade feeder steer. (U.S.D.A. Photo.)*

are somewhat narrow over the back, and light in the hindquarters. They may show evidence of some dairy breeding. Medium steers cannot be expected to grade higher than *good* as slaughter cattle.

Common cattle. Common steers show a lack of thrift and constitution. They are upstanding, narrow chested, narrow over the back and loins, light in the hindquarters, shallow bodied, long necked, and prominent in the hips. They are not straight in the top and underlines and are usually steep in the rump. In type they resemble the dairy breeds more than the beef breeds of cattle. Many of the feeder cattle lots grading *common* are dairy breeds of steers. Medium slaughter steers are about as high a grade as they can be expected to grade after fattening.

Inferior cattle. This is the lowest feeder grade. In addition to having all the faults of common-grade cattle, they are apt to be unhealthy, stunted, and extremely unthrifty. The following table summarizes the classes and grades of feeder cattle.

FIGURE 72. *A feeder steer that would grade good. (U.S.D.A. Photo.)*

FIGURE 73. *A medium grade feeder steer. Note the lack of depth, width, and compactness as compared to the higher grade feeder cattle. (U.S.D.A. Photo.)*

Cows, Bulls, and Stags. Cows, bulls, and stags do not make up a large percentage of the feeder cattle trade. However, when cows become old or nonproductive, they go to market. Some cattle feeders make a practice of buying cows. They fatten them to improve the slaughter grade, thereby increasing the per pound value. The profit on cows usually comes from margin because cows are not very efficient users of feed.

Bulls usually come to the market as singles, and are sold by breeders and commercial producers when they can no longer use them for breeding. A certain percentage of the bulls are castrated, fattened, and sold as stags.

TABLE 4

CLASSES AND GRADES OF FEEDER CATTLE

Sex	Age	Weight	Grade
Steers	Calves Yearlings 2-year-olds	Heavy Medium Light	Fancy, choice, good, medium, common, and inferior
Heifers	Calves Yearlings 2-year-olds	Heavy Medium Light	Fancy, choice, good, medium, common, and inferior
Cows Bulls Stags	All ages All ages All ages	Any Weight	Choice, good, medium, common, and inferior

Score Card for Feeder Cattle. Experience is the only method whereby one can gain sufficient knowledge to grade accurately feeder cattle. However, the beginner may get some help by carefully studying the score card designed for feeder cattle. The most common error made by the inexperienced cattleman is to overemphasize some points in conformation and underemphasize others. One seldom finds even one animal above criticism, let alone a group.

FIGURE 74. *This common grade feeder steer is leggy and lacks depth and width.* (*U.S.D.A. Photo.*)

Therefore it is important to give the proper value to the good points and not to deduct unduly for the faults in conformation.

The following score card attempts to give a point value to the various parts of an animal's conformation based upon the importance of that part of the body to a high-grade feeder.

SCORE CARD FOR FEEDER BEEF CATTLE

Scale of Points	Point Value
A. GENERAL APPEARANCE	
1. Weight for age	10
2. Form—broad, deep, low-set, smooth, compact, straight, top and underline, stylish	10
3. Quality—thrifty and healthy, pliable skin of medium thickness, dense; clean, medium-sized bone; fine, soft, shiny hair coat	12
4. Condition—uniform covering; high degree of natural fleshing giving due consideration to available feeds	6
	38
B. BODY	
5. Chest—full, deep, wide; heart girth, large; crops, full	4
6. Ribs—long, well sprung	8
7. Back—broad, straight, uniformly covered	8
8. Loin—broad, uniformly covered	8
9. Flank full, even with underline	2
	30
C. HINDQUARTERS	
10. Hips—smooth, well blended into body	2
11. Rump—long, wide, level; tailhead, smooth; pin bones, wide apart, not prominent	5
12. Thighs—deep, full	5
13. Twist—deep, plump	5
14. Legs—wide apart, straight, short; shanks, fine, smooth	1
	18
D. FOREQUARTERS	
15. Shoulders—smooth, compact, neat	3
16. Shoulder vein—full	2
17. Brisket—trim, neat; breast, wide and full	2
18. Legs—wide apart, straight, short; arm full, shank fine	1
	8
E. HEAD AND NECK	
19. Muzzle—broad; mouth, large; nostrils, large, open	1
20. Eyes—large, clear, placid	1
21. Forehead—broad, full; ears, medium sized, fine texture	1
22. Face—short; jaws, strong	1
23. Neck—short, thick, blending smoothly with shoulders; throat—clean with light dewlap	2
	6
TOTAL	100

SELECTING FEEDER CATTLE

Feeding programs vary widely. There is a wide choice in weights, grades, ages, and kinds of cattle available to feeders, and there is just as great a variation in feeding conditions. The kind of cattle to buy depends upon so many factors that only a few can be considered here. However, the more important considerations are: (1) kind and amount of feed available, (2) price of feed, (3) spread in prices between feeder and slaughter cattle, (4) future market outlook, and (5) the length of time they are to be fed.

Feed. If high quality slaughter beef is to be produced, the use of liberal amounts of feed grains and good quality forage is usually essential. A cattle feeder with his bins full of feed grains and a barn full of good hay may well consider buying choice grades. Since young beef that grades prime generally tops the market, choice heavy calves or choice light yearlings that can be marketed at from 1,000 to 1,200 pounds in weight should be considered.

FIGURE 75. *These steers are being wintered primarily on hay, and will be finished on grass. (Courtesy Geo. A. Hormel Company.)*

These cattle may be either steers or heifers.   If heifers are purchased the price must be less than that of steers in the same grade.
Heifers finish somewhat faster on the average than steers, but will
not equal steers in dressing percentage.   The market price of fat
heifers is usually lower than that of steers in the corresponding
grade.

FIGURE 76.   *The buyer of these cattle felt that choice light calves would best fit his
conditions.*

It takes both quality cattle and quality feed to produce top beef.
Low-grade feeders, regardless of how well fed, will not make high-
grade slaughter cattle.   If there is available an abundance of low
quality roughage, such as corn fodder, sorgo fodder, and hay that
is coarse or "stemmy," the problem of using this forage profitably
may be solved by feeding it to cattle.   Cattle may be bought in
the fall and used to clean up a cornfield behind the picker or run
out on the pastures as long as there is sufficient feed.   Medium-to-
heavy yearlings, weighing from 600 to 750 pounds, and medium-to-
common grades would be well suited for this purpose.   After the
rough feed in the fields has been eaten up, the cattle may be put
in the feed lot and full-fed roughage with enough protein to meet

the animals' need. Grain should be limited to from 3 to 5 pounds per day until the last thirty to sixty days of the feeding period. A full feed of grain may be used the last month or so. These cattle will market as commercial-to-good slaughter steers and will not require more than 15 to 25 bushels of grain.

It is important that lower-grade cattle be bought at a price considerably under the price of choice grades. Such cattle will not make top grade slaughter animals, and the cattle feeder will receive less for them on a hundredweight basis. They do offer an opportunity to convert low quality feed into a marketable product. High-grade cattle fed on low quality feed will generally not produce the highest grade of beef. The loss in margin usually results in a financial loss when cattle are not fed according to grade. The kind of feed available should determine to a large extent the grade of cattle to buy.

Feed Prices. When prices of feed are high in proportion to finished beef and when feeder prices are low, the cattle feeder generally expects to make his profit on the margin rather than on the gain in weight. Under these conditions heavy cattle weighing from 800 to 1,000 pounds may be the best. These cattle will be ready for market after a gain of from 200 to 300 pounds. The purpose of the gain is to finish the cattle to meet the requirements of their slaughter grade and to bring the feeder an increased price per hundred over the cost of the feeders. In making a marginal profit of from $2 to $3 per hundredweight, he has a profit of from $16 to $30 per head, if he can break even on the gain. If the reverse is true—that is, low-priced feed and high-priced feeders—then the chance for profit is greater on the gain than on the margin. When feed is cheap, light yearlings or calves weighing from 300 to 500 pounds will cost less. With low-priced feed the feeder may put from 600 to 800 pounds of gain per head on the cattle. His profit will result from the gain rather than from the margin.

Spread in Feeder and Slaughter Cattle Prices. If the price of feeders is low compared to the price of slaughter cattle, again the margin is important. Heavy cattle will usually bring in the most profit.

Future Market Outlook. Price prospects for fat cattle are important in determining which weights and grades of feeders to buy. If the immediate future outlook is good but the long-time outlook is very uncertain, then heavy cattle, which will meet the grade most in demand for fat cattle, are more certain to make a profit. Such cattle may be short-fed from 90 to 120 days and moved before the expected price break.

Length of Feeding Period. The amount of feed available usually determines the length of time cattle are fed. Cattle feeders having large amounts of feed they desire to market as beef generally desire light animals of a grade that will correspond to the quality of feed available.

These cattle are often calves bought in the fall, wintered to gain a pound a day, which is only a good growth gain, and turned on pasture the next spring. Some grain may be fed to the cattle while on grass. The second fall they are put into the feed lot and finished according to their grade.

SUMMARY

Feeder cattle are unfinished cattle that are generally either sold to cattle feeders or put into the feed lot by the producer and finished for market.

Feeder cattle vary considerably as to age, weight, and grade. Most feeder cattle are steers or heifers. The weight classes are light, medium, and heavy. The age classes are calves, yearlings, and two-year-olds. Steers and heifers are graded fancy, choice, good, medium, common, and inferior. Feeder cows, bulls, and stags have a top grade of choice. Bulls and stags make up a very small percentage of the feeder cattle trade.

In selecting feeder cattle one should give careful consideration to the available feed, feed prices, spread in feeder and slaughter cattle prices, future market outlook, and length of the feeding period.

QUESTIONS

1. What are feeder cattle?
2. What are the age classifications of feeder cattle?
3. What are the weight classifications of feeder cattle?
4. List the grades of heifers, steers, cows, bulls, and stags.
5. Describe the choice feeder steer.
6. What are the chief factors that determine the grades of feeder cattle?
7. Give an example of when heavy cattle would be a good buy. Of when light cattle would be.

8. Under what conditions would you recommend the purchase of choice feeders? The plainer grades?
9. What are the important factors one should consider in determining the weight and grade of cattle to buy?

REFERENCES

Beresford, Rex, *151 Questions on Cattle Feeding and Marketing,* Iowa State College Extension Bulletin 99, Ames, Iowa.

Heady, Earl O., and Harold R. Jensen, *Farm Management and Economics,* Prentice-Hall, Inc., New York, 1954.

Snapp, Roscoe R., and A. L. Neuman, *Beef Cattle* (Fifth Edition), John Wiley and Sons, Inc., New York, 1960.

Feeds and Feed Utilization by Beef Cattle

Profitable production of beef cattle requires a practical knowledge of feeds and of how cattle can best utilize these feeds. It has been pointed out in the preceding chapters that there is a wide variation in the types of beef production programs. If one is to select and develop a program best fitted to his particular set of conditions, he must be familiar with the feeding value of the various feed stuffs and the kind of cattle best suited for utilizing available feeds.

THE DIGESTIVE SYSTEM OF CATTLE

To understand the food requirements of beef cattle, we should know how they digest and utilize feed. Beef cattle belong to that class of animals known as "ruminants." Ruminants are animals that have four compartments to their stomachs, as contrasted to the simple-stomached animals that have a single-compartment stomach. Examples of ruminants among common farm animals are cattle, sheep, and goats. Hogs are the most common example of simple-stomached animals; poultry, although not classified as simple-stomached animals, have a similar digestive system.

Because of their type of digestive system, cattle do not present so many feeding problems as do animals with a simple stomach. As will be shown later, cattle can actually manufacture many of the vitamins and some protein amino acids that have to be fed the simple-stomached animals. They are also able to digest large quantities of roughage.

The compartments of the ruminant stomach are the *rumen, reticulum, omasum* and *abomasum.*

Function of the Four Compartments. Each compartment of the cattle stomach has important functions to perform.

Rumen. The rumen is the first and by far the largest compartment of the stomach. It serves as a storage area for large quantities of feed, especially roughages, and has a capacity of from 40 to 60 gallons in mature cattle, depending upon the size of the animal.

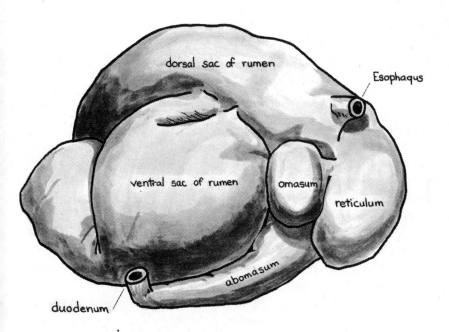

FIGURE 77.   *The stomach of a mature ruminant animal.   Note the size of the rumen compared to the other three stomach compartments.   (Drawing by Harlan Clark.)*

During the process of eating, ruminants chew their food just enough to make swallowing possible. While the food is in the rumen, it is worked upon by millions of bacteria and other microorganisms. These microorganisms are able to transform low quality proteins and even some nitrogen compounds into essential protein amino acids. They also manufacture many needed vitamins, including the vitamin-B complex group. The proteins and vitamins are used by the bacteria, and as the bacteria die, they are in turn digested by the cattle.

After the ruminants have consumed their feed, regurgitation, or chewing the cud, takes place. The food is brought up from the rumen, and the chewing is completed. It is then swallowed again, returning to the rumen for further bacterial action.

The presence of the rumen, and the bacterial action that takes place in it, explains why beef cattle can digest large quantities of roughage and convert it into beef; for this reason, too, the B-complex vitamins and highly complex protein feeds are seldom necessary in their ration. It will be shown later that proteins are an essential part of the beef cattle ration, but that they need not be nearly so varied and complete as for swine and poultry. In very young calves the rumen is not developed, and during the first few weeks they must receive a diet containing most of the food nutrients.

Reticulum. The reticulum is closely associated with the rumen, and it is here that many foreign bodies, such as wire and nails, are retained. If these objects are not pointed or too sharp, they may be held in the reticulum for long periods without any serious damage. The main functions of the reticulum are to furnish additional storage space and to sort out and hold foreign materials that may cause serious damage to the other body organs.

Omasum. The omasum, or third compartment of the stomach, consists of strong muscular walls. Its functions are not too well understood, but seem to be that of squeezing out the water from the feed before it enters the abomasum.

Abomasum. The abomasum is the fourth compartment or true stomach; its functions are similar to those of the simple stomach in swine or similar animals. Gastric juice, which is necessary in protein digestion, is secreted in the abomasum. When the food leaves the abomasum, it goes into the small intestine, where the digestible portion is absorbed into the blood stream; the remainder is passed into the large intestine and eliminated as waste.

Digestive System of Ruminants. The important item to realize about the digestive system of ruminants is their ability to (1) manufacture the B-complex group of vitamins, (2) utilize low quality proteins, (3) convert a certain amount of nitrogen to protein compounds, and (4) digest large quantities of roughage.

Millions of microorganisms found in the rumen and to some extent in the reticulum are responsible for much of the digestive process of beef cattle and other ruminants. It has been said by cattle authorities that if the microorganisms are properly fed, the cow will be well nourished. This statement is partially true, since the rumen should contain a large population of beneficial bacteria so as to obtain the most economical returns for each dollar spent on feed and to maintain the health of the animal.

DIGESTIVE PROCESSES OF YOUNG CALVES

The rumen of the calf does not develop and begin to function until several days after birth.   Until rumination has started, the young calf is unable to manufacture the vitamins and protein amino acids that older ruminants are capable of doing.   Therefore, to get all the essential food nutrients young calves are dependent upon the ration provided for them.   The problems involved in the feeding of newborn calves are very similar to those of swine and other simple-stomached animals.   In addition to vitamins A and D, the B-complex vitamins must be in the ration.   Animal proteins are necessary to insure a complete protein balance.   Most beef cattle-men permit the calves to nurse the cows until they are five to six months old.   Since milk contains enough of the necessary food nutrients for the calf until he is old enough to eat grains and forage, nutritional problems seldom arise (except in the case of a poor milking cow).

FIGURE 78.   *Here we see a comparison of the mature (left) and young (right) ruminant stomach.   (Drawing by David Wright.)*

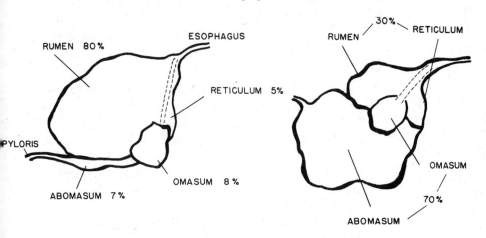

FOOD NUTRIENTS

The term "nutrient" means any single class of food or group of like foods that aids in the support of life and makes it possible for animals to produce the things expected of them. Nutrients are generally divided into five classes: carbohydrates, fats, proteins, minerals, and vitamins. Water is very essential, and may be classed as a sixth nutrient.

Carbohydrates and Fats. Carbohydrates and fats, generally supplied to cattle by feeds high in these nutrients, furnish heat and energy and provide much of the material necessary for fattening. Fats and carbohydrates are very much alike, although fats are more concentrated; fats furnish two and one-fourth times as much heat and energy as do carbohydrates. In other words, one pound of fat will equal two and one-fourth pounds of carbohydrates in heat and energy value.

Carbohydrates are composed largely of sugars and starches and fats of fatty acids. They constitute about three-fourths of all the dry matter in grains, hay, grasses, silage, fodder, and other similar feeds. These feeds are usually grown by the beef producer and supply most of the cattle's needs for these nutrients.

Proteins. The greater part of the muscles, internal organs, skin, hair, hoofs, and horns are made up of proteins. The unborn calf or fetus is dependent to a large extent upon proteins for survival and development. Unless the proper amount of proteins are supplied in the ration for beef cattle, the growth and fattening processes will be much slower and more costly.

Proteins are made up of a group of acids known as *amino acids*. Of the 25 or more amino acids that have been identified, at least ten are considered essential in livestock feeding. The amino acids are sometimes referred to as the building stones for proteins. Feeds that contain all or nearly all the essential amino acids are referred to as complete or nearly complete protein. These complete protein feeds are much more important for simple-stomached animals than they are for beef cattle.

Except for very young calves, any cattle that are fed adequate amounts of any digestible form of protein can manufacture the required amino acids. Therefore, the cheapest source of protein is an important consideration. Legume roughages, pastures, and such by-products of the oil seed crops as soybean oil meal, linseed oil meal, cottonseed meal, and peanut oil meal are important sources of proteins for beef cattle. Other high protein feeds are corn gluten feed, corn gluten meal, soybeans, and many more of lesser importance. Most farm grains and nonlegume roughages are low in protein.

Urea. Urea is a nitrogen compound from which the bacteria in the ruminant stomach may make a certain amount of the amino acids or protein building stones essential to good nutrition. It may be used as a protein substitute within limits, as described in Chapter 8.

Vitamins. Beef cattle utilize a large number of vitamins, but fortunately most of them are manufactured in the digestive system. Except for very young calves, whose rumen has not started to function, vitamins A and D are all that seem to be required in the beef cattle ration. Carotene, which is found in abundance in all

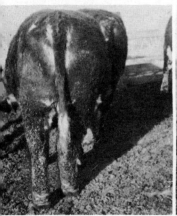

FIGURE 79. *Swelling often develops in cattle suffering from vitamin A deficiency. Note swollen legs (left) and swelling in the abdominal region (right) and dry hair coat. (Courtesy L. L. Madsen, U.S.D.A. Bureau of Animal Industry.)*

high quality forage, is converted to vitamin A by animals. Vitamin D is supplied by sunlight and is also found in sun-cured forage. Except in the case of cattle kept inside and fed poor quality forage, vitamins-A and -D supplements are seldom necessary in older animals' rations.

Occasionally, it may be necessary to hand-feed beef calves. Such conditions arise if the cow produces insufficient amounts of milk

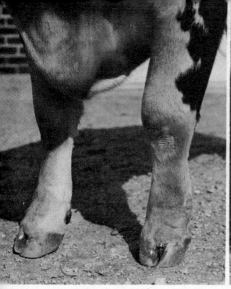
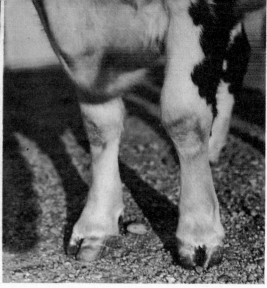

FIGURE 80. *This photo (left) shows swelling in the front legs due to vitamin A deficiency and (right) the disappearance of the swelling following vitamin A therapy.* (*Courtesy L. L. Madsen, U.S.D.A. Bureau of Animal Industry.*)

to nourish the calf properly, or if the mother dies before the calf is weaned. When calves are hand-fed they may benefit from the B vitamins and also from the addition of vitamin-A and -D concentrate added to their milk. Fish liver oils are important sources of vitamins A and D, and brewer's yeast and distiller's solubles will supply most of the additional B vitamins that may be needed by very young calves.

FIGURE 81. *This cow developed rickets early in life when maintained on a vitamin D deficient ration and not allowed exposure to direct sunlight. Note the bowed front legs and enlarged joints.* (*Courtesy L. L. Madsen, U.S.D.A. Bureau of Animal Industry.*)

Minerals.   Minerals are needed in nearly all parts of the animal body but are used primarily in the bones, the teeth, and for milk production of cows that are suckling calves.   When rations are low in this nutrient, growth will be retarded, damage will be caused to the animals' health, and cows may produce insufficient milk for their calves.

Minerals are generally divided into two groups: *major minerals* and *trace minerals*.   The major minerals—salt, calcium, and phosphorus—are needed in the greatest quantity, and are most likely to be lacking in the feed supplied.   The trace minerals are those needed in very small amounts, and yet are essential to the health

FIGURE 82. *This animal (top) is suffering from cobalt deficiency. The administration of cobalt (bottom) brought about remarkable recovery. (Courtesy C. F. Huffman, Michigan Agricultural Experiment Station.)*

of the cattle. They include iron, copper, manganese, iodine, cobalt, sulphur, magnesium, zinc, potassium, and boron.

Legume roughages will supply large amounts of most minerals except salt, but mineral supplements for beef cattle are recommended. Steamed bone meal is an excellent source of both phosphorus and calcium. The trace minerals may be purchased as a trace mineral mixture or supplied by using trace mineralized salt. Salt should either be provided straight or included in the mineral mixture.

Antibiotics. Antibiotics are not considered a food nutrient. However, recent experiments show a marked decrease in incidence of scouring, and growth increases occurred when antibiotics were administered in capsule form to suckling calves. Older calves, especially those on poor to medium quality rations, showed increased gains when given a ration containing antibiotics. The function of antibiotics is not well understood, but they have an important place in beef calf feeding. Four antibiotics—aureomycin, terramycin, bacitracin, and penicillin—have been used in feeding experiments. Aureomycin has given the best results up to the present time.

Hormones. Like antibiotics, hormones are not considered a food nutrient, but recent experimental results show definite increases in gains of fattening cattle when certain hormones, especially diethylstilbestrol, were included in the ration.

FIGURE 83. *The cow on the left received a phosphorus supplement while grazing on a phosphorus deficient range for two and one-half years. The cow on the right received none. Note the thriftier appearance of the cow and calf that received the phosphorus supplement. (From Cooperative Work of the Bureau of Animal Industry, Texas Agricultural Experiment Station, and the King Ranch, Kingsville, Texas.)*

Water. From 70 to 80 per cent of the beef animal's body is made up of water. Approximately 87 per cent of milk is water. Water transports the digested food materials through the intestinal walls into the blood stream, carries away waste products, and aids in the control of body temperature. Each pound of milk a cow produces requires from three and one-half to five and one-half pounds of water in addition to the amount required by the body.

The weather conditions and the kind of feed influence the amount of water required. Water consumption increases rapidly on hot days. When silage or any roughage high in moisture is fed, cattle will drink less water. When water is available at all times to range cattle and cattle in the feed lots, greater gains and more efficient use of feed will result.

CLASSIFICATION OF FEEDS

Feeds are generally classified according to the amount of total digestible nutrients they provide, or according to amounts of a specific nutrient they furnish in the ration. They are usually divided into two general classes: roughages and concentrates.

Roughages. Feeds containing large amounts of fiber or non-digestible materials are called *roughages*. This group includes hays, silage, fodder, and other similar feeds.

Legume roughages. Legumes are plants that use nitrogen which they take from the air. Legumes are higher in nitrogen than most

FIGURE 84. *Plenty of fresh water is essential to economical beef production. (Courtesy Geo. A. Hormel Company.)*

other plants, and since nitrogen is essential in the manufacture of proteins, legumes are higher in protein than are the other roughages. The common legumes are alfalfa, all the clovers, trefoil, soybeans, and lespedeza; various varieties of peas and beans; and a large number of other less widely grown plants.

Nonlegume roughages. Nonlegume roughages as a class are lower in protein than are legumes. When they are fed as the only roughage, they seldom provide enough protein to meet the needs of beef cattle. The use of nonlegumes as the only roughage generally calls for an increased amount of the high protein feeds to balance the ration. The common nonlegume roughages are brome grass, timothy, bluegrass, western prairie grasses, corn fodder, corn silage, and fodder or silage made from the various sorghums.

Concentrates. Concentrates are feeds that have a comparatively high digestibility. They are relatively low in fiber and include all the grains and many by-products of grains and animals, such as wheat bran, soybean oil meal, cottonseed meal, and tankage.

Protein concentrates. Protein concentrates may be classed as a subdivision of concentrates. The term refers to the group of concentrates that furnish a relatively high percentage of protein. The exact percentage of protein a feed must contain before it may be considered a protein concentrate has not been definitely defined, but for the purposes of this book we shall consider any feed that contains 20 per cent or more protein as a protein concentrate.

Protein concentrates may be derived from animal or vegetable sources. Those derived from vegetable material are referred to as *vegetable proteins*, whereas those having an animal origin are called *animal proteins*. The animal proteins are more complete and are usually more expensive. Because of their expense and for reasons already explained, the vegetable proteins are more important in beef cattle feeding.

Fiber and Nitrogen-Free Extract. These are common terms used in discussing livestock feeds. Both have to do with carbohydrates. *Fiber* refers to the less digestible and *nitrogen-free extract* refers to the more digestible part of the carbohydrates.

BALANCING THE RATION

Profitable beef production requires the greatest possible gains at the least possible feed costs. This cannot be accomplished unless the ration is well balanced.   Cattle utilize feed for the maintenance of their bodies, for growth as long as they are immature, for the development of unborn calves, and for milk production.   Nature is rather exacting about the amounts of each nutrient required for these functions.   If the ration does not provide enough of each nutrient, the cattle will be disappointing in the way they perform the functions expected of them.   Also, feed will be wasted.   For example, supposing fattening cattle are fed primarily on nonlegume hay and corn.   They will have more than a sufficient amount of carbohydrates.   In their attempt to get enough protein and other nutrients to meet their needs, they will consume greater quantities of these feeds than needed, eliminating much of the excess carbohydrates as waste.   If the ration is balanced by the addition of the required amounts of other nutrients, feed will not be wasted and more economical gains will result.

Balanced Ration Defined.   A balanced ration is one that supplies in their correct proportion all the food nutrients necessary to nourish the animal properly and to meet the requirements for production during a 24-hour period.

NUTRIENT REQUIREMENTS FOR BEEF CATTLE

The nutritional requirements of beef cattle will depend upon the age, rate of gains expected, and, in the case of cows, whether or not they are suckling a calf.   The nutritional requirements of bulls depends upon both the age and the extent to which they are being used for breeding purposes.   The following tables give the recommended nutrient content of rations best for beef cattle under the various conditions.

TABLE 5

Recommended Daily Nutrient Allowances for Beef Cattle
(Based on air-dry feed containing 90 per cent dry matter)

Body Weight (Pounds)	Expected Daily Gain (Pounds)	Total Feed		Daily Allowances per Animal				
		Per Cent of Live weight	Per Animal (Pounds)	Digestible Protein (Pounds)	Total Digestible Nutrients (Pounds)	Calcium (Grams)	Phosphorus (Grams)	Carotene (Mg.)
Normal Growth, Heifers and Steers								
400	1.6	3.0	12	0.9	7.0	20	15	24
600	1.4	2.7	16	0.9	8.5	18	15	36
800	1.2	2.4	19	0.9	9.5	16	15	48
1,000	1.0	2.1	21	0.9	10.5	15	15	60

TABLE 5 (Continued)

Daily Allowances per Animal

Body Weight (Pounds)	Expected Daily Gain (Pounds)	Per Cent of Live Weight	Per Animal (Pounds)	Digestible Protein (Pounds)	Total Digestible Nutrients (Pounds)	Calcium (Grams)	Phos- phorus (Grams)	Caro- tene (Mg.)
		Total Feed						

Bulls, Growth and Maintenance (Moderate Activity)

Body Weight (Pounds)	Expected Daily Gain (Pounds)	Per Cent of Live Weight	Per Animal (Pounds)	Digestible Protein (Pounds)	Total Digestible Nutrients (Pounds)	Calcium (Grams)	Phos- phorus (Grams)	Caro- tene (Mg.)
600	2.3	2.7	16	1.3	10.0	24	18	36
800	1.7	2.1	17	1.4	11.0	23	18	48
1,000	1.6	2.0	20	1.4	12:0	22	18	60
1,200	1.4	1.8	22	1.4	13.0	21	18	72
1,400	1.0	1.7	24	1.4	14.0	20	18	84
1,600	—	1.6	26	1.4	14.0	18	18	96
1,800	—	1.4	26	1.4	14.0	18	18	108

Wintering Weaning Calves

400	1.0	2.8	11	0.7	6.0	16	12	24
500	1.0	2.6	13	0.8	7.0	16	12	30
600	1.0	2.5	15	0.8	8.0	16	12	36

Wintering Yearling Cattle

600	1.0	2.7	16	0.8	8.0	16	12	36
700	1.0	2.4	17	0.8	8.5	16	12	42
800	0.7	2.3	18	0.8	9.0	16	12	48
900	0.5	2.0	18	0.8	9.0	16	12	54

Wintering Pregnant Heifers
(Weights are for beginning of winter period; gains average for period)

700	1.5	2.9	20	0.9	10.0	18	16	42
800	1.3	2.3	20	0.9	10.0	18	16	48
900	0.8	2.0	18	0.8	9.0	16	15	54
1,000	0.5	1.8	18	0.8	9.0	16	15	60

Wintering Mature Pregnant Cows
(Weights are for beginning of winter period; gains average for period)

800	1.5	2.8	22	1.0	11.0	22	18	48
900	1.0	2.2	20	0.9	10.0	18	16	54
1,000	0.4	1.8	18	0.9	9.0	16	15	60
1,100	0.2	1.6	18	0.8	9.0	16	15	66
1,200	0.0	1.5	18	0.8	9.0	16	15	72

Cows Nursing Calves, 1st 3 to 4 Months After Parturition

900-1,100	None	—	28	1.4	14.0	30	24	300

Fattening Calves Finished as Short Yearlings

400	Average for	3.0	12	1.1	8.0	20	15	24
500	period, 2.0	2.8	14	1.2	9.5	20	16	30
600	pounds	2.7	16	1.3	11.0	20	17	36
700	daily	2.6	18	1.4	12.0	20	18	42
800		2.5	20	1.5	13.5	20	18	48
900		2.3	21	1.5	14.5	20	18	54

Fattening Yearling Cattle

600	Average for	3.0	18	1.3	11.5	20	17	36
700	period, 2.2	3.0	21	1.4	13.5	20	18	42
800	pounds	2.8	22	1.5	14.0	20	19	48
900	daily	2.7	24	1.6	15.5	20	20	54
1,000		2.6	26	1.7	17.0	20	20	60
1,100		2.4	27	1.7	17.5	20	20	66

TABLE 5 (Continued)

Body Weight (Pounds)	Expected Daily Gain (Pounds)	Total Feed — Per Cent of Live Weight	Total Feed — Per Animal (Pounds)	Daily Allowances per Animal — Digestible Protein (Pounds)	Total Digestible Nutrients (Pounds)	Calcium (Grams)	Phosphorus (Grams)	Carotene (Mg.)
			Fattening 2-Year-Old Cattle					
800	Average for	3.0	24	1.5	15.0	20	18	48
900	period, 2.4	2.9	26	1.6	16.0	20	20	54
1,000	pounds	2.7	27	1.7	17.0	20	20	60
1,100	daily	2.6	29	1.8	18.0	20	20	66
1,200		2.4	29	1.8	18.0	20	20	72

SOURCE: A Report of the Committee on Animal Nutrition. National Research Council *Recommended Nutrient Allowances for Domestic Animals*, Revised December, 1950.

TABLE 6

RECOMMENDED NUTRIENT CONTENT OF RATIONS FOR BEEF CATTLE
(BASED UPON TOTAL AIR-DRY FEED [ROUGHAGES AND CONCENTRATES] CONTAINING 90 PER CENT DRY MATTER)

Body Weight (Pounds)	Expected Daily Gain (Pounds)	Daily Feed — Per Cent of Live Weight	Daily Feed — Per Animal (Pounds)	Allowance as per cent of ration or amount per pound of feed — Digestible Protein (Per Cent)	Total Digestible Nutrients (Per Cent)	Calcium (Per Cent)	Phosphorus (Per Cent)	Carotene (Mg. Per Cent)
			Normal Growth, Heifers and Steers					
400	1.6	3.0	12	7.5	58	0.37	0.28	2.0
600	1.4	2.7	16	5.6	53	0.25	0.21	2.2
800	1.2	2.4	19	4.7	50	0.19	0.17	2.5
1,000	1.0	2.1	21	4.3	50	0.16	0.16	2.8
			Bulls, Growth and Maintenance (Moderate Activity)					
600	2.3	2.7	16	8.1	63	0.33	0.25	2.2
800	1.7	2.1	17	8.2	65	0.30	0.23	2.8
1,000	1.6	2.0	20	7.0	60	0.24	0.20	3.0
1,200	1.4	1.8	22	6.5	59	0.21	0.18	3.3
1,400	1.0	1.7	24	5.8	59	0.18	0.17	3.5
1,600	—	1.6	26	5.4	54	0.15	0.15	3.7
1,800	—	1.4	26	5.4	54	0.15	0.15	4.2
			Wintering Weaning Calves					
400	1.0	2.8	11	6.4	55	0.32	0.24	2.2
500	1.0	2.6	13	6.2	54	0.27	0.20	2.3
600	1.0	2.5	15	5.3	53	0.24	0.18	2.4
			Wintering Yearling Cattle					
600	1.0	2.7	16	5.0	50	0.22	0.17	2.2
700	1.0	2.4	17	4.7	50	0.21	0.16	2.5
800	0.7	2.3	18	4.5	50	0.20	0.15	2.7
900	0.5	2.0	18	4.5	50	0.20	0.15	3.0
			Wintering Pregnant Heifers					
		(Weights are for beginning of winter period; gains are average for period)						
700	1.5	2.9	20	4.5	50	0.20	0.18	2.1
800	1.3	2.3	20	4.5	50	0.20	0.18	2.4
900	0.8	2.0	18	4.5	50	0.20	0.18	3.0
1,000	0.5	1.8	18	4.5	50	0.20	0.18	3.3

TABLE 6 (Continued)

Body Weight (Pounds)	Expected Daily Gain (Pounds)	Daily Feed		Digestible Protein (Per Cent)	Total Digestible Nutrients (Per Cent)	Allowance as per cent of ration or amount per pound of feed		
		Per Cent of Live Weight	Per Animal (Pounds)			Calcium (Per Cent)	Phosphorus (Per Cent)	Carotene (Mg. Per Cent)
Wintering Mature Pregnant Cows								
(Weights are for beginning of winter period; gains are average for period)								
800	1.5.	2.8	22	4.5	50	0.20	0.18	2.2
900	1.0	2.2	20	4.5	50	0.20	0.18	2.7
1,000	0.4	1.8	18	4.5	50	0.20	0.18	3.3
1,100	0.2	1.6	18	4.5	50	0.20	0.18	3.7
1,200	0.0	1.5	18	4.5	50	0.20	0.18	4.0
Cows Nursing Calves, 1st 3 to 4 Months After Parturition								
900-1,100	None	—	28	5.0	50	0.24	0.18	11.0
Fattening Calves Finished as Short Yearlings								
400	Average for	3.0	12	9.2	67	0.37	0.28	2.0
500	period, 2.0	2.8	14	8.6	68	0.31	0.25	2.1
600	pounds	2.7	16	8.1	68	0.28	0.23	2.2
700	daily	2.6	18	7.8	68	0.25	0.22	2.3
800		2.5	20	7.5	68	0.22	0.20	2.4
900		2.3	21	7.2	68	0.21	0.19	2.6
Fattening Yearling Cattle								
600	Average for	3.0	18	7.2	65	0.25	0.21	2.0
700	period, 2.2	3.0	21	7.0	65	0.21	0.19	2.0
800	pounds	2.8	22	6.8	65	0.20	0.19	2.2
	daily	2.7	24	6.7	65	0.18	0.18	2.2
1,000		2.6	26	6.5	65	0.17	0.17	2.3
1,100		2.4	27	6.3	65	0.16	0.16	2.4
Fattening 2-Year-Old Cattle								
800	Average for	3.0	24	6.3	62	0.18	0.18	2.0
900	period, 2.4	2.9	26	6.3	62	0.17	0.17	2.1
1,000	pounds	2.7	27	6.3	62	0.16	0.16	2.2
1,100	daily	2.6	29	6.3	62	0.15	0.15	2.3
1,200		2.4	29	6.3	62	0.15	0.15	2.5

SOURCE: A Report of the Committee on Animal Nutrition, National Research Council *Recommended Nutrient Allowances For Domestic Animals*, Revised December, 1950.

MEASURING THE VALUE OF FEEDS

No single method of determining the value of feeds is accurate enough for all purposes. Many factors must be considered if a reasonably correct appraisal of any feed or group of feeds is to be made.

Digestible Nutrients. Since no feed is entirely digestible, one of the most widely accepted methods of determining feed values is based on the total digestible nutrient content of the feed. Modern feeding standards list the total digestible nutrients and also the digestible proteins of the more widely used livestock feeds.

One way to determine the cheapest source of digestible nutrients for beef cattle is to divide the price per bushel, ton, or hundred pounds (whichever is the most common unit of measure) by the pounds of total digestible nutrients contained in the feed. This will give a comparative cost of various feeds based on feeding value. Although the cost per pound of total digestible nutrients is a very good guide to the value of a feed, it is not the whole answer. Tables 7 through 11 give the average composition of commonly used beef cattle feeds.

TABLE 7

AVERAGE COMPOSITION OF CONCENTRATES HIGH IN ENERGY AND FAT-PRODUCING VALUE COMMONLY FED TO BEEF CATTLE (EXPRESSED IN PER CENT)

	Total Dry Matter	Total Digestible Nutrient	Total Protein	Digestible Protein	N-Free Extracts or Carbohydrates	Fats	Mineral Matter	Fiber
Barley	89.4	77.7	12.7	10.0	66.6	1.9	2.8	5.4
Beet Pulp (Dried)	91.2	69.7	8.8	4.1	58.7	0.6	3.5	19.6
Molasses (Dried) ..	91.9	72.1	10.7	7.1	59.4	0.7	5.1	16.0
Corn (No. 2)	85.0	80.1	8.7	6.7	69.2	3.9	1.2	2.0
Citrus Pulp (Dried)	90.1	75.4	5.9	2.5	62.7	3.1	6.9	11.5
Ground Ear Corn ..	86.1	73.2	7.4	5.3	66.2	3.2	1.3	8.0
Feterita (Grain)	89.4	79.8	12.2	9.5	70.1	3.2	1.7	2.2
Kafir (Grain)	89.8	81.6	10.9	8.8	72.7	2.9	1.6	1.7
Milo (Grain)	89.0	79.4	10.9	8.5	70.7	3.0	2.1	2.3
Molasses (Beet)	80.5	60.8	8.4	4.4	62.0	0.0	10.1	0.0
Molasses (Cane)	74.0	54.0	2.9	0.0	62.1	0.0	9.0	0.0
Oats (Hulled)	90.4	91.9	16.2	14.6	63.7	6.1	2.2	2.2
Oats	90.2	70.1	12.0	9.4	58.6	4.6	4.0	11.0
Rye	89.5	76.5	12.6	10.0	70.9	1.7	1.9	2.4
Wheat	89.5	80.0	13.2	11.1	69.9	1.9	1.9	2.6
Wheat Bran	90.1	66.9	16.9	13.3	53.1	4.5	6.1	10.0
Wheat Middlings ..	90.1	79.2	17.5	15.4	60.0	4.5	3.8	4.3

TABLE 8

AVERAGE COMPOSITION OF PROTEIN CONCENTRATES COMMONLY FED TO BEEF CATTLE (EXPRESSED IN PER CENT)

	Total Dry Matter	Total Digestible Nutrient	Total Protein	Digestible Protein	N-Free Extracts or Carbohydrates	Fats	Mineral Matter	Fiber
Brewer's Grains (Dried)	92.9	67.1	27.6	22.1	40.9	6.5	3.6	14.3
Buttermilk (Dried) ..	92.0	83.1	31.8	28.6	43.6	6.1	10.0	0.5
Corn Gluten Feeds ..	90.9	76.0	25.5	21.9	48.8	2.7	6.3	7.6
Corn Gluten Meal ..	91.4	80.2	42.9	36.5	40.1	2.0	2.5	3.9
Cottonseed Meal	92.7	72.6	43.3	35.9	27.4	5.1	6.0	11.0
Distiller's Dried Corn Grains	93.1	80.9	28.8	21.0	41.7	8.9	4.7	9.0

TABLE 8 (Continued)

	Total Dry Matter	Total Digest-ible Nu-trient	Total Protein	Digest-ible Protein	N-Free Extracts or Carbo-hydrates	Fats	Mineral Matter	Fiber
Linseed Meal	91.0	70.3	36.6	30.7	38.3	1.0	5.8	9.3
Milk (Dried Skim) ..	94.0	80.7	34.7	31.2	50.3	1.2	7.8	0.2
Peanut Oil Meal	93.0	82.4	43.5	39.6	23.4	7.6	5.2	13.3
Safflower Seed Oil Meal (Hulled Seed)	91.0	55.5	38.0	32.7	17.0	6.8	8.2	21.0
Soybean Seed	90.0	87.6	37.9	13.7	24.5	18.0	4.6	5.0
Soybean Oil Meal	90.4	78.1	45.7	42.0	31.4	1.3	6.1	5.9

TABLE 9

AVERAGE COMPOSITION OF COMMON DRY ROUGHAGES
(EXPRESSED IN PER CENT)

	Total Dry Matter	Digest-ible Total Nu-trient	Total Protein	Digest-ible Protein	N-Free Extracts or Carbo-hydrates	Fats	Mineral Matter	Fiber
Alfalfa Hay (Average)	90.5	50.7	15.3	10.9	36.7	1.9	8.0	28.6
Alfalfa Hay (High Grade) ..	90.5	52.7	17.5	12.8	39.5	2.4	8.4	22.7
Alfalfa Meal (Dehydrated) ..	92.7	54.4	17.7	12.4	38.4	2.5	10.1	24.0
Bermuda Grass Hay	90.6	44.2	7.2	3.7	48.7	1.8	7.0	25.9
Bluegrass Hay	89.4	54.8	8.2	4.8	42.1	2.8	6.5	29.8
Birdsfoot Trefoil	91.2	55.0	14.2	9.8	41.9	2.1	6.0	27.0
Brome Grass Hay	88.8	49.3	10.4	5.3	39.9	2.1	8.2	28.2
Clover Hay—Red (Good)	88.3	51.8	12.0	7.2	40.3	2.5	6.4	27.1
Clover Hay—Red (Second Cutting)	88.1	54.1	13.4	8.4	40.4	2.9	6.9	24.5
Clover Hay—Alyce ..	89.0	49.4	10.9	6.6	35.5	1.6	5.6	35.4
Clover Hay— Crimson	89.5	48.9	14.2	?.8	37.0	2.2	8.7	27.4
Corncobs (Ground)	90.4	45.7	2.3	0	54.0	0.4	1.6	32.1
Corn Fodder— Medium watered well eared	82.6	53.9	6.8	3.3	46.7	2.1	5.2	?1.8
Cowpea Hay	90.4	51.4	18.6	12.3	34.6	2.6	11.3	23.3
Fescue Hay	89.2	52.7	7.0	3.7	43.2	1.9	6.8	30.3
Hegari Fodder	86.3	52.4	6.1	3.2	52.8	1.7	7.5	18.2
Kafir Fodder	90.0	53.6	8.7	4.5	44.2	2.6	9.0	25.5
Kudzu Hay	89.0	49.2	15.9	10.7	35.1	2.5	6.9	28.6
Lespedeza Hay (Annual)	90.0	45.1	13.1	5.6	42.2	2.5	5.3	26.9
Lespedeza Hay (Perennial)	89.0	41.4	13.2	4.4	42.7	1.7	4.9	26.5
Oat Straw	89.7	44.7	4.1	0.7	41.0	2.2	6.3	36.1
Orchard Grass Hay	88.6	47.8	7.7	3.9	40.7	2.9	6.8	30.5
Prairie Hay Western (Good)	91.3	45.1	6.0	2.0	44.0	3.0	8.6	29.7
Reed Canary Grass Hay	91.1	45.1	7.7	4.8	44.3	2.3	7.6	29.2

TABLE 9 (Continued)

	Total Dry Matter	Total Digestible Nutrient	Total Protein	Digestible Protein	N-Free Extracts or Carbohydrates	Fats	Mineral Matter	Fiber
Sorghum Fodder (Sweet)	88.8	52.4	6.2	3.3	48.1	2.4	7.1	25.0
Soybean Hay (Seed well developed)	88.0	52.5	15.2	10.8	35.2	4.7	6.2	26.7
Sudan Grass Hay	89.6	50.0	11.2	6.3	41.3	1.5	9.5	26.1
Timothy Hay (Good)	89.0	50.8	7.5	4.1	44.4	2.4	4.7	30.0
Vetch Hay (Common)	89.0	55.3	13.3	10.1	43.2	1.1	6.2	25.2

TABLE 10

AVERAGE COMPOSITION OF PASTURE LEGUMES AND GRASSES
(EXPRESSED IN PER CENT)

	Total Dry Matter	Total Digestible Nutrient	Total Protein	Digestible Protein	N-Free Extracts or Carbohydrates	Fats	Mineral Matter	Fiber
Alfalfa	24.4	14.8	4.6	3.5	10.0	0.9	2.2	6.7
Bahia Grass	30.0	15.9	2.4	1.1	14.1	0.5	3.6	9.4
Bluegrass	30.2	20.7	5.5	4.1	13.4	1.2	2.5	7.6
Brome Grass	25.0	18.3	5.1	3.9	10.7	1.0	2.4	5.8
Clover (Ladino)	16.6	12.4	4.1	3.3	7.5	0.8	1.7	2.5
Clover (Red)	25.0	16.8	4.0	2.8	11.2	0.9	2.1	6.8
Clover (Alsike)	22.0	15.7	4.1	3.2	10.4	0.9	1.9	4.7
Clover (Sweet)	20.8	12.8	4.1	3.2	9.2	0.7	1.9	4.9
Fescue	30.5	18.8	3.0	1.6	14.0	1.0	2.4	10.1
Lespedeza (Annual)	25.0	12.7	4.1	2.0	9.2	0.5	3.2	8.0
Rape	16.3	12.8	2.9	2.4	8.0	0.6	2.2	2.6
Sudan Grass	21.6	14.3	3.3	2.4	10.2	0.6	1.9	5.6
Timothy	23.9	15.4	4.7	3.5	11.1	0.9	2.6	4.6
Trefoil	22.7	13.3	3.4	4.5	9.5	0.8	2.3	5.6

TABLE 11

AVERAGE COMPOSITION OF COMMON KINDS OF SILAGE AND ROOTS
(EXPRESSED IN PER CENT)

	Total Dry Matter	Total Digestible Nutrient	Total Protein	Digestible Protein	N-Free Extracts or Carbohydrates	Fats	Mineral Matter	Fiber
Alfalfa Silage	36.0	21.3	6.0	4.1	13.7	1.4	3.2	11.7
Beetroots (Common)	13.0	10.1	1.6	1.2	8.9	0.1	1.5	0.9
Beetroots (Sugar)	16.4	13.7	1.6	1.2	12.6	0.1	1.1	1.0
Corn Silage	27.6	18.3	2.3	1.2	16.2	0.8	1.6	6.7
Grass Legume Silage	33.3	19.1	5.2	2.9	14.2	1.3	3.8	8.8
Grain Sorghum Silage	30.0	17.1	2.6	1.4	18.6	0.7	2.1	6.0
Mangels Roots	9.2	7.0	1.3	0.9	6.0	0.1	1.0	0.8
Peavine Silage	24.5	14.0	3.2	1.9	11.0	0.6	2.2	7.3

Source: Tables 7 through 11 adapted by special permission of the Morrison Publishing Company, Ithaca, New York, from *Feeds and Feeding* (22nd Edition), by F. B. Morrison.

Carbohydrates and Fats as Measures of Feed Value. Feeds are generally selected to do a specific job in the animal's body. When feeds that will furnish a large amount of energy and fattening value are required, the nitrogen-free extract or carbohydrates and fats as well as the total digestible nutrients must be considered.

Proteins as a Measure of Feed Value. Many feeds are purchased primarily for their protein content. They are used to increase the protein percentage in the ration, and cost should be determined on a digestible-protein basis. Such protein concentrates as cottonseed meal, soybean meal, or linseed meal will produce nearly equal results when fed to beef cattle. The cost per hundred pounds of digestible protein may be used to determine which one to feed. Example:

If soybean meal costs $5 per 100 pounds, then $\dfrac{\$5}{42.0} \times 100 =$ the cost of 100 pounds of digestible protein.

Generally, grains and roughages are not fed primarily for their protein content. Yet if they are high in this important nutrient, the cost of feeding is generally lower because less protein meals or concentrates are necessary. For example, cattle fed legume hay will require much less protein meal to grow and fatten than those receiving a low protein roughage. The protein content of roughages and grains is important in determining feeding value.

Minerals and Vitamins as a Measure of Feed Value. Grains and roughages are seldom fed primarily for their mineral or vitamin content. However, the mineral and vitamin content of good leafy legume forage improves it as a feed and is important in determining its food value. The high carotene or vitamin A content of yellow corn explains the chief difference between yellow and white corn as a livestock feed. Beef cattle receiving a full feed of good quality legume forage and an ample amount of grain seldom suffer from a mineral or vitamin deficiency.

Palatability as a Measure of Feed Value. Beef cattle must consume large quantities of feed if they are to make rapid gains. How well cattle like the taste of their feed determines to a large extent how much they consume. For example, rye is equal to most of the other grains in nutrient value, but it is not palatable to beef cattle. If too large a portion of the ration is made up of rye, feed consumption is reduced and the rate of gain will be lowered. Molasses is very palatable and when mixed with other ingredients in the ration will often induce cattle to consume greater quantities of feed.

QUALITY OF FEEDS

The amount of nutrients varies considerably in the same kind of feed, depending upon its quality.

Many factors, such as variety, type of soil, weather conditions, and age, affect the value of a feed and explain the wide range of digestible nutrients in the same kind of feed.

Corn may vary from 6 per cent to over 9 per cent in protein, and alfalfa will range from 8 to 19 per cent in protein. It is important to carefully consider the quality of the product in judging the value of a feed.

Factors Affecting Quality of Feeds. Varieties of the same crop will differ in food value. The amount of protein in wheat varieties grown under the same conditions will vary from 10 to 16 per cent. Oats that produce a plump berry with thin hulls are much higher in digestible nutrients than are those with a large proportion of hulls. State agricultural experiment stations can be relied upon to furnish information regarding varieties of crops for their particular states, together with comparative feeding values.

Soils. Recent experiments and analyses have shown that feeds produced on soils well supplied with plant foods have a higher feeding value than do those produced on poor land.

The mineral content of alfalfa and the protein in corn may vary depending upon the soil. Land well supplied with nitrogen, from which plants make protein, will produce higher protein corn than will soils deficient in this plant food. Alfalfa grown on soils that are well supplied with lime and phosphorus will be higher in these elements than will alfalfa grown on deficient soils.

The appearance of a forage or grain may not be the best guide to its food value. A knowledge of the area, or even the farm where it was grown is important.

Weather. Unfavorable weather conditions influence feed values. Corn that is high in moisture as a result of cold, wet seasons will have much fewer digestible nutrients per pound than will dry corn. Small grains may have a high percentage of hull to berry. Therefore, the proportion of fiber is increased as a result of hot, dry weather conditions, particularly when the kernels are forming.

Analyses show that the same kind of crop will vary in feeding value from year to year. The temperature, length of growing season, and amount and distribution of rainfall all affect the nutrient value of crops.

COMMERCIAL MIXED FEEDS

There are many companies engaged in the business of producing livestock feeds. Commercially mixed feeds for all classes of livestock are available in almost every community. When questions arise as to the value of one company's product as compared to that of another, the reliability of the manufacturer and the success that feeders have had with his products must be considered. A study of the analysis given on the container may be helpful. Most states permit feed companies to sell under what is known as the *closed formula* or *open formula*.

Feed Analysis Tags. *Closed formula.* Under the closed formula, feed companies are generally required to give the minimum crude protein, minimum crude fat, minimum nitrogen-free extract, and maximum amount of fiber contained in the feed. They must also list the ingredients that were used in making the product, but, except for mineral or ash, they are not required to disclose how much of each ingredient has been used. Some states require that the percentage of mineral be listed. For example, a feed may be listed as containing soybean oil meal, tankage, meat scraps, and bone meal. Although this is a true statement of the ingredients used, it fails to give *the amount* of each product in the feed. Many feed companies prefer the closed formula because it prevents duplication of their products by other companies or livestock feeders.

The following is a typical closed-formula label that might appear on the feed bag:

WEIGHT 100 LBS. NET
A-1 CATTLE FATTENER

Crude protein not less than 26.00%
Crude fat not less than 4.50%
Nitrogen-free extract not less than 43.00%
Crude fiber not more than 8.50%

Ingredients: Alfalfa meal, wheat bran, linseed oil meal, soybean oil meal, cotton seed meal, rolled oats, yellow corn, molasses, antibiotic, and vitamin supplement, calcium 6.0%, phosphorous 1.3%, salt 5.0%, iodine .0002%.

Open formula. Feed companies selling open-formula feeds must list the minimum percentage of protein, fat, nitrogen-free extract, maximum amount of fiber, and the weight of each ingredient contained in the feed. Following is an example of an open-formula feed label:

ACE CATTLE FATTENER
GUARANTEED ANALYSIS

Crude protein, not less than 35.00%
Crude fat, not less than 4.00%
Crude fiber, not more than 8.50%
N.F.E., not less than 28.00%

Lbs. Per Ton
730........Soybean oil meal
600........Cottonseed oil meal
400........Linseed oil meal
140........Cane molasses
 60........Ground limestone
 35........Steamed bone meal
 20........Salt
  5........Trace mineral concentrate
 .6........D-Activated plant sterol
 10........Hydrogenated fat

(Trace mineral concentrate contains steamed bone meal, manganese sulphate, iron oxide, sulphur, magnesium sulphate, charcoal, cobalt, carbonate, potassium iodide and copper sulphate.)

SUMMARY

The stomachs of ruminants, such as cattle, sheep, and goats, have four compartments. The rumen is by far the largest compartment and serves as a storage place for bulky feeds and as a place for bacterial action.

Because of bacterial action, which is part of the digestive process, ruminants can digest large quantities of fiber and convert low quality proteins into essential amino acids. The microorganisms also manufacture most of the B vitamins, which are later absorbed by the animal.

Swine and poultry have a simple digestive system and must rely directly upon the feed they consume to obtain all classes of nutrients. They have much less ability to digest fiber than do ruminants.

The term nutrient is applied to any single class of food or group of like foods that aid in the support of life and make it possible for animals to produce what is expected of them. The five classes of food nutrients are: carbohydrates, fats, proteins, minerals, and vitamins. Water is very essential and may be classed as a sixth nutrient. Carbohydrates and fats furnish heat and energy for animals and provide much of the material necessary for fattening. Proteins make up the greater part of the structure of muscles, internal organs, skin, hair, hoofs, and horns, and the fetus of the unborn calf. Vitamins are essential nutrients, but with the exception of very young calves, vitamins A and D are all that seem to be required in beef cattle rations. Minerals are needed in nearly all parts of the animal body, but are used primarily in the bones and teeth. Antibiotics, while not considered a food nutrient, have shown beneficial results when fed under certain conditions to cattle. Recent experiments have shown increased rates of gain when hormones have been added to the ration. Unless water is readily available the rate of gain and feed efficiency is reduced.

Hays, fodders, and grains are the chief sources of carbohydrates and fats for cattle. Linseed oil meal, cottonseed oil meal, soybean oil meal, corn gluten feed are examples of high protein feeds commonly fed to cattle. Salt may be supplied "free choice" (that is, separately and self-fed) or mixed with the regular ration. Most feeds contain the other minerals, but mineral supplements are generally recommended for cattle. Pasture, high quality cured forages, and grains generally contain enough vitamins to meet cattle requirements. Where vitamin supplements are needed, they may be purchased commercially. Antibiotics may be purchased in ready-mixed feeds or as antibiotic supplements.

Many factors must be considered in evaluating feed. Among the more important considerations are (1) the kind of animal to be fed, and (2) the purpose for which the particular feed is being used.

Feeds that are intended as fattening feeds must be judged primarily for their carbohydrate content and total digestibility. However, their protein, mineral, and vitamin contents are also important because the percentage of these nutrients in the feed determines the amount of other concentrates needed to balance the ration. The quality and percentage of digestible protein in a feed that is fed largely for its protein content is the chief measure of its value.

Mineral and vitamin concentrates are measured in terms of the essential minerals and vitamins present.

Quality of feeds are affected by weather, soils, harvesting, and varieties of crops.

The value of any feed in a ration is determined largely by how well the ration is balanced. Feeding more of any nutrient than the animal requires is wasteful. Commercial feeds are sold under open-formula or closed-formula analysis. More information is given on the label when the open-formula is used. The value of commercial feeds is determined largely by the reliability of the company and the success feeders have had with its product.

QUESTIONS

1. Name the four compartments in the ruminant stomach.
2. What is the principal digestive process that takes place in the rumen?
3. Why do we have less difficulty in supplying older cattle with B vitamins than we have with young calves?
4. Explain why ruminants can convert comparatively low-quality protein feeds and a certain amount of nitrogen compounds into usable amino acids.
5. What is meant by the term nutrient?
6. List the classes of nutrients.
7. What is the main function of each nutrient class?
8. How do fats and carbohydrates differ in their ability to produce energy and fatty tissue?
9. What are the major minerals?
10. Why are trace minerals so called?
11. Why is an abundance of clean, fresh water important to cattle production?
12. What has been the result of feeding antibiotics to calves?
13. What is meant by digestible nutrient?
14. What is the difference between a ration and a *balanced* ration?
15. What are the two main classes of feeds?
16. How do roughages and concentrates differ?
17. Why are legumes higher in protein than are other roughages?
18. What are some of the common feeds known as concentrates?
19. What are protein concentrates?
20. List the feeds commonly fed for their carbohydrate content.
21. What vitamins are most likely to be lacking in beef cattle rations?

REFERENCES

Morrison, Frank R., *Feeds and Feeding* (22nd Edition), The Morrison Publishing Company, Ithaca, New York, 1956.

Recommended Nutrient Allowances For Beef Cattle, Report of the Committee on Animal Nutrition (Revised) 1950, National Research Counsel, Washington, D. C.

6

Feeding and Management of the Breeding Herd

The breeding herd must be properly fed and managed if a good calf crop is to be attained. The calf crop represents the earnings from the herd. The owner's income results largely from the sale of animals not needed in the breeding herds. The percentage of calf crop, the vigor and size the calves attain by market time, and the feeding efficiency largely determine the profit realized. A one hundred per cent calf crop is seldom obtained, but should be one of the goals set by the producer. A second goal is to feed the herd as cheaply as possible without sacrificing the percentage and vigor of the calf crop, or reducing the productive life of the cows.

FIGURE 85. *Plenty of roughage is essential for economical feeding of the breeding herd. (Courtesy Rath Packing Plant.)*

FIGURE 86. *A strong healthy calf is the first step toward profitable raising of beef cattle. (Courtesy American Hereford Association.)*

Recent studies and research in cattle nutrition has shown that cows can utilize an amazingly large amount of low quality roughage when properly balanced with minerals, vitamins, and protein and still produce a strong, healthy calf crop. We now know that roughages such as corncobs, and corn stalks, once thought of as waste products from the farm and good only for fertilizing the land, may be successfully utilized as cattle feed. Pastures, legume and grass hays, silage, and fodders, while superior to corncobs and corn stalks in feeding value and more expensive, also provide a relatively cheap source of cattle feed. The most successful cow herd owners are those who have learned to utilize all available feed produced on their farms or ranches to the greatest possible advantage. Unless ample amounts of pasture and other rough feeds are available at comparatively low cost, it is doubtful whether a cow herd can be profitably maintained.

FIGURE 87. *Good pasture and plenty of it will reduce the feed bill. (Foster photo, Courtesy* The Farm Journal-Country Gentleman.)

FEEDING THE HERD ON PASTURE

When an ample amount of good pasture is available, summer feeding problems of the breeding herd are easily solved. Young growing plants are generally high in most food nutrients and represent a fairly well-balanced ration for two-year-old heifers and cows.

Studies reveal that cattle will spend not much more than eight hours per day grazing. Whenever a pasture fails to provide in eight hours of grazing sufficient forage to satisfy the animal's requirements, maintain its weight, promote the milk production of the cows, and provide for reasonable growth in young stock, additional feed should be provided.

Supplementing the Grass. Whenever the pasture is insufficient to provide adequate nutrients to meet the needs of the cattle, for best results it will be necessary to supplement the pasture with additional feed.

Feeding additional forage to cattle on pasture. When additional feed is required, a good quality dry forage, or silage may be used successfully. The amount of additional forage will depend upon the amount and quality of the grass available. Ten pounds of good legume hay, 30 pounds of legume silage, 20 to 25 pounds of sorghum or corn silage will replace by about one-half the pasture requirements for mature cattle. When a lower quality forage is used the amount will need to be increased. If available, silage is an excellent supplement when the grasses are dry or mature. Dry forages are superior additional feed when the pasture grasses are green and succulent.

Many farmers use extra forage to supplement the pasture early in the season to prevent the cattle from cropping the grass too short. When it is known that the amount of pasture is insufficient as the sole forage for cattle during the season, it may be extended by feeding additional forage from the start of the pasture season. Pastures that have been closely grazed will not recover during the dry weather that is common during July and August over much of the cattle country.

Feeding additional grain to cattle on pasture. Grain may be used to replace part of the pasture requirements for breeding cattle. Three to five pounds of corn, barley, wheat, or sorghum grain, will replace about one-half the pasture requirements for mature breeding cattle.   If oats are used it will require from 7 to 5 pounds. *Feeding additional minerals to cattle on pasture.*   Salt should be within easy reach of the cattle at all times.   In many sections of the country, pastures provide the other essential minerals; however, there are some areas in which deficiencies of phosphorus and some of the trace minerals, particularly cobalt, are common.   One cannot be sure whether the pasture will provide adequate minerals.   As the land is cropped or grazed, more and more mineral deficiencies become apparent.   As an insurance against mineral starvation and since mineral mixtures are relatively cheap, a good mineral mixture should be kept before the cattle at all times. Following are some good mineral mixtures recommended for various sections of the United States:

MINERAL MIXTURES FOR AREAS
WHERE ONLY ADDITIONAL SALT, CALCIUM, AND PHOSPHORUS
NEED TO BE PROVIDED

(1) 200 pounds steamed bone meal
     100 pounds common salt

(2)   50 pounds steamed bone meal
      25 pounds ground limestone
      25 pounds common salt

MINERAL MIXTURES FOR AREAS
WHERE ONE OR MORE TRACE MINERALS MAY BE DEFICIENT
IN ADDITION TO SALT, CALCIUM, AND PHOSPHORUS

(1) 100 pounds common salt
     25.5 pounds ground limestone
     50.0 pounds steamed bone meal
     25.0 pounds red oxide of iron
      2.5 pounds pulverized copper sulfate
      1.0 ounce cobalt sulfate

(2)   23 pounds iodized trace mineral salt
      25 pounds ground limestone
      50 pounds steamed bone meal
       2 pounds iron (ferric oxide)

(3)   50 pounds bone meal
      25 pounds ground limestone
      20 pounds iodized salt
       5 pounds trace mineral premix *

* Trace minerals can be purchased as a trace mineral mixture and added to the other ingredients.

Vitamin supplements for cattle on pasture.   Green forage has an abundance of vitamins needed in cattle nutrition.   It is seldom necessary to supplement good pasture with any vitamin supplement. Vitamins A and D are the only ones likely to ever be deficient in the rations of cattle a month or more of age.   Green plants contain an abundance of vitamin A and sunlight will provide the D requirements.   Cattle can store vitamin A in abundant quantities and can draw upon this reserve for several months.   Only when cattle have been grazed for several months on poor quality dry pastures is there a danger of a vitamin A deficiency.

Cattle suffering from a vitamin A deficiency show an inability to see in dim or subdued light, have a staggering gait, and excessive running of the eyes and nose.   If a vitamin A deficiency is suspected, they may be fed one pound per day of fresh dehydrated alfalfa meal or two pounds of high-grade alfalfa hay.   When these feeds are not available a vitamin supplement, prepared commercially, containing 3,000 international units of vitamin A per gram may be fed at the rate of one-fourth pound per animal per day.   If this supplement is fed over a period of from 10 to 15 days, enough vitamin A will be provided to correct the condition.   After that one or two feedings per week should prevent a recurrence of the trouble.

Feeding protein supplements to cattle on pasture.   When an ample amount of green pasture forage is available, mature breeding cattle seldom need additional protein.   If the pasture is short or if poor quality and low protein forage is used to supplement the pasture, then from one-fourth to one pound per head of protein concentrate such as cottonseed cake or meal, soybean, linseed or peanut oil meal will be needed to balance the ration.

The practice of using salt mixed with the protein supplement, as a means of controlling the intake of protein when the mixture is self-fed to cattle, is gaining in popularity among ranchers in some sections of the range country.   The salt protein mixture permits the self-feeding of protein which reduces labor and provides for a more even consumption of the supplement and more uniform grazing of the range than does hand feeding.   It is necessary to have plenty of water available when a salt protein mixture is fed.   Constant adjustment of the salt protein ratio is necessary to provide for the correct intake of protein.   As the salt is increased or decreased in proportion to the protein meal, consumption of the mixture increases or decreases. The salt is used to govern the protein intake. The amount and quality of the pasture determines the needed level of protein intake.

In tests carried out by the Oklahoma Agricultural Experiment Station, daily consumption of protein meal by 700-pound cattle was held to 2 pounds per day by mixing seven-eighths of a pound of salt with each 2 pounds of meal. California tests showed that by shifting the salt content from 10 to 30 per cent in a ration made up of equal parts of cottonseed meal and barley, consumption could be controlled. When grass was high in quality, a higher percentage of salt reduced the amount of supplement eaten.

A commercially prepared protein block, consisting of oil seed meals and a binder such as molasses pressed into a hard block similar to a salt block, may be located in a place where it is available to the cattle. Although the protein block provides an easy way to supplement pasture, there is some danger that cattle may consume more than is required and thus increase feeding costs.

Water. Water is usually the cheapest and most essential element in livestock nutrition. The need for plenty of fresh, clean water within easy reach of the cattle cannot be overestimated. Cattle make faster gains and utilize feed more efficiently when plenty of water is available. Range cattle tend to feed more in the vicinity of the watering place. When watering facilities are too far apart the range is grazed unevenly. Some areas will be grazed so close that the grass will be destroyed and will be replaced by undesirable weedy plants.

FIGURE 88. *Cows and calves grow faster and make more efficient gains when water is within easy reach. (Courtesy American Hereford Association.)*

Under corn belt farm conditions the cattle herds are usually not large and the pastures are close to the buildings.   Cattle are thus able to come up twice a day to the well, where a stock tank is usually located, and do not travel over one or two miles per day. Where large herds are maintained on the range, water must be provided in the pastures.   This may be done by creating ponds or reservoirs to catch and hold the excess water during the rainy season and store it for the dry periods.   Where the free water table is close enough to the surface, wells may be drilled over the range at distances of one to two miles apart.   Cattle should never have to travel more than two miles for water.   An excess amount of walking to water uses up feed that would otherwise be utilized for growth and fattening.

Pastures Compared.   There is a wide variety of pasture plants. Weather, soil, and moisture conditions determine the pasture crops best adapted for each locality.   Pasture crops are divided into two general classes: legumes and grasses.

Legumes.   Legumes have the ability to use atmospheric nitrogen. Since nitrogen is important in the building of proteins, these plants are usually higher in protein than are the grasses.   They are heavy feeders of phosphorus and calcium and, when grown on land well supplied with these elements, are rich in these essential minerals. Legumes are usually higher in total food value than are grasses and, in general, are very palatable to cattle.   Most of the common pasture legumes are deep rooted and stand dry weather well, thus extending the pasture period.   However, when legumes are used alone as a pasture crop, there is danger of bloat.   The loss from bloat has been so great that straight legume pastures are not recommended.   Scientists are studying the cause of bloat and some information has been revealed (see Chapter 9).   Prospects are that a method of bloat prevention may soon be discovered.   For the present, therefore, legumes should be grown in combination with grasses when used for pasture because grasses greatly minimize the danger of bloat.   Legumes should not make up more than one-half of the plant stand, and care should be used in seeding to obtain an even mixture of the two types of plants.   If the seeding is uneven, cattle may graze where the heavy stand of legumes occur and bloat will result.

Wherever legumes are adapted, they should make up part of the pasture mixture.   Experiments conducted at several stations have shown that when a legume and grass pasture is used, it is superior to grass alone. Some of the advantages of legumes used in conjunction with grasses are: (1) faster gains, (2) longer grazing season, and (3) greater carrying capacity of the pastures.

Some of the more common pasture legumes are: alfalfa, alyce clover, alsike clover, trefoil, crimson clover, kudzu, ladino clover, lespedeza, red clover, sweet clover, vetch, and white dutch clover. Most areas of the United States have one or more legumes adapted to the particular region. Legumes do not grow well under arid or semiarid conditions. In the drier sections they may be grown on irrigated land as hay or pasture crops.

Grasses. Like legumes, there are many types of pasture grasses. Various areas have a number of grasses adapted to their climatic conditions. In selecting grasses for permanent pasture seeding, those that will produce the most forage over an extended period and that are palatable to livestock are recommended; for example, bluegrass is common in the central and northern corn belt. It pro-

FIGURE 89. *Legumes and grasses combine to make excellent cattle pasture. (Courtesy* Wallaces' Farmer and Iowa Homestead.)

duces excellent forage during the cool, moist months of spring but becomes more or less dormant during the hot dry months of summer and early fall.   Brome grass, although no more palatable than blue-grass, stands dry weather better and will produce more forage in an average season.

The list of grasses used for pasture in the United States is almost endless.   Many are native to certain areas, such as the western and southern range, and are well adapted to the weather and soil con-ditions that prevail there.   Agronomists have imported grasses from outside the United States for the improvement of the range and pas-tures in various sections.   In the typical range country, pastures are permanent, and only those grasses known to be well adapted should be used for reseeding.   Some of the better grasses to be used in mixtures for temporary and semipermanent pastures in the Midwest are: bluegrass, brome grass, tall fescue, orchard grass, redtop, per-ennial rye grass, sudan grass, and timothy.   All of these grasses are perennials except sudan grass, which is an annual.

Mixtures.   There are many combinations of legume and grass seed mixtures used for seeding pastures.   The length of time a pas-ture is expected to last is important in selecting a mixture.   In areas of the United States where the amount and distribution of the rain-fall are sufficient for growing cultivated crops, many farmers use rotation pastures as a means of providing forage and maintaining soil fertility.   Under a crop rotation system pastures may be left from one to four years.   The land is then plowed and planted to a row crop such as corn or cotton.   Land that is too wet or whose topography is too rough for cultivation is left in permanent pasture. Many permanent pastures become unproductive, and a reseeding and fertilization program is necessary.   A third type of pasture, known as an emergency pasture, is used when there is need for more grazing area than has been provided for.   Quick growing grasses that will provide forage the same year they are seeded make the best emergency pastures.

There is such a wide variety of soil and climatic conditions pre-vailing in the United States that no attempt will be made to give recommended pasture seed mixtures for all areas.   This information may be secured from the local vocational agriculture instructor, the county extension director, or the nearest agricultural college.   Some recommended mixtures for the midwestern states that have wide adoption in other sections are listed in the following table.

TABLE 12
Grass and Legume Mixtures Recommended for the Midwest
(Seeding Rate per Acre in Pounds)

Rotation Pastures

1. Alfalfa 6-8 Smooth Brome Grass 5-10
2. Alfalfa 6-8 Meadow Fescue 6-8
3. Alfalfa 6-8 Smooth Brome 6 Meadow Fescue 2
4. Alfalfa 6-8 Smooth Brome 4-5 Timothy 1-2
5. Alfalfa 7-8 Red Clover 3 Orchard Grass 6
6. Alfalfa 5-6 Ladino ½ Smooth Brome 8
7. Alfalfa 3 Ladino ½ Red Clover 3 Smooth Brome 8
8. Alsike 3 Ladino ½ Red Top 2-4 Timothy 2-3
9. Red Clover 6-8 Timothy 4-6

Permanent Pastures

1. Birdsfoot Trefoil 4-6 Bluegrass 3-4 Smooth Brome 6-8 Timothy 2
2. Birdsfoot Trefoil 4-6 Alfalfa 3-4 Smooth Brome 6-8 Timothy 1-2

Emergency Pastures

1. Sudan Grass 15-25
2. Sudan Grass 5-10 Soybeans 60-80

Developing a Pasture Program.   For economical beef production, plans should be made for pasturing the cattle as much of the year as possible.   Studies at Purdue University showed that 55.4 per cent of the feed cost for an entire year occurred during a 127-day wintering period.   The cost of wintering rations was two and a half times as much as the cost of pasture per day.

If a careful selection of variety and kinds of pasture mixtures are used, the grazing season can be extended in most areas and be a year around program in much of the southern part of the United States. Fall seeded grain, such as wheat or rye, will provide early spring pastures in the northern zone and winter pasture in the Southwest. Sudan grass and soybeans will provide midsummer pastures, giving the regular rotation or permanent pasture an opportunity to recover and to provide more late fall feed.   An example of a pasture program, suitable for the Midwest, that could be adapted to many other sections by changing the selection of crops to meet the local conditions is seed rye in the fall for late winter and early spring pasture. This will provide pasture until May 1 or later.   Cattle may then be turned on the permanent or rotation pasture which will be well started. The rye pasture may be plowed and planted to a row crop. Sudan grass, soybeans, or a mixture of both may be seeded in the spring after danger of frost is past. These crops will provide excellent midsummer grazing and relieve the regular pasture. When the rotation or permanent pasture has recovered, it will provide fall grazing until hard freezing occurs.

FIGURE 90. *These cattle are on an improved Georgia pasture. (Courtesy American Aberdeen-Angus Breeders Association.)*

Precautions to take when using sudan grass and other sorghums. When sudan grass is used for pasture, there is some danger of poisoning from prussic acid unless the following precautions are taken.

1. Do not pasture until the grass is 18 inches high.
2. Feed the cattle some dry forage before turning them on sudan grass pasture, especially for the first time.
3. Do not pasture sudan grass following frost or a prolonged drouth.
4. Soils growing sudan grass should be well fertilized if it is low in any of the major plant foods. Prussic acid is less likely to develop when the crop is grown on fertile soil.

The foregoing rules apply to other crops belonging to the sorghum family if they are pastured or fed green. Dry forages or silage made from the sorghums are not likely to cause prussic acid poisoning.

Nutrient Value of Pasture Varies. The nutrient value of pasture crops does not remain the same during the season. As plants become more mature, the fiber content increases and the protein and vitamin content decreases. The same is true when the growth of plants is retarded because of dry weather. Many pastures that have provided the entire ration successfully during one part of the season will need to be supplemented with considerable amounts of additional forage and grain at other times. Young pasture grass will average from 18 to 22 per cent protein and 70 to 80 per cent total digestible nutrients on a dry matter basis (water removed) as compared to about 5 to 9 per cent protein and 40 to 50 per cent total digestible nutrients for matured grasses. Not only does young pasture grass contain more protein, but it is of a highly digestible nature.

Management of Pastures and Grazing Systems. Turning the cattle into the entire pasture area early in the spring and leaving them there for the season is not conducive to making the most efficient use of pasture. Under free range conditions it may be the only way, but whenever possible drift fences or electric fences should be used to limit the area cattle graze over during any one period. The whole area is usually too large for cattle to graze evenly. The sections that have been eaten off will grow up tender and cattle will then continue to graze on these areas. As the season advances, the ungrazed portion becomes coarse, unpalatable, and lower in food value, whereas the grazed areas may not recover and will grow up to weeds and undesirable plants.

Rotation grazing. By using a temporary fence to divide the pasture into three or four sections and limiting the cattle to a smaller area and rotating them every two to four weeks, more and better grazing will be provided per acre of pasture land. If it becomes evident that any areas will grow more than necessary to provide late fall feed, they may be clipped and put up for hay or silage.

Deferred grazing. Under range or permanent pasture conditions the forage production will be greater over a longer period of time if the pasture is allowed to rest and reseed itself. The area may be divided into three to five sections and one section allowed to grow

FIGURE 91. *A forage chopper and self-unloading wagon used for hauling pasture to the cattle.* (*Courtesy of Reuben Albaugh, C. F. Kelly, and H. L. Belton,* Beef Handling and Feeding Equipment, *University of California Circular 414.*)

up and go to seed. The grazing is delayed on this area in the spring until the new plants have had a chance to become established. The next year a second section is allowed to reseed and the process is continued each year. When a deferred system of grazing is accompanied by a proper fertilization program, pastures will continue to be productive.

Cutting and hauling pasture forage. Green-lot feeding is a term applied to the practice of cutting and hauling pasture to the cattle that are confined to a dry lot. Experiments conducted at several stations show that by this system one can expect to produce from 20 to 30 per cent more beef per acre than can be produced from grazing. Many of these experiments showed faster gains when pasture was hauled to the cattle than occurred with any of the grazing systems. In addition to more carrying ability of the pastures and faster gains on the beef cattle, fences may be eliminated and bloat is seldom a problem.

Forage should be cut daily and in the amount that will be consumed by the cattle in a 24-hour period. Larger amounts will mold and result in waste. The taller legumes and grasses have shown considerable increase in total yield from green-lot feeding. The shorter crops have shown little if any increase. The practice of green-lot feeding is more adaptable to legume and grass pastures grown in rotation than to permanent pastures.

While there are the advantages mentioned in the preceding paragraphs, there are also many disadvantages to green-lot feeding.

Some of the more important disadvantages are that (1) the job must be done each day, creating a labor problem, (2) that considerable investment is needed in machinery, wagons, and other equipment, and that (3) rainy spells and wet spots are a problem with heavy machinery. One must carefully weigh the advantages and disadvantages before changing from a grazing system to green-lot feeding. The large operator may consider the possibility of hauling pasture to his cattle. It is doubtful that the small herd owner would find the extra investment and labor needed economically sound.

Fertilization programs for pastures. Many pastures have become unproductive due to the depletion of plant foods in the soil. It should be remembered that plants utilize nitrogen, phosphorus, potash, and many trace elements which they convert to carbohydrates, fats, proteins, and mineral nutrients that provide livestock with food materials. Each time an animal is removed from the farm or ranch it carries in its body plant food derived from the soil.

FIGURE 92. *Unloading fresh cut forage. (Courtesy of Reuben Albaugh, C. F. Kelly, and H. L. Belton,* Beef Handling and Feeding Equipment, *University of California Circular 414.)*

Pastures that have furnished much of the feed for livestock, will eventually need fertilization if they are to continue to produce. Unless the plant food is replaced in part, grasses and legumes will grow slowly. When they do not produce abundantly, cattle will graze the area too short, further destroying desirable plants and allowing undesirable weeds to get started. Weeds compete with the grasses and legumes for the limited supply of plant food, further decreasing the stand and growth of the desirable plants. When this condition exists a pasture fertilization, weed destruction, and reseeding program will be necessary.

Weeds may be destroyed by chemicals, controlled burning, or cultivation. The weed destruction methods used will depend upon the plants and recommended practices for the area.

Soil tests should be taken of the pasture areas, and a fertilization program should be carried out in accordance with the soil's needs. When pastures consist entirely of nonlegumes and the soil is in need of nitrogen, these grasses will be low in both protein and total yield. Land needing lime and phosphorus will produce poor yields

FIGURE 93. *This pasture has been overgrazed and inadequately fertilized, resulting in poor productivity.* (*Courtesy of R. J. Delorit and H. L. Ahlgren,* Crop Production: Principles and Practices [*New York: Prentice-Hall, Inc., 1953*], *Fig. 234, p. 469.*)

of forage that is deficient in calcium and phosphorus. For an abundance of nutritious pasture, a sound fertilization program is essential in most areas.

Reseeding methods and pasture mixture should be those recommended for the area.   Wherever they are adapted, legumes should make up a part of the plant stand.

FEEDING THE HERD IN DRY LOT

Dry lot feeding of the breeding herd, such as is necessary in areas of the United States too far north for winter pastures, presents more problems than pasture or summer feeding. It has been pointed out that good quality green forage is high in vitamins, many of the minerals, and protein. Unless reasonable precautions are taken, winter or dry lot rations may have nutritional deficiencies that will result in a small percentage calf crop or weak calves.

Danger of Nutritional Deficiencies. Protein, vitamin A and mineral deficiencies may occur in cattle confined to a dry lot especially when low quality forages are used without supplements. However, breeding cows can utilize large quantities of corncobs, corn stalks, and other low quality feeds if they are properly supplemented and still produce a good calf crop.

Use of Various Types of Roughages for Wintering the Cow Herd. If the roughage used is at least one-half good legume hay or legume silage and the cows are fed liberal amounts, they will go through the winter in good condition and produce a strong calf with no extra feed except for a mineral mixture and salt self-fed. Legume hay or silage is high in protein, vitamins, and most of the minerals. When an ample amount of legume roughage is available, the problem of a wintering ration is pretty nearly solved.

When low quality roughages, like corncobs, corn stalks, or coarse stemmy hay is fed as the only roughage, some high energy feed, such as molasses, sorghum grain, barley, corn, wheat, or oats, and a complete supplement that contains the needed vitamins, minerals, and protein, are needed to properly balance the ration.

Experiments conducted at Purdue University have shown that cows receiving 14.5 pounds of ground corncobs, one pound of dehydrated alfalfa meal, 3.5 pounds of Purdue Cow Supplement (fed daily), and a mineral mixture (fed free choice), wintered and produced as good a calf crop as did cows receiving 20 pounds of alfalfa-brome-timothy hay plus minerals. The Purdue Supplement used in the cow-feeding trials consisted of 636.8 pounds of soybean meal, 285.8 pounds of 45 per cent molasses feed, 51.4 pounds of bonemeal, 17.2 pounds of iodized salt, and 2.5 pounds of vitamin A concentrate.

FIGURE 94. *Legume and grass silage makes excellent roughage for winter rations.* (*Courtesy* Wallaces' Farmer and Iowa Homestead.)

Recent work at the Iowa and other stations has shown that if corn is picked when it is about 30 per cent moisture and the stalks are harvested and made into silage, this silage will provide good feed if properly supplemented. Corn belt farmers are exhibiting considerable interest in picking corn early and drying it artificially. This practice permits the harvesting of the stalks while they still retain most of the leaves and many of the stalks are still green. Silage made from these stalks will be higher in protein than corncobs, but if fed as the only roughage would probably not provide enough protein for the needs of the breeding cows.   Cows receiving two pounds of grain and five pounds daily of good legume hay, plus a full feed of corn stalk silage and minerals, fed free choice, could be expected to winter well and produce a good calf crop.

Silage should not be used as the only roughage in breeding-cattle rations.   Experiments have shown that when at least three to five pounds of dry roughage are fed in addition to the silage, better utilization of the silage results.   The roughage need not be of high quality.   Four to five pounds of ground corncobs or an equal amount of coarse hay may be used.

When the silage consists of corn or sorghum (grain included), no additional grain will be required.   However, unless the dry roughage consists of high-quality legume hay, one or two pounds of 30 to 40 per cent protein supplement should be fed daily.

Grazing Winter Pastures and Crop Residues.   Under corn belt conditions corn fields and small grain fields are usually grazed until covered with snow.   Feed gleaned from these fields will provide some cheap roughage, but should not be relied upon for the entire ration.   Such feed is low in protein, minerals, and essential vitamin A.   Therefore, either five to ten pounds of legume hay daily or one to two pounds of protein supplement plus one or two pounds of grain should be fed.

Minerals may be fed free choice.   In the northern range it is common practice to hold the cattle off from part of the range, thus allowing the grass to grow for winter pasture.   This type of winter forage provides good feed, but is low in protein.   Cattle will winter well on the range if given minerals free choice and one to two

FIGURE 95. *These cows are receiving part of their ration by gleaning a harvested corn field.*

pounds daily of a good protein supplement.   If the range becomes grazed too short or covered with snow, supplemental feeding of hay is essential.   In the southern areas wheat or other small grain pastures provide excellent grazing and allow the permanent pastures to make a recovery for later grazing.

The preceding discussion will show that there are many combinations of roughages that may be used for wintering the cow herd. The wise cattleman will plan his program so as to winter the cattle as cheaply as possible without damage to the health of the cows or the calf crop.

Weight Gains Cows Should Make.   Ordinarily cows should gain during the winter in weight equal to the weight gain of their unborn calf, the fluids, and the membranes of advanced gestation. This would equal about one-third pound per day.   However, the condition of the cow at the beginning of the wintering period must be considered.   When the range has been exceptionally good, cows will enter the winter season in high condition and some loss in weight will not injure them nor their calves.   On the other hand, poor pasture conditions may mean thin cows that will need to gain a pound or more per day to be in condition for calving and nursing a calf.

Rations for Wintering Beef Cows.   The number of rations one may develop for the successful wintering of cows is large.   Rough-

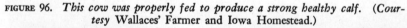

FIGURE 96.   *This cow was properly fed to produce a strong healthy calf.*   (*Courtesy* Wallaces' Farmer and Iowa Homestead.)

ages must serve as the basis of all wintering rations if economical beef production is to be accomplished. The nutritional deficiencies of roughages will need to be compensated for by feeding proper supplements. Cows should have a wintering ration that will range from 8 to 10 per cent protein (air dried basis) plus adequate minerals and vitamin A. Following are several rations for cows in dry lot during the winter.

TABLE 13

RATIONS FOR WINTERING BEEF COWS

Ration	Feed	Pounds Fed Daily
1.	Legume hay	15-20
	Mixed minerals	Free choice
2.	Legume hay	5-10
	Oat straw	10-15
	Mixed minerals	Free choice
3.	Corn or sorgo silage	30-40
	Legume hay	5
	Oat straw	5-7
	Mixed minerals	Free choice
4.	Ground corncobs	14-15
	Dehydrated alfalfa meal	1
	Purdue Cow Supplement	3.5
	Mixed minerals	Free choice
5.	Corn or sorgo silage	30-40
	Chopped dry corn stalks	10
	Cottonseed, linseed, or soybean meal	1
	Mixed minerals	Free choice
6.	Legume and grass silage	25-30
	Legume and grass hay	5-10
	Mixed minerals	Free choice
7.	Corn stalk silage	30-40
	Legume hay	5-10
	Grain	2
	Mixed minerals	Free choice
8.	Corn stalks in field	Graze at will
	Legume-grass hay	10
	Mixed minerals	Free choice
9.	Dry winter range	Graze at will
	30-40% protein supplement	2
	Mixed minerals	Free choice

NOTE: Mineral mixtures are the same as those recommended for cattle on pasture, salt should be fed free choice in addition to the mineral mixture.

Estimating the Amount of Feed Required for Wintering the Herd. If the feed supply is not sufficient to carry the herd through the winter it is generally cheaper to make needed purchases in the fall. Hay, grains, and other feeds tend to increase in price toward spring. The wise cattleman will, therefore, take stock of his feed supply in the fall and either make arrangements for needed feed or reduce his herd accordingly.

The average cow will require from 15 to 20 pounds of good quality legume grass mixed hay per day or the equivalent in other feeds. If good hay is to be used as the sole ration except for minerals and salt, from 450 to 500 pounds per cow per month should be provided. The herd owner should decide upon the ration he will use and estimate his feed requirements. The rations in the preceding table are based upon the average daily needs of a bred cow. By selecting one ration and multiplying the amount of each ingredient by the number of days in the average wintering period, a fairly accurate estimate of feed needs can be made except for the minerals. The consumption of minerals is not great and they can be purchased during any season at about the same price.

Mating. There are many problems the cattleman must solve relative to mating animals for the purpose of producing a calf crop. The first of these is the selection of breeding stock, which was discussed in Chapter 3.

Heat periods. The period of heat or oestrum is the time when the female will be receptive to the bull and the act of mating will occur. A few hours after the heat period is over an egg or female germ cell is released from the ovary. Under normal conditions conception will take place providing the male germ cells (sperms) have been placed in the vagina by the act of breeding during the heat period of the female.

The duration of the heat period will vary from 12 to 30 hours with individual cows. The average heat period is from 12 to 18 hours. The egg or female germ cell is released (ovulation) from 6 to 20 hours after the heat period. If the cow is to receive only one service from the bull, it is better to have it occur toward the end of heat to insure good strong sperms for fertilization. Experiments have proven that higher rates of conception take place when the females are bred toward the end of the heat period.

The time between heat periods will vary from 17 to 26 days, depending upon the individual animal, with an average of about 21 days.

Signs of heat. Cows vary in their individual behavior during the heat period. However, most cows exhibit considerable nervousness. They will attempt to mount other cows which in turn will mount them. There may be a reddening and swelling of the vulva. Usually there is a slight mucous discharge.

Gestation periods. The time from conception until the cow calves is known as the gestation period. The gestation period will vary from 270 to 290 days, with individual cows and with different breeds. Most authorities agree that 283 days is about the average length of the gestation period.

TABLE 14

GESTATION TABLE FOR COWS (283 DAYS)

Day of Month Bred	Jan.	Feb.	Mar.	Apr.	May	June	July	Aug.	Sept.	Oct.	Nov.	Dec.
EXPLANATION: Find date cow was bred in first column and month bred in top line. The date in column below opposite date bred will be the time at which the cow is due to calve.											
	Oct.	Nov.	Dec.	Jan.	Feb.	Mar.	Apr.	May	June	July	Aug.	Sept.
1	11	11	9	9	8	11	10	11	11	11	11	10
2	12	12	10	10	9	12	11	12	12	12	12	11
3	13	13	11	11	10	13	12	13	13	13	13	12
4	14	14	12	12	11	14	13	14	14	14	14	13
5	15	15	13	13	12	15	14	15	15	15	15	14
6	16	16	14	14	13	16	15	16	16	16	16	15
7	17	17	15	15	14	17	16	17	17	17	17	16
8	18	18	16	16	15	18	17	18	18	18	18	17
9	19	19	17	17	16	19	18	19	19	19	19	18
10	20	20	18	18	17	20	19	20	20	20	20	19
11	21	21	19	19	18	21	20	21	21	21	21	20
12	22	22	20	20	19	22	21	22	22	22	22	21
13	23	23	21	21	20	23	22	23	23	23	23	22
14	24	24	22	22	21	24	23	24	24	24	24	23
15	25	25	23	23	22	25	24	25	25	25	25	24
16	26	26	24	24	23	26	25	26	26	26	26	25
17	27	27	25	25	24	27	26	27	27	27	27	26
18	28	28	26	26	25	28	27	28	28	28	28	27
19	29	29	27	27	26	29	28	29	29	29	29	28
20	30	30	28	28	27	30	29	30	30	30	30	29
21	31	Dec. 1	29	29	28	31	30	31	July 1	31	31	30
22	Jan. 1	2	30	30	Mar. 1	Apr. 1	May 1	June 1	2	Aug. 1	Sept. 1	Oct. 1
23	2	3	31	31	2	2	2	2	3	2	2	2
24	3	4	Jan. 1	Dec. 1	3	3	3	3	4	3	3	3
25	4	5	2	2	4	4	4	4	5	4	4	4
26	5	6	3	3	5	5	5	5	6	5	5	5
27	6	7	4	4	6	6	6	6	7	6	6	6
28	7	8	5	5	7	7	7	7	8	7	7	7
29	8	—	6	6	8	8	8	8	9	8	8	8
30	9	—	7	7	9	9	9	9	10	9	9	9
31	10	—	8	—	10	—	10	10	—	10	—	10

Determining Pregnancy. Veterinarians and animal scientists are carrying on research work in an attempt to find a simple sure way of determining pregnancy during the early stages. However, for the present the only sure way is an internal examination of the uterus made through the rectum. The uterus and ovaries lie just beneath the colon and can easily be felt through the wall of the large gut. If the cow is pregnant the fetus can be felt. Later in pregnancy the uterus is pulled down and cannot be felt by the examiner. The vagina, however, will be drawn forward over the outer edge of the pelvis and the forward portion of the uterus, forming a thick firmly stretched band passing downward toward the abdominal cavity and out of the reach of the examiner.

Early examination for pregnancy by a veterinarian or trained operator can be carried out on small beef cow herds. Many times cows fail to get with calf due to some organic difficulty which may be corrected by a veterinarian in time for the animal to produce a calf in the current season. On large herds under range conditions the process of examination would be more difficult.

Age to breed heifers. The age to breed heifers is much disputed among cattlemen. Heifers that have made a good growth for their breed may successfully be bred as yearlings to calve as two-year-olds. However, in a questionnaire sent to Nevada ranchmen by the University of Nevada, 63 per cent of the ranchers stated that heifers calving as two-year-olds failed to produce a calf as three-year-olds. Heifers calving as two-year-olds frequently fail to conceive while nursing calves and therefore fail to calve the next year. The Nevada study further revealed that ranchers who bred their heifers for calving the first time when three-year-olds produced 12 per cent more calves than did those who followed the practice of having heifers calve at two years of age.

Small herd owners who can give their heifers exceptionally good care both before and after calving may profitably breed heifers for calving at two years of age. Heifers should weigh at least 850 pounds when bred. Unless they are up to this weight, small stunted cows may result from early calving.

Age of the bull. Under range conditions a bull should be two years old before he is turned out with the herd. Bulls past seven years old may not be depended upon to meet the strenuous conditions of the range and breed their quota of cows. However, where conditions are such that they can be properly cared for, many bulls will breed when 12 or more years old.

Under small herd conditions where the number of cows a bull serves can be regulated, a young bull 15 months old, if hand-mated, can be depended upon to breed ten to fifteen cows.

Ratio of cows to bulls. The number of cows to run with a bull varies widely. Where the range is rough and brushy, 15 cows per bull is enough. Under good conditions a vigorous bull between the ages of two and seven will serve up to 40 cows when running with the herd. If hand-mating is practiced, and the breeding program is carried out to produce both spring and fall calves, one bull may be sufficient for 50 to 60 cows.

Time for calving.   When warm housing is available early calving is recommended.   Calves that are two to three months of age when the pasture season arrives will utilize more grass and the feed cost will be reduced.   When cows must calve outside, it will be necessary to delay calving until the weather is warm.   In the northern part of the United States, the weather usually will not permit outdoor calving before April.

Length of time the bull should run with the herd.   If a uniform calf crop is desired, the bull should not be allowed to run with the herd for more than three months, especially under range conditions. A survey made in Colorado showed that 10 per cent more calves were produced on ranches where the bull was allowed to run with the herd only three months than on those where he remained with the herd the entire season.   Under Midwest conditions, where late calves may be given special care, a higher per cent calf crop may result from allowing the bull to remain with the herd.   However, the facts should be taken into consideration that (1) calves will be uneven, (2) late calves in the colder areas do not grow as well, and (3) wet cows are harder to winter and require more feed.

FIGURE 97.   *A vigorous healthy range bull in good breeding condition.   (Courtesy American Hereford Association.)*

Signs of Parturition. When a cow is nearing the time when she will drop her calf, she will exhibit certain signs well known to the trained cattleman. The first of these is a noticeable falling away or sinking in the regions of the tailhead and pin bones and a softening of the flesh in this area. Second, the lips of the vulva will appear swollen and inflamed. Third, there will be an enlargement of the udder and a change from a watery secretion to the thick somewhat yellow colored colostrum.

Care of the Cow at Calving Time. Cows should be observed closely for signs of calving and help given those that are in trouble. Where calving is done on the range, it will usually pay to have a rider watch the cows closely. Where cows are confined to small pastures the herd should be checked once daily. The rider or farmer can give assistance to cows having difficulty calving. Some cows give more milk than the calf will take the first few days and will need to be milked out. Other cows may not be producing enough milk and will need additional feed and care. Weak calves may be helped to nurse, and the calves should be rubbed dry if the cows fail to lick them.

When cows calve on the pasture, conditions are usually sanitary and there is little danger of infection. However, when they calve early and barns or sheds are used, the cows should be placed in a clean, disinfected and well-bedded stall. Disinfecting the navel of the newborn calf with a tincture of iodine will help to prevent navel infection which is common when cows calve in barns where manure and other filth has accumulated. Even cleaning and disinfecting may not destroy all of the germs.

Assistance in delivering the calf. After the cow starts to labor, observe closely to see if she is progressing normally. If the cow has difficulty in calving, either call your veterinarian or help the cow. The first step is to determine whether the calf is in the proper position for delivery. The front legs should be extended forward with the head resting on or between them. It may be necessary to push the calf back to correct its position for calving. When the calf is in proper position for delivery, pull gently outward and upward. Pull only when the cow attempts to labor. The hand and arm of the operator should be washed and disinfected before making entry. Provide the cow with plenty of water to drink. Remove the afterbirth as soon as the cow has been cleaned to prevent her from eating it. Cows will eat the afterbirth, probably due to instinct developed by their wild ancestors to prevent the odor from attracting marauding animals. If the cow does not expel the after-birth completely within 48 hours, call your veterinarian.

SUMMARY

Since the calf crop represents the profit from the breeding herd, it is important that the brood cows produce a high percentage of calf crop and that the calves are strong and healthy. The resulting calf crop depends largely upon the proper feeding of the breeding herd. We repeat that cows should be fed as cheaply as possible, but without reducing the percentage and vigor of the calves nor the sacrificing of any of the productive life of the cows.

Plenty of roughage is the key to the economical production of calves. An ample amount of pasture will maintain the herd during the pasture season, exept for minerals and salt which should be provided at all times.

When pastures are inadequate, they should be supplemented with dry forage, silage, or grain. When pastures are dry and low protein feeds are used to supplement them, a protein concentrate should be added to the ration. The protein may be hand-fed or mixed with salt and self-fed. A commercially prepared protein block is a convenient way to supply protein.

Since pasture grasses are high in vitamins, there is seldom a need for them to be provided in the supplement for cows on pasture. Cows that are on very poor quality pasture for a considerable length of time may develop a vitamin A deficiency which can be corrected by feeding one pound per day of fresh dehydrated alfalfa meal, or two pounds daily of high-grade alfalfa hay, or one-fourth pound of a commercial vitamin supplement.

Cattle should not have to travel more than two miles for water. The range and pastures will be grazed more evenly and cattle will make more efficient use of feed when water is readily available.

Legumes grown in combination with grasses provide excellent grazing of a highly nutritious nature. Wherever they are adapted, legumes should be grown as part of the pasture crop.

Pastures should be managed so as to produce an abundance of feed over the longest possible season. Good pasture management depends upon either deferred, rotation, or green lot feeding (which-ever is best suited to the local situation), and a fertilization pro-gram.

Dry lot feeding involves more problems than pasture feeding. There is a danger of mineral, vitamin, and protein deficiencies when cattle are fed in dry lots unless proper precautions are taken in formulating the ration.

Mature cattle can utilize large quantities of low quality roughages such as corn stalk silage, corncobs, and straw, if a supplement containing protein, minerals, and vitamins is provided. When good legume hay or legume hay and silage is fed as the major part of the ration, bred cows can be expected to winter well and produce a calf with little else except salt and minerals self-fed.

Bred cows should normally gain about one-third pound per day. Thin cows will need to put on more flesh to be in condition for calving, while cows in exceptionally good flesh may lose some weight without injury.

The feed needs for wintering the herd should be estimated in the fall and adjustments, if required, should be made.

The heat period for cows will vary from 12 to 30 hours with an average of from 12 to 18 hours. Ovulation takes place from 6 to 20 hours after the heat period. A higher conception rate results when cows are bred near the end rather than early in the heat period. The time between heat periods will vary from 17 to 26 days with an average of about 21 days.

The gestation period is about 283 days with some variation between breeds and individual animals.

Pregnancy may be determined by an internal examination by way of the rectum.

Heifers that are well grown out may be bred to calve as two-year-olds but under most conditions it is recommended that they drop their first calves when three years of age.

When hand-mated, a young bull 15 months of age may be used to breed up to 15 cows. Bulls should be at least two years old and not more than seven when turned on the range. Older bulls, when properly handled, may be used for limited service up to 12 years of age.

Under good conditions the ratio of bulls to cows may be as high as one to 40. Where the range is brushy and grass is sparse, it may be necessary to keep one bull for each 15 cows.

Calves should be born as early in the spring as conditions will permit. Calves two to three months old will utilize more grass and be heavier in the fall.

If a uniform calf crop is desired, it is better to allow the bull to run with the herd not more than three months of the year.

Cows nearing the calving period will show a falling away or sinking in the regions of the tailhead and pin bones, a softening of the flesh in this area, a swelling and inflamed appearance of the vulva, and the formation of colostrum in the udder.

At calving time the herd should be closely observed, a clean, dry place should be provided for cows about to calve, and help given in delivering the calf when needed.

QUESTIONS

1. What are the important considerations in feeding the cow herd?
2. Under what conditions will it be necessary to supplement pasture?
3. Give several examples showing how, when, and the kind of additional feed you would provide for cows on pasture.
4. Give some mineral mixtures that could be used under various conditions.
5. How may additional vitamin A be provided for cows on pasture?
6. How do grasses and legumes compare as pasture plants?
7. Why should grasses and legumes be grown in combination?
8. List the common pasture legumes.
9. Give some pasture mixtures suitable to your area.
10. Develop a pasture program suitable to your area.
11. What precautions should one take in pasturing sudan grass?
12. Explain how the nutrient value of pastures will vary.
13. How should pastures be managed in your area for greatest production?
14. Why is there more danger of nutritional deficiencies when cattle are fed in dry lot?
15. Explain how various quality roughages can be utilized successfully.
16. Give several rations that can be depended upon to winter beef cows successfully.
17. What is the duration and length of time between heat periods?
18. When does ovulation occur?
19. When should cows be bred for the highest conception rate? Why?
20. What are the signs of heat?
21. What is meant by the gestation period, and what is the average length of the gestation period?
22. How can pregnancy be determined early in the gestation period?

23. When should heifers be bred?   Explain.
24. How old should bulls be before being put into service?
25. What is the recommended ratio of cows to bulls?
26. When should cows calve?   Why?
27. How long should the bull be allowed to run with the herd?   Why?
28. What are the signs of parturition?
29. Explain how the cow should be cared for at calving time.
30. When and why should the navel be disinfected?

REFERENCES

Beeson, W. M., and T.W. Perry, *Chopped Forage vs. Pasture for Feeding Cattle*, Agricultural Experiment Station Mimeo A. H. 122, 1953, Purdue University, Lafayette, Indiana.

Beresford, Rex, *Raising Beef Cattle in Iowa*, Extension Bulletin P-102, 1952, Iowa State College, Ames, Iowa.

Hauser, E. R., and J. J. Lacey, *Beef Cattle in Wisconsin*, College of Agriculture Extension, Circular 413, 1952, University of Wisconsin, Madison, Wisconsin.

Lindgren, H. A., *Feed Requirements and Values for Livestock*, Extension Bulletin, 639, 1951, Oregon State System of Higher Education, Corvallis, Oregon.

Ralston, F. A., *Beef Production in Montana*, Extension Bulletin 272, 1951, Montana State College, Boseman, Montana.

Results of Cattle Feeding Experiments, A. H. 753, 1958; A. H. 779, 1959; A. H. 813, 1960; Iowa State University, Ames, Iowa.

Smith, Harry H., and Ford C. Daugherty, *Beef Production in Colorado*, Extension Bulletin 389-A, 1950, Colorado A & M College, Fort Collins, Colorado.

Snapp, Roscoe R., and A. L. Neuman, *Beef Cattle* (Fifth Edition), John Wiley and Sons, Inc., New York, 1960.

Totusek, Robert, E. C. Hornback, T. W. Perry, and W. M. Beeson, *Corncobs for Wintering Beef Cows*, Mimeo. A. H. 94, 1952, Purdue University, Lafayette, Indiana.

Feeding and Management of Calves

Death losses of calves at calving time and slow gaining calves due to poor feeding and bad management practices, reduce profits for the cattleman. Inefficient management may mean the difference between a profit or a loss for the year's operations. The cattleman must necessarily take a number of risks. Among these are seasonal conditions that may materially reduce his feed crops and pastures. He also has the problems of disease and, at times, unfavorable market prices for his product. Therefore, it is essential for profitable production that he take every means possible to reduce those risks over which he has some control.

MANAGEMENT OF YOUNG CALVES

When a cow has been kept in the breeding herd for the purpose of producing a calf, that calf must go to market if the feed bills and other costs of maintaining the cow are to be paid and still provide a margin of profit for her owner.

Care of the Newborn Calf. Nature has intended that the newborn calf shall live and if given a reasonable chance to do so, most of them will. The percentage of calves that survive may be increased if the operator is on hand to give the newborn calf the needed attention.

When the calf is born, the mucus and phlegm should be cleaned from the nose and mouth. If the calf does not start to breathe, it should be held by the rear legs and lifted with the head down. This procedure is a form of artificial respiration and will often produce results if repeated several times. Alternate compression and relaxation of the chest will often start the calf breathing when other methods fail.

As soon as the calf is breathing properly, the navel should be disinfected.   Squeezing out the navel cord and painting the navel with tamed iodine (an iodine product which has had most of the blistering properties removed) or methylate will help avoid infection.   If the cow does not lick her calf dry, or if the weather is cold, the operator should wipe the calf to hasten drying.

FIGURE 98. *Disinfecting the navel of a newborn calf.* (*Courtesy C. F. Huffman, Michigan State College.*)

If the cow calves in a barn or shed where there is danger of disease germs being present, the cow's udder should be washed with a chlorine solution to prevent any infectious organisms from being taken in through the calf's mouth during the first feeding.   If the calf is normal, it will stand and suck within 30 minutes.   If it fails to do so, it should be given assistance in getting a feeding of the first or colostrum milk.   The colostrum or first milk secreted by the cow is nature's especially prepared food designed to start the calf's digestive system operating.

Within two hours after the calf has had its first feed, its bowels should move to eliminate the material accumulated in the digestive tract before it was born.   If this does not pass in due time, an enema consisting of one-half teaspoonful of soda in a quart of warm water may be given.

Providing Clean Dry Quarters.   When calves are dropped during warm weather and out on the range or pasture, they usually are allowed to remain with their mothers and pens are not required. When cows calve during cold weather it is a common practice to keep the calves shut up in pens located in barns or sheds as protection against the cold.   The calves are turned out with the cows morning and night so that they may nurse.   This practice permits the cows to graze the corn stalk fields or winter pasture without exposing the young calves to severe cold.

Well-lighted, well-ventilated, clean, dry pens, adequately bedded and free from drafts are essential to the successful raising of calves born during cold weather.

Observation pens.   Some beef cattlemen prefer to use individual observation pens for calves until they are a week or ten days old. This gives the operator an opportunity to observe and detect any infection or communicable disease and reduces the danger of spreading such infections to healthy calves.   Observation pens are tem-

FIGURE 99.   *These winterborn calves are located in a well-bedded, well-ventilated pen.   (Courtesy Geo. A. Hormel and Company.)*

porary and may be constructed from hinged panels, which can be taken apart and stored when not in use.

Group pens. Regardless of whether observation pens are used or not, calves usually are transferred to group pens within a few days following birth. Most cattlemen prefer to leave the cow and calf together continuously for the first two or three days. Then the cow may be turned out and the calf transferred to either an observation pen, later to a group pen, or directly to the group pen.

It is important not to overcrowd the pens and to group the calves according to size and age. Very young calves placed with older ones will be crowded away from the feed boxes and hayracks, resulting in slower average gains and unequal consumption of feed, especially grain.

Calf pens should be equipped with a feed box, a hayrack, and watering facilities. Feed boxes should be about 10 inches wide, 6 inches deep, and long enough to provide two feet of feeding space for each calf. They should be 20 inches from the floor and away from the waterer. The hayrack should be constructed to prevent waste and provide at least one foot of feeding space per calf.

Sanitation. Calves confined to dry lots, barns, or sheds are more susceptible to diseases, such as scours, digestive difficulties, and parasite infestation than are those that are on pasture. Good sanitation is always important in cattle production, but is especially important in the management of young calves under confinement.

Calf pens should be cleaned and disinfected at regular intervals. They should be kept dry, well lighted, and ventilated. When it becomes necessary to hand-feed milk, or other liquid feeds, the utensils used should be washed after each feeding. Feed boxes and waterers should be kept clean especially when contaminated with calf droppings. Calves showing signs of scours or other infectious ailments should be isolated and treated. The successful calf raiser is alert and can detect quickly calves that are beginning to show some difficulty. A healthy, vigorous calf will have clear, bright eyes and erect ears, show alertness, and display a smooth, glossy hair coat. Calves showing discharge from nostrils, coughing, or rapid breathing, need immediate attention.

DEHORNING

While horns that have been well trained and polished add to the attractiveness of show cattle of the horned breeds, commercial cattle should have the horns removed.

Advantages of Dehorned Cattle.   Cattle should be dehorned for the following reasons:

1. More room is needed for horned cattle in sheds, barns, and lots.
2. Cattle with horns inflict more damage on equipment.
3. There is more danger to the operator in handling cattle with horns.
4. Horned cattle that are inclined to fight will keep others away from the feed.
5. Cattle with horns inflict bruises on each other that may result in heavy economic losses.

When to Dehorn.   The age to dehorn calves depends upon the conditions and the method used in performing the operation. Generally the sooner it can be done the less inconvenience is suffered by the calf.   Under range conditions, from a time and labor standpoint, it may be better to wait until most of the calves have been dropped.   This will mean that some calves will be three months of age before dehorning.   Under corn belt conditions where the calves are confined or can be rounded up without much difficulty the operation can be done on one or two calves at a time, if necessary, within a few days after birth.

Methods of Dehorning.   There are a number of methods that may be employed for dehorning cattle.   The age of the calf to be dehorned and other facilities available determine which one is best.

Chemical method of dehorning.   The horn buttons may be prevented from growing by burning with chemicals.   This method is most successful if done before the calf is ten days old.   The chemicals that are commonly used are caustic potash or caustic soda. They come in a white stick about the size of blackboard chalk or in a commercially prepared dehorning paste.   Care should be used in handling them to prevent serious burns to the operator.   The hair should be clipped around the horn button and a ring of heavy grease applied to the clipped area to prevent the burning action of the chemical from spreading too far.   If using the caustic stick, dip the end in water to moisten it and rub with a rotary motion on the horn button.   If the paste is used, it may be smeared on with a swab or flat wooden spatula.   In a few days, a heavy scab forms over the horn; the scab drops off in about ten days.   The calf suffers little inconvenience, and there is no open wound with its attendant danger of infection.

While removing horns by chemicals is effective in eliminating the horns, there is a tendency for the face to appear longer as the animal matures. This is due to the frontal bone becoming somewhat oval in outline and extending above the point where the horns would normally have been. For this reason, the use of caustic for dehorning is objected to by those who desire to show their animals at the fairs and other shows.

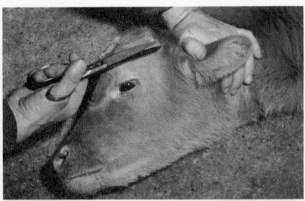

FIGURE 100. (top) Clipping the hair from around the horn button. (center) Applying a ring of Vaseline around the horn button. (bottom) Applying the caustic stick to the horn button. (Courtesy C. F. Huffman, Michigan State College.)

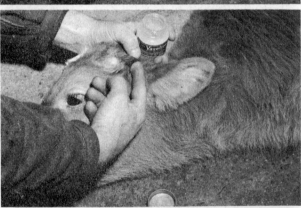

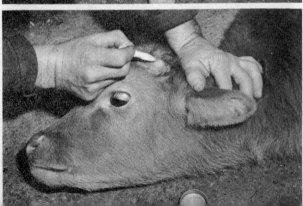

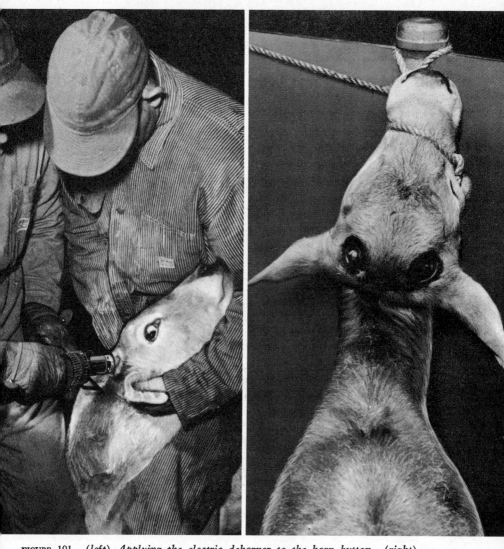

FIGURE 101. (left) *Applying the electric dehorner to the horn button.* (right) *This is the way the horn buttons will appear a few days after the hot iron has been applied.* (*Courtesy Sunbeam Corporation.*)

Hot iron. Burning the horn button with an electric dehorner or hot iron is a method being used on some farms for dehorning young calves. Calves should not be over three months old if burning is to be effective in preventing horn growth. Electric dehorners have an automatic control that maintains temperatures at about 1000° F. Applying the electric dehorner to the horn button for ten seconds is sufficient to destroy the cells and prevent growth of the horn.

Spoons and tubes.   There are a number of instruments, such as spoons and tubes, on the market for dehorning.   Up to three and a half months of age, horns are only skin appendages and may be gouged or scooped out with a tube which is cylindrical in shape with a hand grip on one end and a sharpened edge on the other. After the age of three and a half months the horns become fastened to the skull and tubes are not an effective means of removing them.

FIGURE   102.   *Dehorning with a dehorning tube.*   (*Courtesy Tony Fellhauer, University of Wyoming.*)

Dehorning tubes come in several sizes varying from three-fourth inches to one and one-eighth inches in diameter.   Since the horn sizes vary with individual calves, several different sizes of tubes should be made available.   In using tubes (1) select a sharp tube of the proper size to fit over the horn base, (2) place the cutting edge straight down over the horn, (3) push and twist both ways until a cut of from one-eighth to three-eighths deep has been made.

Calves nearing three months of age will require the deeper cut. Do not go deeper than necessary to cut through the skin as excessive bleeding will result, (4) turn the tube down to a 45-degree angle and lift the horn button out.

An open wound results from the use of either tubes or spoons and therefore it is better to perform the operations in cool weather. Otherwise use a good fly repellent on the wound.

Clippers and saws. When older cattle are to be dehorned, especially designed clippers or saws are used. A considerable

FIGURE 103. *Clippers are often used for dehorning after the horns have grown out too far to use tubes, spoons, or chemicals.* (*Courtesy* Successful Farming.)

amount of bleeding may follow the operation. To prevent bleeding the main horn artery should be tied off with a cotton or silk thread. This may be done by sliding a sewing needle under the artery to pull thread in place before tying.   It is necessary when sawing or clipping the horns to take about one-half inch of skin in order to remove the horn roots.   Since an open wound results, it is better to perform the operation during cool weather when there are no flies.   In warm weather, a good fly repellent should be smeared over the wound.

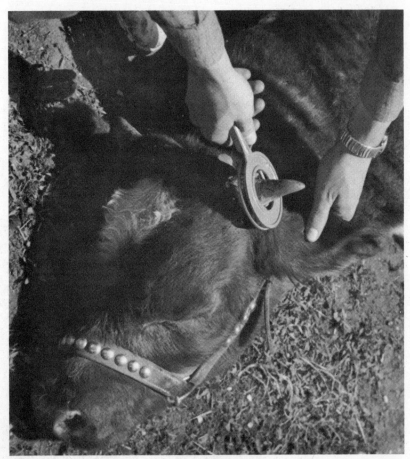

FIGURE 104.   *This photo shows how to apply rubber bands for dehorning.*   *(Courtesy Don Collinson.)*

Rubber bands.   Some farmers have reported successful dehorning of older cattle by using the rubber band method.   The chief advantage of this system is that a large open wound, such as is left by clippers or saws, is avoided.   The dehorning is accomplished by first making a groove around the base of the horn in about the same place it would be cut with a saw or clipper, and then using the elastrator to slip a rubber band over the horn and into the groove.   The rubber band shuts off the circulation and the horn gradually comes off.

FIGURE 105. *The elastrator used in placing rubber bands over horns and the ridger used for grooving horns to keep bands in place. (Courtesy Don Collinson.)*

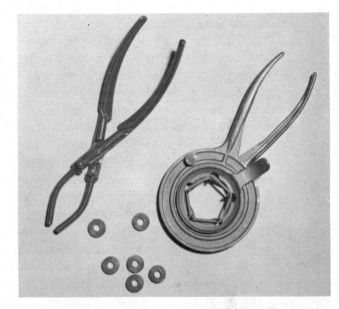

FIGURE 106. *This animal has been dehorned by using the rubber band method. (Courtesy Don Collinson.)*

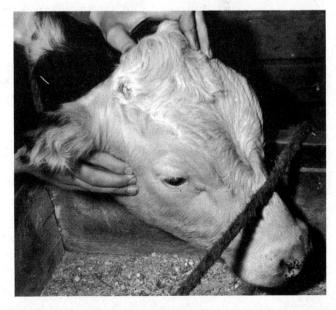

CASTRATION

All male calves that are not to be used for breeding purposes should be castrated. Castrating is essential to the production of a high quality carcass and to prevent both inbreeding and the breeding of females by undesirable males.

Time to Castrate. Castrating, like dehorning, should be done in cool weather to prevent screw worm infestation or other infections. Between the ages of one and three months is probably the ideal time to perform the operation although many cattlemen prefer to castrate when the calves are one to two weeks of age. Generally speaking, the younger the calf is the less inconvenience it suffers. The only objection to castrating very young calves is the difficulty the operator experiences in grasping and holding the testicles while performing the operation.

Methods of castrating. Pulling downward on the scrotum and cutting off the lower one-third, exposing the testicles from below, is a common method of castrating. For show cattle where a well-developed cod is desired, one testicle is pulled down at a time and held firmly with the left hand so that the skin of the scrotum is tight over the testicles. An incision is then made on the outside of the scrotum next to the leg, both through the scrotum and the membrane surrounding the testicle. The pressure exerted by the left hand will expose the testicles so that it may be grasped and held in the right hand. The left hand may be used to separate it from the supporting tendons. While holding the testicle with the left hand, the tendons should be cut close at their lower attachments. The spermatic cord should now be stripped of all surrounding membranes and severed by scraping rather than cutting, as less bleeding will result. As much of the spermatic cord as possible should be removed. This may be accomplished by pulling downward on the testicle drawing the cord out as far as possible before it is severed.

A specially constructed instrument known as the Burdizzo has found some favor in the South. This consists of castrating pincers designed to crush and destroy the spermatic cord and the blood vessels that supply the testicles, leaving the testicles to dry up and be absorbed. The operation is bloodless and no open wound is left for infestation by screw worms or infection. However, unless it is used by a skilled operator the cord and blood vessels will not be completely destroyed.   The result will be a calf known as a *slip*, which will show stagginess when about a year old.

The elastrator similar to the one described in dehorning cattle may be used to slip a rubber band over the scrotum tight up against the groin.   The rubber band shuts off the circulation and the scrotum and testicles slough off.

MARKING

Marking is essential to good management.   It permits identification of animals as to ownership and breeding.   If permanent, it is also a deterrent to thieves as marked cattle may be more easily identified.   Purebred associations require marking as a prerequisite to registration.   There are many marking systems employed. Some leave a permanent identification mark on the animal itself. Others consist of attaching an identifying number to the animal either as neck chains or ear tags.   The purpose or purposes for which cattle are marked and the region will largely determine the kind of marking system best adapted.

Hide Brands.   Hide brands are probably the oldest system used in marking cattle.   They were employed by the ancient Egyptians and have been common in the western United States since the development of the cattle industry in that area.

Hide brands are used primarily as a means of identifying cattle as to ownership on the open ranges of the West.   A rancher cannot ordinarily lay claim to cattle unless they carry his brand.   Most western states have made provisions for the recording of brands to prevent duplication.   One operating a ranch close to the border of another state can generally record his brand in both states.   Hide branding is usually accomplished by having irons shaped into the letters, numbers, or design to be used.   The irons are heated in a fire and applied to the body of the animal.   The identifying brand is seared into the hide leaving a permanent identifying brand. Only a few seconds is required and slips should be avoided.

A second method is what is known as the cold iron operation. This is done by dipping a cold branding iron into chemicals consisting of caustic materials and applying the iron to the hide.   For best results the hair should be clipped.   This operation has not been nearly as popular as the hot iron method.

A good brand is one that is simple and easy to read but cannot be easily changed.   It is necessary to firmly secure the animal to prevent slips.   Calves may be roped and dragged to the place of branding.   Older cattle can be handled more easily in a specially constructed chute.

Hide brands are probably the best identifying marks so far designed from the standpoint of being easily read, but they are unsightly and are not generally recommended for breeding cattle that are to be shown at livestock shows.

FIGURE 107.   *These calves have just been branded. Note the horseshoe brand design.   (Courtesy American Aberdeen-Angus Breeders Association.)*

Ear Notches.   Ear notches are easy to identify and may be used for ownership as well as breeding records.   They disfigure the cattle and for that reason are not popular.   Like the hide brand, they have developed as a means of leaving a permanent identifying mark which will not easily be lost.

Tattoo Method.   One of the best marks for permanent identification of cattle is that of tattoing the inside of the ear with indelible ink.   This is accomplished by using a tattoo earmarking instrument which is equipped with letters, figures, and ink.   The ink is forced into the skin where it leaves a permanent mark.   The letters and figures may be arranged into any one of several combinations.

Most breed associations require an ear tattoo before accepting animals for registration.

To properly tattoo the ear, first place the figures or letters you plan to use in the jaw of the marker, close the lock and try it out by punching a cardboard to be sure the letters or figures are correct and right side up. Hold the animal securely and select a spot near the center of the ear, being careful to avoid the ribs or cords. Thoroughly clean this spot in the ear with a wet cloth. Place the ear between the jaws of the pliers with the figures on the inside of the ear, close the jaws quickly and release quickly. Avoid tearing the ear. With the finger smear ink over the punctures and rub thoroughly until each hole is well filled. If there is an excessive flow of blood it will be necessary to use more ink and rub longer. Next make a written memorandum of the mark and keep the · memorandum in a safe place.

FIGURE 108. (left) Correct placement of the tattooing pliers. (right) A good clear tattoo for permanent identification. (Courtesy University of Wisconsin.)

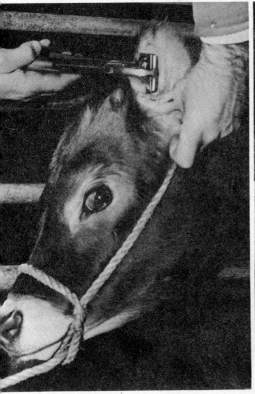 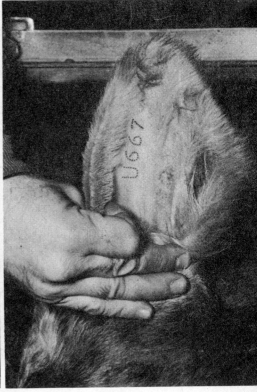

Horn Brands.   Horn brands may be used as an easily identifiable mark on mature horned cattle.   They are commonly used to identify cattle for sale purposes, the horn brand corresponding with the number in the sale catalogue.

FIGURE   109. *This   cow has been identified by a horn   brand.   (Courtesy American Hereford Association.)*

Ear Tags.   Metal ear tags or buttons with letters and numbers may be inserted in the ear as a means of identification of calves. Tags may be purchased or made to order with initials, names, and numbers in almost any combination.   There is some danger that the tags may be torn out and identification lost.   They should be used with some other identifying mark.

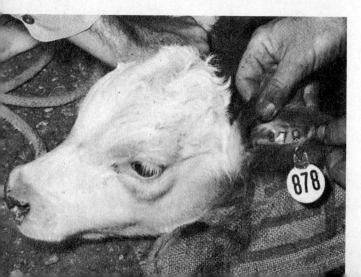

FIGURE 110. *An ear tag has been placed on this calf for quick identification, but the tattoo will not be lost, and serves as a permanent mark. (Courtesy* The Farm Journal-Country Gentleman.)

FIGURE 111. *Neck chains with metal numbers attached are a good means of identification. (Courtesy American Aberdeen-Angus Breeders Association.)*

Neck Straps and Chains. Leather neck straps or neck chains with a number plate attached, make an easy method of identification. Like the ear tags, there is some danger that they will be lost.

FEEDING SUCKLING CALVES

Beef cattlemen usually follow the practice of letting the calves nurse the cows. Whether or not it will be profitable to feed concentrates to suckling calves will depend upon the pasture conditions, the age that calves will be marketed, the cost of the supplemental feed, and whether the calves will be sold or kept in the herd for breeding purposes. The feeding of concentrates to calves that are to be sold as yearling feeders may not be profitable where pastures are good and there is plenty of good roughages for winter feeding. However, calves that are to be sold or kept for breeding purposes or sold as feeder calves may profitably pay for additional feed while nursing. Creep-fed calves may be expected to gain approximately one-third pound per day more than the average calves receiving only their mothers' milk and pasture. When the cows' milk flow is heavy and pastures are good, less response will result from creep-feeding concentrates. If additional feed is fed, the common practice is to erect a creep on the pasture or in a dry lot (if the cows have not been turned on the pasture) and provide a concentrated ration for the calves. The creep should be constructed in such a way as to permit the calves to feed but prevent the cows and other older cattle from getting to the feed.

Creep-Feeding Calves. The practice of creep-feeding calves has the following advantages: (1) The calves will have more weight at weaning time, (2) the cows are suckled down less, (3) calves will not miss their mothers as much at weaning time, (4) calves will be more uniform in size as creep feeding helps to make up for any shortage while nursing, (5) calves that are to be fattened will be in better condition when they go into the feed lot, and the fattening period will be shortened, (6) heifers and bulls that are to be kept or sold as breeding animals will have more growth, (7) fat is a good seller even of feeder calves. Creep-fed calves are usually fatter than other calves and therefore sell better either as feeders or for breeding purposes.

Starting calves to eat. Suckling calves are sometimes slow in starting to eat concentrates. A creep, easily accessible to the calves, may be placed in one end of the cattle shed (if cows and calves are in a dry lot) or near the watering place on the pasture. If one feeds both cows and calves a small amount of concentrates on the ground or in low down bunks, calves that have not learned to eat grain will be encouraged to do so by watching the cows. After the calves have learned to eat, the feed may be placed in a creep. For best results, fresh clean feed should be in the creep at all times.

Feeds for suckling calves. A large variety of feeds may be successfully fed to suckling calves. Availability and price should largely determine those that are selected.

FIGURE 112. *A good calf creep.* (*Courtesy* Successful Farming.)

Grains.   Corn, oats, barley, sorghum grain, or wheat are all good grains for self-feeding suckling calves.   The price per pound of digestible nutrients should be the determining factor in making a selection.   Grains are the principle concentrates used in creep-feed mixtures.

Protein supplements.   Since milk is high in protein it is seldom necessary to include a protein concentrate in the creep-feed mixture. When pastures are poor or if the milk flow of the cows is low, then it is advisable to include a recommended protein concentrate in the creep feed.   If the herd is in a dry lot and low protein forage is fed, then the addition of a protein supplement is recommended.

Soybean oil meal, linseed oil meal, cottonseed meal, peanut oil meal, or corn gluten meal are all satisfactory protein supplements for beef calves.   In addition to these there are a large number of reliable commercially prepared protein supplements ranging from 30 to 45 per cent protein that will give satisfactory results.   The price per pound of protein should be considered when making a selection.

Mineral supplements.   If a good mineral mixture is available for the cow herd, and fed in a place easily accessible to the calves, it may not be necessary to provide a mineral supplement in the creep ration.   However, many good cattlemen reserve a small section of the creep where a mineral supplement is placed separately for the calves.

Forages for calves.   When calves are kept in a dry lot it is important that they have a good grade forage available at all times. Legume hay is preferred, but a good quality grass hay is usually satisfactory if some additional protein is provided.   Small calves may be fed some silage, but most beef cattlemen prefer that at least part of the roughage be in the form of hay rather than all silage.

Calves that are on good pasture will not need additional forage. When pastures are poor they should be supplemented with a good hay or silage.

If there is plenty of good forage available the cows and calves may eat together.   If there is only a limited amount of high quality forage, it should be saved for the calves and fed in a separate area not accessible to the cows.

Antibiotics for suckling calves.   Experiments conducted at Purdue University showed a marked reduction in scouring among suckling calves and a growth stimulation when aureomycin was fed at

the rate of 24 mg. per 100 pounds live weight.   Calves receiving
aureomycin administered in capsule form daily at the above rate
seldom showed any signs of scouring, while the control group receiving the same ration except for the aureomycin, developed several
cases of severe scouring.   The aureomycin fed calves averaged
14.5 pounds per calf more at 80 days of age than the control calves
not fed the antibiotics.

Judging from the Purdue experiments and similar results from
other agricultural experiment stations, it seems advisable to include
aureomycin in the creep ration.

Preparations of Grain for Calves.   Unless a mixed ration including a protein or antibiotic supplement is to be fed, the grinding or
rolling of corn and oats is not necessary.   Barley, wheat, and sorghum grains are improved by grinding or crushing.   These seeds
especially the sorghums are so hard that they pass through the
cattle without being digested unless they are ground or rolled.   To
facilitate uniformity in a mixed ration, the grinding of all grains is
necessary.

Rations for Suckling Calves.   Using the concentrates discussed
in the preceding paragraphs, a large number of creep rations may
be formulated all of which would give satisfactory results.   The
following table lists some suggested rations for creep feeding calves.

TABLE 15

SUGGESTED RATIONS FOR CREEP-FEEDING SUCKLING CALVES

With Good Pasture or Legume Hay		Poor Pasture, Low Protein Forage, or Poor Milking Cows	
(1) Ground Oats	1,000 lbs.	(1) Ground Oats	1,000 lbs.
Ground Corn	1,000 lbs.	Ground Corn	800 lbs.
*Antibiotics		Linseed, Soybean, or	
		Cottonseed Meal	200 lbs.
(2) Ground Oats	1,000 lbs.	*Antibiotics	
Ground Barley	1,000 lbs.		
*Antibiotics		(2) Ground Oats	1,000 lbs.
		Ground Barley	850 lbs.
(3) Ground Barley	1,000 lbs.	Corn Gluten Meal,	
Ground Sorghum Grain	1,000 lbs.	Soybean, Cottonseed	
*Antibiotics		or Linseed Oil Meal	150 lbs.
		*Antibiotics	
(4) Ground Oats	500 lbs.		
Ground Wheat	500 lbs.	(3) Ground Sorghum Grain	1,000 lbs.
Ground Corn	500 lbs.	Ground Barley	800 lbs.
Ground Sorghum Grain	500 lbs.	40% Commercial Protein	200 lbs.
*Antibiotics		*Antibiotics	

* An antibiotic supplement which will provide 40 grams of aureomycin per ton of feed.

FEEDING REPLACEMENT HEIFERS

After the replacement heifers have been weaned, it is important to feed them separately from the cows. Heifers need a better quality ration than do mature cows if they are to reach normal size at breeding time.

FIGURE 113. *A group of replacement heifers.* (*Courtesy American Aberdeen-Angus Breeders Association.*)

Whenever it is possible, during the first and second winters, breeding heifers should receive at least 5 pounds of good legume hay, plus additional amounts of sorgo or corn silage in the colder regions. In the South, if good winter pastures are available, additional forage is not essential.

Unless a roughage that will supply some grain (like sorghum silage or corn silage) is fed, grain in addition to good forage will speed up the growth and maturity of heifers. It is important to raise the replacement heifers as cheaply as possible, but without sacrificing growth and development.

Antibiotics for Growing Heifers.   As previously stated, experimental results reported at Kansas State College and Purdue University indicate that antibiotics fed to calves after weaning and up to 18 to 20 months of age, if they are receiving a ration consisting largely of roughage, will increase gains and efficiency of feed utilization.

At Kansas State College, two groups of heifers were fed a wintering ration of sorghum silage, 4 pounds of milo grain and 1 pound cottonseed meal.   One group received 36 mg. of aureomycin daily. The aureomycin-fed heifers gained an average of 1.16 pounds daily over a 119-day feeding period as compared to 1.03 pounds daily gain for the heifers not receiving aureomycin.

The level of aureomycin fed daily is important.   Purdue scientists recommend a level of about 10 mg. to 100 pounds of live weight. When greater amounts are fed, the antibiotics have a depressing effect on the appetite of the cattle.

TABLE 16

SUGGESTED RATIONS FOR HEIFERS FROM WEANING TO TWO YEARS OF AGE

Dry Lot		On Pasture	
Feed	Pounds Daily	Feed	Pounds Daily
(1) Legume Hay	5	(1) Mixed Grain per hundred	
Sorgo or Corn Silage	10-20	lbs. live weight	½
(2) Legume Silage	15-30	(2) Ground Ear Corn, per	
Mixed Grains per hundred lbs. live weight	½	hundred pounds live weight	¾
(3) Grass Hay	5		
Sorgo or Corn Silage	10-20		
40% Protein Supplement	½		
(4) Grass Hay	10		
Straw	Unlimited		
Mixed Grains per hundred lbs. live weight	½		
40% Protein Supplement	½-1		

NOTE: Minerals self-fed.
   Aureomycin premix may be added to the rations to provide 10 mg. aureomycin per hundred pounds live weight.

FEEDING YOUNG BULLS

The feeding of young bull calves up to the time they will be put into service does not differ greatly from that of replacement heifers.

Owing to somewhat faster growth, their feed requirements are greater. The grain ration should be increased over that recommended for heifers. In addition to an unlimited amount of good cured roughage or pasture, young bulls should receive about a pound of grain per hundred pounds live weight daily. If the roughage is of a low protein nature half a pound to one pound of protein supplement should be fed daily in addition to the grains. A mineral supplement should be available free choice (self-feeding).

Young bulls about to be put in service should be in good flesh but not overly fat. Bulls in service will usually stay in condition on the same rations fed to the cows unless they are used exceptionally heavily over a considerable length of time. If so, an additional amount of concentrates will be required to maintain them.

SUMMARY

The care a newborn calf receives largely determines its chances for survival. Normally the calf does not need a great deal of attention providing the cows have been placed in a clean, warm pen for calving. During warm weather cows can calve out on the pasture. The phlegm should be cleaned from the nose and mouth of the newborn calf and the navel should be disinfected. If it is slow in starting to breathe artificial respiration may save the calf. If the calf is weak assistance should be given it in getting a feeding of the colostrum. If the calf's bowels do not move within two hours an enema should be given.

During cold weather, clean, dry, well lighted and ventilated pens should be provided for the calves. They may be turned out with their mothers morning and night for nursing. When the weather is warm and the cows are on pasture, the calves may run with the cows. Observation pens may be used to hold newborn calves in for the first few days to determine whether they have any contagious ailments that might spread to healthy calves. Pens should not be overcrowded and calves should be grouped according to age and size. Pens should be equipped with hayracks, feed boxes, and watering facilities.

The operator will need to give more attention to sanitation conditions when calves are confined to pens than will be required by those on pasture.

The commercial cattleman should dehorn his cattle. Dehorning may be accomplished by chemicals, hot iron, dehorning spoons and tubes, saws, clippers, or rubber bands. The method used will depend upon the age of the calf and the experience of the operator.

Calves may be castrated any time after they are a few days old. Most experienced cattlemen prefer to perform the operation when they are from two to three months of age. The operation may be accomplished by removing the testicles with a knife or crushing the spermatic cord with a castrating pincer.

The wise cattleman marks his calves. Hide brands, ear notches, and tattooing will provide permanent marks that will not be lost. Other methods include horn brands, neck chains or straps, and ear tags.

Suckling calves will grow quite satisfactorily on milk and grass or other good forage. However, growth and weight gains will be faster if a concentrated ration is provided in a creep. Grains are usually all the nutrients that need to be provided in the creep if good pasture or high protein forage is available to the calves. If pastures are poor or low protein roughage is fed the addition of a protein supplement will produce faster gains. Minerals may be placed in the creep or located where both cows and calves have access to them.

Antibiotics have increased the rate of gain and reduced the incidence of scours among suckling calves. It is recommended that they be included in the creep ration.

Corn and oats need not be ground or crushed unless they are to be used in a mixed formula. Barley, wheat, and sorghum grains should be ground or crushed.

Replacement heifers need a better ration than is ordinarily necessary for mature cows. They should be separated from the cow herd and given some grain in addition to good roughage. When the ration is made up primarily of roughage, antibiotics will increase the rate of growth of young stock up to 18 to 20 months of age.

Young bulls may be fed the same as replacement heifers except that they will require more feed.

QUESTIONS

1. State the steps you would take in caring for the newborn calf immediately after birth.
2. What steps would you take to provide sanitary conditions for young calves?

3. Describe the type of pens you would recommend for young calves housed in barns or sheds.

4. Why should calves be dehorned?

5. Describe the various methods of dehorning cattle and give the advantages of each.

6. When should calves be castrated?

7. Explain the methods used in castrating calves.

8. Why is it important to mark cattle?

9. Describe the various systems of marking beef cattle.

10. What advantages are there in creep-feeding calves?

11. Under what conditions would you consider it uneconomical to creep feed?

12. What advantages has the feeding of aureomycin shown in suckling calves?

13. At what level should antibiotics be fed to suckling calves?

14. Give several good creep rations for calves to be fed under various conditions.

15. Discuss the preparation of grains for young calves.

16. How would you feed replacement heifers and young bulls?

17. What advantages are there in feeding antibiotics to young stock from weaning to 20 months of age?

18. At what level should antibiotics be fed young stock after weaning?

REFERENCES

Anderson, W. T., and Henry Mayo, *Producing Beef Calves in Indiana*, Extension Bulletin 371, Purdue University, Lafayette, Indiana.

Beresford, Rex, *Raising Beef Cattle in Iowa*, Extension Bulletin P-102, Iowa State College, Ames, Iowa.

Lindgren, H. A., *Feed Requirements and Values for Livestock*, Extension Bulletin 639, Oregon State System of Higher Education, Corvallis, Oregon.

Perry, T. W., W. M. Beeson, and M. T. Mohler, *Aureomycin for Growing and Fattening Beef Animals*, Agricultural Experiment Station, Mimeo A. H. 120, 1953, Purdue University, Lafayette, Indiana.

Feeding and Management of Stockers and Fattening Cattle

The cattle feeding business is risky, especially for the inexperienced. The cattle feeder usually is one who has produced grain and roughage which he expects to convert into beef. He is generally located in a grain producing area. However, there are a number of commercial cattle feeders who buy all of their feed. In addition to the initial cost of the cattle, the feeder has his feed tied up in his cattle. If his feeding operations go wrong, through mistakes in judgment, he will lose heavily.

Securing Cattle. Farmers who have a considerable amount of grassland along with several acres of grain crops often maintain a cow herd and raise their own feeders. These cattle are later put into the fattening yards and finished on the grain produced on the farm. The farmer may produce more cattle than he has grain for fattening and may either buy additional grain or sell part of his cattle as feeders. Most of the cattle that go into the feed lots are purchased from the ranchers during the late summer and fall months and shipped into the grain producing areas for fattening.

SOURCES OF PROFIT FROM FEEDING CATTLE

It has been pointed out in Chapter 1 that the cattle feeder depends primarily upon two sources of income for profit from his cattle fattening operations. They are margin and value of the gain over feed cost. It should also be noted that many cattle feeders located

166

on grain producing farms regard the fertilizing value of the manure as a very important source of income, since it results in greater yields of grain crops. This is especially true where the cattle are fed out on the farm land or when care has been taken to preserve the manure, hauling it onto the crop land with minimum losses of fertilizing elements.

Profits from Margin. Unless there is a general price decline in cattle, or conditions that have created unusually high prices for feeder cattle, the feeder can reasonably expect to sell his finished cattle for a higher price per hundred pounds than he paid. This increase in price is known as margin. To assure himself of getting a margin he should finish his cattle to meet the best market grade they are capable of making. For example, choice feeders usually sell at a higher figure than cattle grading *standard to good.*

FIGURE 114. *These feeder cattle are waiting for shipment from the western range into the corn belt for fattening. (Courtesy American Hereford Association.)*

Choice feeder cattle when properly finished should grade as *choice to prime* slaughter cattle and bring the top prices.   If he finished these cattle only to the extent that they will grade *good*, he may receive considerably less than he paid per hundred pounds.   If it is the intention of the feeder only to finish cattle to *good* or a lower grade, he will generally have to purchase lower-quality feeders if he expects to make a margin under average condition.

Profits from Gains.   Profits from gains result from receiving a greater total price from the increased weight than it cost to put on the gain.   For example, suppose that it takes 50 bushels of corn, 150 pounds of supplement, and one ton of hay to put 400 pounds of gain on a steer.   If the corn is worth $1.50 per bushel, supplement $5.00 per hundredweight, and hay $20.00 per ton, the feed cost will be $75.00 for corn, $7.50 for supplement, and $20.00 for hay, or a total feed cost of $102.50.   If $10.00 extra is allowed per steer for equipment, labor, and other expenses, there is a total cost of $112.50. If the steer sells for $29.00 per hundred, the increased weight is worth $116.00, a profit on gain of $3.50 per hundred.

Profits Resulting from Manure Value.   The value of the manure is indirect and more difficult to determine than are margin and gain profits.   Manure value must be determined in terms of increased crop production as a result of the fertilizing value of the manure and the amount of commercial fertilizer replaced by the manure.

When corn, small grains, and hay are sold from the farm as cash crops, the soil has lost all of the plant food contained in these crops.

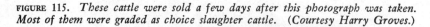

FIGURE 115.   *These cattle were sold a few days after this photograph was taken. Most of them were graded as choice slaughter cattle.   (Courtesy Harry Groves.)*

If these are fed to the cattle and reasonable care has been exercised to preserve the manure, a return can be expected of at least 50 per cent of the total plant food contained in the feed that has been fed.

How manure loses its value.   Nitrogen, phosphorous, and potassium are the principal plant foods.   Loss of plant food from manure results from leaching by rain, heating of the manure pile, loss of urine, and confining cattle to muddy lots where the manure cannot be recovered.

Preventing plant food losses from manure.   Manure packed in a shed, where it is not exposed to the weather, will not lose much of its value provided that there is enough moisture to prevent heating. Many farmers do not realize that the urine or liquid portion of the manure has a greater fertilizing value pound for pound than do the feces.   Unless an absorbent type of bedding such as chopped straw or ground corncobs is used, much of the urine will be lost.

By adding superphosphate to the manure as it is made, the loss of nitrogen may be greatly reduced.   The phosphorous will improve the fertilizing value of the manure, as it is one of the major plant food elements.

Paved lots enable the feeder to scrape up the manure easily with a power loader and the paving will also serve to keep the cattle out of the mud.   Many feeders scatter corncobs or straw in the feed lot for the purpose of conserving the manure.

When cattle are fed on rotation pastures the manure will be dropped directly on the land and much of the loss is thus prevented.

FIGURE 116.   *Paved lots save manure and keep the cattle out of the mud.   (Courtesy Harry Groves.)*

The amount and value of manure produced by fattening cattle.
The average fattening steer or heifer will produce from 7 to 8 tons
of manure including bedding, per year.   The value of this manure
depends upon the feeds fed and the prices of commercial fertilizers
as well as the price received for the increased yield of crops.   The
figure will vary considerably, but a conservative estimate would be
from $2.00 to $3.00 per ton.

FIGURE 117. *The cattle feeder should consider the value of the manure in terms of
increased crop production when determining the profits from his feeding operations.*
(Courtesy Deere & Company.)

TABLE 17

PLANT NUTRIENTS IN ONE TON OF AVERAGE CATTLE MANURE

(INCLUDES SOLIDS, LIQUIDS, AND BEDDING)

Nitrogen (N) pounds	Phosphoric Acid (P_2O_5) pounds	Potash (K_2O) pounds	Tons Manure Produced Per Year Per 1,000 Lbs. Body Weight
11.4	3.1	9.9	15

The farmer who would make a choice between feeding cattle or selling grain and hay may well consider the value of manure from cattle in attempting to determine which to do.

DRY ROUGHAGES FOR STOCKER AND FATTENING CATTLE

Cattle feeds are many and varied.   The rations used depend upon the kind of cattle to be fed and the cost and availability of feeds. The feeding value of different feeds will be discussed in such a way as to enable the cattlemen to select the feeds best suited to his conditions.

Roughages should make up a large part of the cattle ration. They are economical and when properly fed, decrease the cost of gain.   Roughages vary considerably in feeding value.

Legume Hays.   As previously stated (see Chapter 6) high-quality legume hay is recognized as the best roughage from a nutritional standpoint.   It is high in protein, minerals, and vitamins.   Alfalfa, the clovers, lespedeza, soybeans, and cowpeas are all common legumes used for hay and silage.   However, when straight legume hays are fed to cattle that are on a full feed of grain, there is a tendency for them to scour.   Many cattle feeders, therefore, prefer a mixed grass-and-legume or a straight grass hay for cattle on a full feed of grain.   Legumes will vary in food value depending upon the stage of maturity when harvested, the harvesting methods, the ability of the operator to retain the leaves of the plant, and the soil fertility.   Coarse, mature, stemmy hay, even though it is a legume, may be low in food value.

Grass Hays.   Many of the grasses, such as brome, fescue, orchard grass, and western native grasses, are excellent roughages but low in protein and minerals compared to legumes.   One pound of a 40 to 45 per cent protein supplement is usually all that is needed when legume hay is used as the entire roughage.   If grass hay is fed as the only roughage, an increase of one-half to one pound of protein supplement will be required to balance the ration.   More attention will need to be given to the mineral and vitamin content of the ration to make up for the roughage deficiency.   Feeding a mineral mixture free choice and one or two pounds of dehydrated alfalfa meal per head daily will compensate for the mineral and vitamin deficiencies of the grass hays.

Mixed Hays. The term mixed hay usually applies to a mixture of grasses and legumes. The food value of mixed hay will be somewhere between that of legume and grass hay depending upon the percentage of legumes in the mixture.

Beet Tops. Fresh beet tops have a very high feeding value but lose much of their value if left too long in the field. They should be harvested and stored to conserve their feeding value or they should be made into silage.

Dehydrated Hays. Dehydrated hays are the result of harvesting green plants and artificially drying them. This process saves the leaves and results in a higher protein and vitamin A content. How-ever, since vitamin D is absorbed in the hay from the sunshine while curing in the field, sun cured hay is generally higher in vitamin D.

Cattle that are exposed to direct sunshine will be unlikely to suffer from a vitamin D deficiency. Therefore, the vitamin A content of forage is more important than the vitamin D content.

Corncobs. Corncobs have been used successfully when properly supplemented for growing and fattening cattle. Corncobs are high in fiber and very low in protein, vitamins, and mineral content. If cattle were fed corncobs alone they would probably slowly starve. Experiments at Purdue University, Iowa State College, and other agricultural experiment stations, as well as the experience of prac-tical cattle feeders have shown that cobs produced gains comparable to hay and corn when fed as the only roughage together with a full feed of ground ear corn and a complete supplement. The sup-plement must contain the necessary amount of protein, vitamins, and minerals, and must be fed in the quantity needed to make up for the deficiencies of cobs in these nutrients. Ohio Agricultural Ex-periment Station tests have shown that choice calves and yearlings full-fed on a corn and cob meal mixture containing one-third cobs by weight, 2 pounds of soybean oil meal, plus mixed hay, salt, and minerals fattened to grade choice in from 200 to 250 days. Since ground ear corn would be about 20 per cent or one-fifth cobs, the Ohio rations would have contained about 13 per cent more cobs than ground ear corn.

Dry Chopped Corn Stalks. Like corncobs, corn stalks when properly supplemented will produce substantial gains on fattening cattle. Tests at the Iowa Agricultural Experiment Station showed that steers receiving 7.01 pounds of dry chopped corn stalks, 2.12 pounds of complete supplement, 3.12 pounds of mixed hay, 9.7

pounds of cracked corn, minerals and salt, gained an average of 1.76 pounds daily.

These experiments show that cheap roughages have a place in beef-cattle feeding. In wintering rations, when the feeder desires to produce a limited growth gain of from one to one and one-fourth pounds daily and plans to fatten his beef cattle on grass or on grain the following fall, low-quality roughages may be used very successfully for cattle weighing 500 pounds or more. Lighter-weight calves should have some high-quality forage. Such roughages will have to be lower in cost per pound of food value than the better roughages if they are to be economical. If high-fiber roughages are to be utilized by cattle, they will need to be fed in conjunction with some high-energy feed, such as molasses, corn, or sorghum grain, plus substantial amounts of protein supplements fortified with vitamins and minerals.

The bacteria that are responsible for the ability of cattle to digest high-fiber feeds must be supplied with enough energy, protein, mineral and vitamin nutrients for their own growth. Unless these bacteria are well fed, ruminants fail to get enough food value from cobs, corn stalks and similar feed to survive and produce gains. If the bacteria are properly fed, they grow and digest the high-fiber feed. As the bacteria die, they are in turn digested by the ruminants. It should be remembered that feeds like dry corncobs and corn stalks furnish little excepting carbohydrates. They are usually a cheap source of this nutrient. However, the other nutrients must be supplied if digestion and assimilation of the carbohydrates is to be accomplished.

SILAGES FOR STOCKER AND FATTENING CATTLE

Silage is produced by putting feeds containing a high percentage of moisture into one of several types of silos, or by packing the feed in a compact stack known as a silage stack. While straight grains may be made into silage, it is common practice to use the grasses, legumes, or the entire grain plant for the purpose of making silage. The more common practice is to cut the plants while they are high in moisture, chop them, and put them in the silo. Unless the proper amount of moisture is present, the necessary type of fermentation to preserve and produce a high quality silage will not take place. Dry forages and grains may be converted to silage by adding the proper amount of water. Silage forms when crops are stored to ferment in the absence of air. Unless the air is excluded by complete packing, silage will mold and spoil. Good preservation requires that lactic and acetic acids develop in the fermentation.

Grass and Legume Silage. When alfalfa, brome grass, oats, and other legumes, grasses, or small grain crops are made into silage it is generally referred to as grass silage; actually it would be more nearly correct to refer to silage made from legumes as legume silage, that from grasses other than small grains as grass silage, and that made from small grains as small grain silage.

These crops all vary considerably in their nutrient content. Silage made from legumes will contain more protein than that made from grasses.

Why make grass silage? Grass silage can be made during weather unfavorable for curing hay in the dry form. Since there will be very little loss of leaves, grass silage has a much higher nutrient value than weather damaged hay. Very little carotene and protein are lost when grasses and legumes are made into silage. Studies show that 15 to 20 per cent more protein and 10 times as much carotene or vitamin A will be conserved when legumes or grasses are made into silage as compared to the same crops made into hay.

Moisture content. Silage may be successfully made when crops average from 65 to 80 per cent moisture if the proper precautions are taken. At 70 to 80 per cent, grasses and legumes will need to have some molasses, other sugar materials, or grain added to aid fermentation and preserve the silage. When it is over 70 per cent moisture there will be considerable seepage and loss of nutrients unless some dry materials like ground corncobs or ground grains are added to absorb the excess moisture. If the ensiled forage is made when the moisture content is below 65 per cent, it will heat and spoil. Water should be added to bring the moisture content up to 65 per cent. Forages ranging from 65 to 70 per cent moisture will make good silage without either preservatives or added water.

Use of preservatives. There are two general types of preservatives that may be used in making grass silage, those that both preserve and add additional nutrients and those that serve only to prevent spoilage. Among those that increase the nutrient value are molasses, ground grains, and powdered whey. They all contain some form of sugar and while acting as a preservative also increase the food value of the silage. Table 18 shows the recommended amount to use of these preservatives.

Among the preservatives that have been successful in preventing spoilage but add nothing in food value is sulphur dioxide. Sulphur dioxide comes in a cylinder under high pressure. A high-pressure hose and a special probe and valve to apply the gas is required. The probe is pushed down into the freshly cut and packed forage and the gas is released at the rate of 5 pounds of sulphur dioxide per ton of silage.

TABLE 18

AMOUNT OF PRESERVATIVES TO USE PER TON OF GRASS OR LEGUME SILAGE

	Pounds Recommended per Ton of Silage		
Preservatives	Legumes	Legumes and Grasses	Grasses and Small Grains
Molasses, liquid	80-100	70-80	60-70
Molasses, dry	60	40	30
Ground Shelled Corn or Grain	150	125	100
Ground Ear Corn	200	150	125
Dried Whey	45-50	30-40	25-30

FIGURE 118. *(left) The common upright silo which is permanent but more expensive than other types. (top, center) A silo constructed by lining rings of welded wire with waterproof paper; a cheap but temporary silo. (Courtesy Iowa State College.) (bottom, center) A bunker type silo, made by using wooden or concrete sides supported by earth. This type of silo is permanent and provides cheap storage. They may be used for self-feeding by placing a moveable manger at one end. (Courtesy Iowa State College.) (right) The silage stack may be used for storing grass and legume silage. Packing is essential if spoilage is to be prevented. (Courtesy Geo. A. Hormel Company.)*

Wilted silage. Good grass silage may be made without preservatives by cutting it and leaving it in the swath or windrow until the moisture is reduced to 65-70 per cent. To check the moisture the squeeze method may be used. Give a handful of chopped forage a hard squeeze. If a few drops of moisture show between the fingers or a tight wet ball forms, it is too wet. If the handful falls apart easily, it is too dry. When the ball holds its shape in a loose form, the moisture content is right for wilted silage.

Corn and Sorghum Silage. Corn and the sorghums make excellent silage. The silage from these crops will be lower in protein than legume or legume and grass mixed silage, but higher in carbohydrates. There is enough sugar contained in the grain so that a preservative is seldom necessary.

Stage to cut sorghums and corn for silage. For the highest quality silage, corn should be cut when the ears are dented and the lower leaves of the plant have started to dry. However, corn may be put into the silo at almost any stage. If exceptionally high in moisture some dry materials such as hay or grain may be needed to absorb the excess moisture. If too dry, water is required.

Sorghums should not be ensiled until the seeds are hard. If the plants are immature, the silage will be sour. If only a little juice is visible after twisting the stalks with the hand, the sorghum is probably about right in moisture content to make good silage.

Corn Stalk Silage. Corn stalk silage is made from the stalks after the ears have been harvested. Water may be needed to increase the moisture as the stalks are usually too dry for silage when the corn is ready for harvest. The addition of molasses as a preservative would improve the feeding value and prevent possible spoilage.

Recent feeding trials using corn stalk silage has revealed that a considerable amount of food value, especially carbohydrates, is present in corn stalks. When they are ensiled, the palatability is increased and cattle will eat them quite well. If the corn is harvested when the ears are about 30 per cent moisture and artificially dried, the stalks, when ensiled, will contain from 1 to 2 per cent protein on a silage basis. Cattle have made rather substantial gains in feeding trials on a full feed of corn stalk silage, 2 to 3 pounds of corn daily and 1 to 3 pounds of a complete protein supplement containing minerals and vitamins. These trials indicate that a considerable amount of additional cattle feed may be made available on many farms by ensiling corn stalks.

TABLE 19

COMPARATIVE VALUE OF ROUGHAGES WHEN ALFALFA IS WORTH $20 PER TON

Roughage	Value	Roughage	Value
Alfalfa hay	$20.00	Prairie hay	$13.00
Red Clover hay	18.00	Timothy hay	12.00
Soybean hay	16.00	Sudan Grass hay	12.00
Lepedeza hay	15.00	Legume and Grass silage	8.00
Brome Grass hay	13.00	Corn silage	8.00
Soybean hay	16.00	Sundan Grass hay	12.00
Lepedeza hay	15.00	Legume and Grass silage	7.00
Brome Grass hay	13.00	Corn silage	8.00
Sorghum silage	$7.50	Oat Straw	$5.00
Corncobs (ground)	6.50	Corn Stalk silage	3.00
Corn Stalks (dry chopped)	6.00		

Haylage. Haylage is a term given to hays stored under oxygen-free conditions. These storage facilities are provided by upright glass-lined steel silos or silos made from other materials and coated on the inside with substances that make them completely airtight. Hay stored under completely airtight conditions will go through the fermentation cycle necessary for silage with less moisture than is required for regular silage. It may be stored at 40 per cent moisture. Since oxygen is not present, the material will not heat or burn, nor will it spoil.

Haylage is preferable to silage because it is much lower in moisture. It eliminates much of the labor required in haymaking. The product is made by cutting the green materials and allowing them to wilt until they have a moisture content of from 40 to 50 per cent. Then it is chopped with a field chopper and blown into the silo with a silo filler or blower.

The resulting product is a sweet-smelling feed, highly nutritious because little food value has been lost.

GRAINS AND GRAIN SUBSTITUTES FOR STOCKER AND FATTENING CATTLE

The grains are the most important concentrates used for fattening cattle. Corn, barley, sorghum grain, wheat, and rye are the major grains.

Corn. Corn is the standard fattening grain, and all other grains or grain substitutes are compared to corn in determining their value. Corn may be fed shelled, cracked, or as ground ear corn. Shelled or cracked corn furnishes more nutrients per pound than does ground ear corn and will produce faster gains when full fed. It takes more experience to feed shelled or cracked corn because there is greater danger of the cattle overeating and then going off feed. Although gains will be somewhat slower, ground ear corn can be fed more safely and has the advantage of utilizing the cob.   When shelled corn is fed without grinding, a larger percentage passes through the animal undigested.   Unless hogs follow the cattle to utilize the undigested corn, it will pay to grind it.

Barley.   Barley may be substituted for corn.   Barley has about 85 per cent of the value of corn for cattle feed.   Feeding tests show that from 12 to 15 per cent more pounds of barley are used per 100 pounds gain.   Feeding whole barley is wasteful.   Barley should be rolled for greatest feed efficiency.

Wheat.   Wheat may replace all or any part of the corn fed pound for pound, but it is better when it does not exceed 50 per cent of the ration.   Wheat is from 2 to 5 per cent higher in protein than is corn.   Wheat should be cracked or rolled. When fed whole, much of it passes through the animal undigested.   However, if it is finely ground, it is less palatable.

Oats.   Oats are better for young calves than for older fattening cattle.   They are considered more of a growing feed than a fattening feed.   Oats provide bulk when added to corn.   If cattle are to be fed on shelled or cracked corn, adding oats to queal one-half of the ration at the start will eliminate part of the danger of cattle going off feed from overeating.   When used as a fattening ration, they are low in food value compared to corn.

Rye.   Rye is not palatable to cattle, and if fed in large quantities for a long period, it may slow down feed consumption, resulting in slower gains.   Rye should not exceed 25 per cent of the grain ration.   It can be used as a corn saver if the price is right.

Grain Sorghums.   Grain sorghums can replace corn in the cattle fattening ration, and it will produce nearly equal results.   Experiments conducted at the Texas Agricultural Experiment Station showed that milo or feterita produced as much daily gain as corn, but more pounds of feed were required per 100 pounds of gain than for corn-fed cattle.   Grain sorghums are hard and grinding improves them for cattle feed.

Molasses.   Molasses is well liked by cattle and is often used as an appetizer.   When unpalatable feeds, especially low quality roughages are fed, cattle may be induced to eat them by sprinkling molasses over the feed.   Molasses is not a protein but a carbohydrate feed and a partial replacement for grains.   Liquid molasses has a feeding value equal to about 70 per cent of corn pound for pound. Because of its palatability, its chief value is in increasing feed consumption. Molasses may be purchased in liquid or dry form. Mixed protein supplements, designed to be fed in conjunction with low quality forages, often contain molasses as a source of high energy feed to stimulate bacterial growth in the rumen. Rumen organisms require carbohydrates in order to digest roughages.

Dried Beet Pulp. Dried beet pulp is a by-product of the sugar beet industry. It is either produced as straight dry pulp or mixed with molasses and dried. In feeding value it is equal to oats for cattle if mixed about equal parts with grain.

Proso Millet. Proso millet has a value of about 85 per cent of corn for cattle feed. It should be ground. Best results are accomplished when it is mixed with other grains.

Animal Fats. Animal fats such as tallow and lard are often surplus products of the packing industry. Considerable research is now in process to determine to what extent these products may be used in livestock feeds. Experiments at Nebraska University and Texas Agricultural Experiment Station indicate that animal fats may be successfully used in livestock feed. At the University of Nebraska, the addition of five per cent tallow to a high roughage cattle ration brought cattle to market weight with about half as much corn. One pound of fat equals two and one-fourth pounds of carbohydrates. Since corn is largely carbohydrate, one pound of tallow will equal about two pounds of corn. Twenty-five bushels of corn with tallow added, produced nearly the same gains as 50 bushels of corn without tallow.

Fats must be heated to 150° to 160° F. to be mixed with other feed substances which requires special mixing facilities. Since the average cattleman would not have the necessary equipment, feeds containing animal fats would need to be purchased commercially.

Experimental work has not progressed far enough that specific recommendations can be made for feeding animal fats at the time of the writing of this book. However, cattlemen should follow the research and make use of new developments in the feeding of animal fats.

The following table gives the comparative value of grain and grain substitutes for fattening cattle, the standard bushel weights and approximate weight of one quart. It should always be remembered that livestock rations should be figured on a pound, rather than on a bushel, basis. Grains vary as to bushel weight.

TABLE 20

COMPARATIVE FEED VALUE ON A PER-POUND BASIS OF GRAINS AND GRAIN
SUBSTITUTES FOR FATTENING CATTLE

Feed	Bushel Weight (pounds)	Value Compared to Corn (%)	Approximate Quart Weight (pounds)
Shelled Corn	56	100	1.7
Corn (ear, ground)	70	85	1.4
Barley (ground)	48	90	1.1
Wheat (cracked)	60	100	1.7
Oats (ground)	32	70-75	.7
Rye (cracked)	56	70-80	1.5
Sorghum Grain (ground)	50-60	95-100	1.4-1.5
Molasses (liquid)		70	3.0

Under most conditions, one of the feed grains will be lower in price relative to feeding value than any other grain. The problem the farmer or feeder must solve is which one is the most economical. The scale shown in Figure 119 will enable the feeder to determine quickly the cheapest grain at any given time. Suppose you are going to buy feed and corn can be purchased locally for $1.50 per bushel. Barley can be shipped in for $1.10 per bushel. Which is the better buy? To find the answer locate $1.50 on the corn line and lay a straight edge vertically to this line so that the price of barley can be read. You will note that the price of barley is about $1.30 per bushel. This means that when corn is worth $1.50 per bushel, barley is an equal buy at $1.30. Therefore, barley at $1.10 per bushel is cheaper than corn at $1.50 per bushel.

High-Moisture Grains. Several experiments have been conducted in recent years comparing high-moisture corn and sorghum grains with dry grain (containing 15 per cent moisture or less). The new types of glass-lined or coated silos (described under "Haylage") permit the storing of shelled or ground ear corn or sorghum when the moisture content is from 20 to 32 per cent. Although the exact results of these experiments have varied, the average shows that cattle fed high-moisture corn will produce as much gain on 10 per cent less corn consumption as cattle fed low-moisture corn.

Rolling or grinding shelled corn and sorghum grain stored under high-moisture conditions considerably increases digestibility and is recommended even when the grain appears very soft.

PROTEINS AND PROTEIN SUBSTITUTES FOR STOCKER AND FATTENING CATTLE

Usually 100 pounds of protein supplement in a fattening ration for beef cattle will save from 250 to 300 pounds of corn or corn substitutes. If the cost of the protein is greater than the value of the feed saved, its value in the ration may be questioned. The need for a protein supplement is largely determined by the protein content of other feeds in the ration. Cattle feeding experiments have indicated that fattening cattle require a ration from 9.5 to 10 per cent protein; more or less than this amount decreases efficiency of gain. Agronomists have been doing considerable work to raise the protein content of corn through breeding and fertilization. Corn as high as 12 per cent protein has been produced. If corn 10 per cent in protein and legume hay or legume silage are used to make up most of the ration, the need for additional protein would be doubtful.

There are a large number of protein concentrates suitable for cattle feeding. The cost per pound of protein should be the chief consideration in making a selection.

Soybean Oil Meal. Soybean oil meal is becoming popular as a cattle protein supplement. It is equal or higher in protein per cent than other protein meals. With the increase in soybean acreage it is often cheaper than other similar feeds.

Linseed Oil Meal. Linseed oil meal has long been a favorite source of protein among cattle feeders. It gives cattle a sleek hair coat and is especially popular among cattlemen who fit animals for the fairs and shows. Many feeders use a mixture of protein meals including linseed oil meal.

Cottonseed Meal. Cottonseed meal is a widely used protein supplement. It is especially popular as a cheap source of protein among cattlemen in the cotton belt. It is not considered as good as linseed or soybean oil meal for calves under four months of age. It may prove toxic to young calves if fed in too large quantity.

Dehydrated Alfalfa Meal or Pellets. Dehydrated alfalfa meal or pellets will range from 17 to 20 per cent protein and therefore closely approach what we may term a protein concentrate. Dehydrated alfalfa may be used to replace a part of the protein in the cattle ration. It is also a rich source of carotene and several essential minerals.

Peanut Oil Meal. Peanut oil meal is about equal to cottonseed, soybean, and linseed oil meal for fattening cattle. In some experiments it was slightly inferior, but for all practical purposes it may be used as a protein supplement for cattle, the price per pound of protein being the deciding factor.

Soybeans. Ground soybeans provide a good source of protein, but the price is generally too high to make them an economical feed. However, when soybeans are a cheaper source of protein than the other common protein feeds, they provide a good home-grown protein supplement.

Corn Gluten Feed and Meal. Corn gluten feed and meal are by-products of the manufacture of cornstarch and glucose. They differ in protein content. Corn gluten feed contains corn bran and is about 22 per cent digestible protein; the meal has a digestible protein content of 35 to 37 per cent. Since the protein is of the same quality as that in corn, neither of these feeds would add any protein variety to rations high in corn. They could be used to better advantage in rations that do not contain corn.

Distiller's Grains. This is the product left over from the grains that are used in the production of distilled liquors and alcohol. It is usually dried and sold as feed. Since several grains may be used the nutrient content of dried distiller's grains will vary. They should be purchased on the basis of their analysis.

Dried Brewer's Grains. This is the by-product of the barley left from the manufacturing of beer. It is usually dried and sold as livestock feed, but it is sometimes sold wet. The dried brewer's grains have a protein content ranging from 14 to 27 per cent.

Tankage, Fishmeal, and other Animal Proteins. Animal proteins may be used to make up a part of the protein content of the rations if they are more economical than the vegetable proteins. Otherwise, experiments show that they have no advantage over the vegetable proteins in rations for cattle over three months of age.

Urea. Urea is a nitrogen compound. Cattle can convert a certain amount of urea to protein. This is accomplished through the bacterial action which takes place in the rumen. Protein is made by combining the urea nitrogen with carbohydrates into the correct chemical combination. It is essential that some good source of carbohydrates be fed if urea is contained in the ration. Molasses or grains are usually recommended. It should be remembered that urea is not a protein. The feeding form of urea is known as *262* for it has a protein equivalent of 262 per cent. In other words, one pound of urea will combine with the carbohydrates to make 2.62 pounds of protein. When urea is fed, 1 pound mixed with 6 pounds of grain will replace 7 pounds of the oil seed meals. Urea may be mixed with soybean or linseed meal and fed as a protein supplement. When mixed, 0.1 pound of urea plus 0.75 pounds of linseed oil meal are equal to 1.5 pounds of linseed oil meal, or 1,760 pounds of linseed oil meal plus 240 pounds of urea are equal to 4,000 pounds of linseed meal in protein equivalent. If soybean oil meal is used with urea, 0.1 pound of urea plus 0.65 pounds of soybean oil meal equals 1.25 pounds of soybean oil meal.

If urea is mixed with one of the common proteins, meals like linseed oil meal, the following example will serve to show how the per cent protein equivalent of the mixture may be calculated.

```
1,900 lbs. Linseed oil meal = 35% protein = 665 lbs. protein
  100 lbs. Urea feed = 262% protein equivalent = 262 lbs. protein equivalent
─────                                           ───
2,000 lbs. total feed                           927 lbs. protein equivalent
        927 ÷ 2,000 = 46.35% protein equivalent
```

Precautions in feeding urea. It should be remembered that urea, if fed in too great quantities, will cause considerable difficulty. It is toxic if overfed; it will make cattle sick and could possibly be fatal. It is important to have urea evenly mixed with grain or protein supplement. Good mixing facilities, therefore, are required. Urea should not exceed 1 per cent of the total dry matter in the ration, 3 per cent of the concentrate mixture, or 5 per cent of a high protein supplement. A protein supplement, containing more urea than the recommended 5 per cent, may be safely fed, if the maximum daily allowance per animal is observed. The maximum safe limit is 0.3 pound of urea per day per animal over 800 pounds, 0.2 pounds for animals between 500 and 800 pounds, 0.1 pound for those between 300 and 500 pounds. *Smaller animals should not be fed urea.*

Urea has no advantage over other recommended protein concentrates except as an economy measure. Its value should be determined in terms of replacing the protein value of other feeds. Urea has no energy, mineral, or vitamin value. This should be considered if urea is to be fed. Urea should not be mixed with raw soybeans or untoasted soybean oil meal. These feeds contain an enzyme that causes urea to become toxic to the animal.

Mixed Supplements. There are a variety of mixed cattle supplements designed for various types of feeding programs. Where good quality forage is used as the primary roughage, almost any of the protein meals that have been discussed, will prove satisfactory. When low quality roughages are used, a protein supplement reinforced with additional vitamins and minerals is recommended. If urea is to be used to replace part of the protein in the ration, it is usually fed in a mixed supplement. Following are some mixed supplements that are especially designed to be fed with low quality roughages but may be used in any ration.

MIXED SUPPLEMENTS CONTAINING 30 TO 35 PER CENT PROTEIN
OR PROTEIN EQUIVALENT

1. Purdue Cattle Supplement with Urea

Feed	Pounds
Soybean oil meal	400.5
Molasses feed (50% molasses)	280.0
Corn or its equivalent	208.0
Urea	40.0
Bone meal	52.0
Salt (mineralized)	17.0
*Vitamin A and D concentrate	2.5
	1,000.0

2. Purdue Supplement A

Feed	Pounds
Soybean oil meal	650.5
Molasses	140.0
Alfalfa meal	140.0
Bone meal	52.0
**Salt with cobalt	17.0
*Vitamin A and D concentrate	.5
	1,000.0

MIXED SUPPLEMENT CONTAINING 48 TO 52 PER CENT PROTEIN EQUIVALENT

Iowa Supplement

Feed	Pounds
Linseed oil meal	666
Distiller's grains	666
Molasses	268
Urea feed	214
Bone meal	134
Iodized salt	36
Trace mineral mixture	8
Vitamin A and D oil (2,250-300)	8
	2,000

* Vitamin A & D concentrate contained 2,250 I. U. of A and 300 I. U. of D per gram.
** One ounce of cobalt sulfate added per 100 pounds of salt.

Purdue University cattle researchers developed a supplement designed to be fed with grass silage. Since grass silage is relatively high in protein and vitamins, the Purdue G supplement is lower in protein and the vitamin A and D concentrate was not included.

Purdue Supplement G

Feed	Pounds
Alfalfa meal	400
Molasses	329
Dried brewer's grains	132
Bone meal	105
Salt with cobalt	34
	1,000

The Iowa Experiment Station has developed an economy supplement consisting of 10 milligrams of stilbestrol per pound, 10 per cent urea, 10 per cent minerals, 15 per cent molasses, and the balance a cheap carrier such as ground corncobs. The supplement is known as 10-10-10-15. Following is a list of the ingredients used per ton.

Iowa Economy Supplement

Feed	Pounds
Carrier (ground corncobs)	1250
Molasses	300
Urea	200
Dicalcium phosphate	110
Limestone	75
Salt	40
*Stilbosol	20
Trace mineral premix	5

* Stilbosol is a stilbestrol premix carrying 1000 milligrams of stilbestrol per pound.

On the basis of several experiments, this supplement can be expected to compare favorably with all others when it is fed to cattle weighing 500 pounds or more at the rate of one pound of supplement to a minimum of four pounds of corn and three pounds of good legume hay, per head daily. It is not recommended for cattle under 500 pounds. This supplement depends upon the nitrogen in the urea combining with the carbohydrates furnished by the other ingredients to provide the necessary protein. Since the farmer cannot purchase the stilbestrol premix, he would have to get a feed company, licensed to buy and mix stilbestrol, to prepare the Iowa economy supplement.

Protein Blocks. Protein blocks containing a mixture of the oil seed meals, salt, mineral, and molasses and made in the shape of a salt block (approximately 10 by 10 by 12 inches) provide an easy way to supply protein to cattle on the range or grazing a corn field. A typical block weighs about 33 pounds and is made hard enough so that it must be licked and not chewed. This limits consumption to about one to one and a half pounds per day.

TABLE 21

COST PER POUND OF CRUDE PROTEIN AT VARIOUS PRICES

Price per ton	Soy-bean meal 44%	Soy-bean meal 41%	Cotton-seed meal 42%	Lin-seed meal 35%	Lin-seed meal 31%	Peanut oil meal 45%	Corn gluten meal 43%	Tank-age 60%	Meat scraps 50%	Fish meal 63%
	Cents	Cents	Cents	Cents	Cents	Cents	Cents	Cents	Cents	Cents
$ 50	5.7	6.1	6.0	7.1	8.1	5.6	5.8	4.2	5.0	4.0
55	6.2	6.7	6.5	7.9	8.9	6.1	6.4	4.6	5.5	4.4
60	6.8	7.3	7.1	8.6	9.7	6.7	7.0	5.0	6.0	4.8
65	7.4	7.9	7.7	9.3	10.5	7.2	7.6	5.4	6.5	5.2
70	8.0	8.5	8.3	10.0	11.3	7.8	8.1	5.8	7.0	5.6
75	8.5	9.1	8.9	10.7	12.1	8.3	8.7	6.2	7.5	6.0
80	9.1	9.8	9.5	11.4	12.9	8.9	9.3	6.7	8.0	6.3
85	9.7	10.4	10.1	12.1	13.7	9.4	9.9	7.1	8.5	6.7
90	10.2	11.0	10.7	12.9	14.5	10.0	10.5	7.5	9.0	7.1
95	10.8	11.6	11.3	13.6	15.3	10.6	11.0	7.9	9.5	7.5
100	11.4	12.2	11.9	14.3	16.1	11.1	11.6	8.3	10.0	7.9
105	11.9	12.8	12.5	15.0	16.9	11.7	12.2	8.7	10.5	8.3
110	12.5	13.4	13.1	15.7	17.7	12.2	12.8	9.2	11.0	8.7
115	13.1	14.0	13.7	16.4	18.5	12.8	13.4	9.6	11.5	9.1
120	13.6	14.6	14.3	17.1	19.4	13.3	14.0	10.0	12.0	9.5
125	14.2	15.2	14.9	17.9	20.2	13.9	14.5	10.4	12.5	9.9

Copyright 1953 by Doane Agricultural Service, Inc., St. Louis, Missouri. Reprinted by permission.

MINERALS AND VITAMINS FOR STOCKERS AND FATTENING CATTLE

Minerals. A mineral mixture for cattle recommended for the area (see Chapter 6) fed free choice will generally meet the mineral requirements of stocker and fattening cattle if a high quality roughage, such as legume hays is fed to the extent of five pounds or more per day. Where the roughage consists mostly of low quality materials such as corncobs and corn stalks, a supplement containing minerals is recommended as assurance that the animal will consume enough needed minerals for proper nutrition.

Vitamins. Usually vitamins A and D are all the cattle feeder needs to be concerned with. When high quality forage is used to make up 50 per cent or more of the roughage part of the ration, and the cattle are exposed to sunshine, these vitamins will be supplied in sufficient quantities.   When low quality roughage is used almost exclusively, a supplement containing vitamin A and D concentrate is recommended.

FEED ADDITIVES FOR CATTLE

Recent experimental work at Iowa and other agricultural experiment stations has shown that a number of feed additives when added to cattle rations improve the rate and increase the efficiency of gain.

Stilbestrol. Stilbestrol is a manufactured chemical that will produce effects similar to the hormone estrogen *estradiol*, which is secreted by certain glands in the animal body.   Stilbestrol is incorporated in the feed for fattening cattle.   Liveweight gains may be stimulated as much as 30 per cent on high-grain fattening rations. Cattle fed high-roughage rations gained from 10 to 15 per cent faster and feed costs were reduced 10 to 20 per cent when stilbestrol was added to the ration.

Feeding Stilbestrol.   Stilbestrol is a highly potent chemical and must be fed with extreme caution.   The recommended feeding level is not less than five milligrams and not more than ten milligrams daily.   Recent experiments indicate that faster gains and greater feed savings result when the level of feeding stilbestrol is increased to 20 milligrams during the last three months of the feeding period for steers; however, most authorities do not recommend more than ten milligrams.   For cattle on grass, a lower level not to exceed five milligrams for the early part of the feeding period and up to ten milligrams for the last three months is recommended. The reason given is that fresh grasses apparently contain hormone-like substances which may cause ill effects when combined with too high a level of stilbestrol. Heifers have shown nearly as much increase in gain as steers from the feeding of stilbestrol.   However, prolapsed uteri, excessive teat and udder development, and other undesirable effects have been noted when amounts in excess of ten milligrams were given.   For this reason ten milligrams is the maximum amount recommended for heifers.

Stilbestrol should be removed from the ration at least 48 hours prior to the slaughtering of the animal.

Because of the dangers involved in overfeeding, and the possibility of human beings' getting some of the materials into their mouths as a result of handling, rigid controls for selling feed containing stilbestrol have been instituted. At the present time only commercial feed manufacturers who have adequate mixing and control facilities and can meet federal and state regulations are licensed to purchase the stilbestrol premix for mixing purposes.

Stilbestrol Premix. Stilbestrol premix usually contains 10,000 milligrams of stilbestrol incorporated into ten pounds of soybean meal and vegetable oil. This ten pounds of premix is then incorporated into a cattle supplement which produces a protein supplement containing from 2½ to ten milligrams of stilbestrol per pound.

Protein supplements containing 2½, five, 7½, and ten milligrams per pound are available from commercial feed companies in several states. This variation in the stilbestrol content of the protein supplement permits the cattle feeder to feed the maximum recommended level of ten milligrams of stilbestrol daily without feeding more than one pound of protein supplement. He may feed up to four pounds of supplement daily containing 2½ milligrams of stilbestrol without exceeding the maximum of ten milligrams of stilbestrol daily.

How to Purchase Stilbestrol Mixed Supplements. A large number of commercial feed companies are making a variety of supplements containing stilbestrol. The cattle feeder may purchase supplements with a wide range in protein percentage or complete protein, mineral, and vitamin supplements to meet nearly every feeding condition. Until more is known about the product, feeders will probably have to rely on commercial feeds if they desire to feed stilbestrol.

Precautions in Feeding Stilbestrol. Unless research proves otherwise, *stilbestrol should not be fed to any animals that are to be kept for breeding purposes.* Breeding swine should not be allowed to follow cattle receiving stilbestrol in their rations. Stilbestrol should be limited to cattle intended to be sold for slaughter purposes.

A few experiments have been completed and a number of others are in progress to determine whether or not stilbestrol will adversely affect bred heifers or bred sows following cattle that are fed stilbestrol. These experiments indicate no adverse effects when stilbestrol is fed to breeding cattle or to brood sows following cattle receiving stilbestrol in their rations. However, until sufficient experimental results are available, cattlemen are advised to keep stilbestrol away from any breeding animals.

Recent experiments indicate that young growing cattle on pasture may benefit from the feeding of stilbestrol. However, the work up to the time of the writing of this book has not been sufficient to warrant such a recommendation. Ranchers and farmers are advised to follow closely the results of further experiments which will determine to what extent it may be advisable to use the drug in rations of young growing cattle.

Implanting Hormones. Stilbestrol pellets of 12 milligrams each may be implanted at the base of the ear with an instrument especially designed for this purpose. Cattle are placed in a squeeze chute and from 24 to 36 milligrams of stilbestrol are implanted in pellet form. The lesser amount is used for pasture-feeding or for short-fed cattle and the greater amount for dry-lot cattle. The pellets are absorbed over a period of 120 to 180 days. The gains of implanted cattle compare favorably with those made by animals fed stilbestrol, and the cost of the stilbestrol is less when implanted. However, the labor and equipment necessary for implanting must be considered before deciding which method to use. More undesirable effects have resulted from implanting heifers than from feeding them the hormone.

ANTIBIOTICS FOR FATTENING CATTLE

Experiments have shown that cattle fed aureomycin, terramycin, erthromycin, and penicillin at the rate of 70 to 80 milligrams daily gained from .09 to .25 pound per day faster than those receiving the same ration without antibiotics. Feed efficiency was improved from 5 to 15 per cent. Of the four antibiotics used, penicillin gave the least response, while the others produced similar amounts of gain.

Cattle receiving rations high in roughage have shown the greatest percentage of gain, while those receiving a high-energy ration consisting of full grain feeding and high-quality roughage have shown the least response from antibiotics. Most of the advantage from antibiotic feeding has occurred during the first three or four months of the feeding period.

The addition of an antibiotic premix providing from 70 to 80 milligrams of either erthromycin, aureomycin, or terramycin, for at least the first half of the feeding period, would probably be profitable in view of the results of recent feeding trials.

Tapazole. Tapazole, a trade name for a product known chemically as 1-methyl-2-mercaptoimidazole, is a white powder in its pure state. It has a blocking effect upon the thyroid gland in animals.

Although Tapazole shows promise as a gain booster, it has not been approved by state and Federal authorities. Therefore, no recommendation can be made for its use until further experiments have been made and approval granted. It looks promising, however, and cattlemen should follow the research results.

Rations for Fattening Cattle. Using the feeds that have been discussed, a large variety of fattening rations may be developed. Many areas produce feeds, not included here, that may be successfully substituted. It is important to use rations that will supply needed nutrients as cheaply as possible. Home-grown feeds are usually cheaper than feeds shipped in. In selecting a ration, the age and quality of cattle should be considered. Cattle being finished for high choice or prime grades are usually limited on roughages in order to induce them to consume more fattening feeds. Cattle of the plainer grades, which are unable because of quality to finish into top slaughter grades, may utilize roughages free choice. Since the selling price of plain cattle is less, cheaper gains are essential. The following are some suggested rations for finishing cattle for market.

RATIONS FOR CATTLE THAT ARE INTENDED TO MAKE
CHOICE OR PRIME GRADES

Feed	Pounds
1. Legume hay	½ lb. per cwt. live weight, daily
Shelled crimped corn	*Full feed*
Linseed, soybean, or cottonseed meal, or a 30 to 35% protein commercial supplement containing stilbestrol	1 lb. daily
2. Legume hay	½ lb. per cwt. live weight, daily
Ground ear corn	*Full feed*
Linseed, soybean, or cottonseed meal, or a 30 to 35% protein commercial supplement containing stilbestrol	1 lb. daily

Feed	*Pounds*
3. Legume hay	½ lb. per cwt. live weight, daily
Rolled barley	*Full feed*
Any recommended protein meal or 30 to 35% protein commercial supplement containing stilbestrol	1 lb. daily
4. Legume hay	¼ lb. per cwt. live weight, daily
Legume & grass silage	2 lbs. per cwt. live weight, daily
Ground sorghum grain	*Full feed*
Protein meal or 30 to 35% protein commercial supplement containing stilbestrol	1 lb. daily
5. Legume hay	½ lb. per cwt. live weight, daily
Legume-grass silage	2 lbs. per cwt. live weight, daily
Corn	500
Sorghum grain	450
Protein meal or 30 to 35% protein commercial supplement containing stilbestrol.	50
6. Legume & grass hay	½ lb. per cwt. live weight, daily
Corn	825
Oats	100
Protein meal or 30 to 35% protein commercial supplement containing stilbestrol.	75
7. Legume & grass hay	½ lb. per cwt. live weight, daily
Ground ear corn	875
Protein meal or 30 to 35% protein commercial stilbestrol supplement.	125
8. Grass hay	½ lb. per cwt. live weight, daily
Sorghum or corn silage	2 lbs. per cwt. live weight, daily
Corn or sorghum grain	850
Protein meal or 30 to 35% protein commercial supplement containing stilbestrol.	150

Note: If a commercial supplement containing stilbestrol is used, do not feed more than is required to provide 10 mg. stilbestrol daily in the rations. A combination of a protein meal and stilbestrol containing supplement may be used. Minerals may be fed free choice.

The experience of cattle feeders and the results of experiments show that cattle may be successfully fattened on all concentrate rations without hay, silage, or any of the coarse roughages. Most of the feeding trials have been carried out using ground ear corn or rolled barley. Ground ear corn consists of 20 per cent roughage, coming mostly from the cob, whereas barley is about 15 per cent roughage, which is supplied by the hull.

When ground ear corn is used, the procedure is to start cattle on a full feed of hay and from three to six pounds of ground ear corn. The hay is reduced gradually and eliminated when the cattle are consuming 12 pounds of ground ear corn per head. All further feed increases are made by adding crimped or rolled shelled corn to the ear corn ration. Protein supplement is fed to give a protein percentage of 9.5 to 10 per cent. Minerals are provided free choice and a vitamin A supplement is added to the protein supplement. The 12 pounds of ground ear corn will supple about 2.4 pounds of roughage, which seems to be all that is required once the cattle are adjusted to full feeding.

When barley is used as the grain concentrate, the procedure is the same except that the vitamin A supplement is increased, because barley is much lower in vitamin A than is corn. Less protein supplement is required to bring the total protein percentage up to the 9.5 to 10 per cent level, because barley is higher in protein than is corn.

If the feeder has an abundance of low-quality forage, he may desire to buy plain grades of cattle and utilize this roughage. Such cattle may not be expected to grade much above the slaughter grade of *good*, but his gains will not be as expensive as if he full-fed grain. Following are some suggested rations using low grades of roughages.

RATIONS FOR FATTENING CATTLE USING LOW GRADE FORAGE

Feed	Pounds fed daily	Probable daily gain pounds
1. Chopped corn stalks	10-12	
Mixed hay	2-3	1.5-2.0
Crimped shelled corn	4.5	
Purdue Supp. A. or a similar commercial supplement with stilbestrol	3.5	
2. Corn stalk silage	*Full feed*	1.5-2.0
Mixed hay	2.0	
Crimped shelled corn	7.0	
Iowa Supp. or a similar commercial supplement containing stilbestrol	2.5	
3. Ground corncobs	11-12	
Mixed hay	2	1.5-2.0
Crimped shelled corn	5.25	
Iowa Supp.	2.25	
4. Ground corncobs	11-12	1.5-2.0
Liquid molasses	2-4	
Crimped shelled corn	2-3	
Iowa Supp.	2.75	

Rations for Wintering Feeders. Feeders who have an abundance of pasture which they wish to utilize often buy 400- to 600-pound calves or yearlings in the fall, carry them through the winter on a growing ration, and turn them on grass in the spring. Young cattle that are wintered should be fed a ration that will produce from one to one and a half pounds per day gain, which is considered a normal growth rate. Following are some suggested rations for wintering feeders intended to be fattened at a later period.

WINTERING RATIONS FOR FEEDER CATTLE

Feed	Pounds fed daily
1. Legume-grass hay	*Full feed*
Minerals	*Free choice*
2. Ground corncobs	10-14
Purdue Supp. A	3-3.5
3. Legume-grass hay	5
Corn or sorghum silage	15-25
35-40 protein meal	½
Minerals	*Free choice*
4. Legume-grass hay	5
Legume-grass silage	15-25
Minerals	*Free choice*
5. Legume-grass hay	5-8
Corn & cob meal	2-3
Minerals	*Free choice*

Note: Recent experiments conducted by Iowa State University indicate that stilbestrol will save feed and increase gains when fed to cattle being wintered for later fattening. When stilbestrol was discontinued there was no decrease in gains beyond the gain expected from other recommended rations that do not include stilbestrol.

Preparing Feed for Cattle. Many experiments have been conducted to determine the best methods of preparing feed for cattle. Pelleting, grinding, rolling, crimping, and no treatment have all been tried, with varying results.

Pelleting. Pelleting consists of grinding the feed and running it through a pelleting machine, which forms it into small pellets ranging in size from that of a pea to two or three times as large. Pelleted feeds may consist of the complete dry part of the ration, including hay, grain, and supplements mixed and pelleted, or any portion of the ration.

Pelleting has generally resulted in increased gains and greater feed efficiency. In various feeding trials, pelleted hay, when compared with long hay or chopped hay, has produced increased gains of from 10 to 30 per cent and a feed saving of from 4 to 10 per cent. When mixed rations (consisting of roughage, grain, and supplement) were pelleted and compared with the same rations ground, pelleting showed the greatest advantage when the rations consisted of 50 per cent or more roughage. Pelleting high-concentrate rations showed little if any advantage over grinding or rolling.

The advantages of pelleting may be summarized as follows:

1. Somewhat greater gains and increased feed efficiency.
2. Less wastage.
3. Less storage space required (especially for roughage).
4. Easier self-feeding.
5. Consumption of a balanced ration.
6. Consumption of larger quantities of feed, especially when low-quality roughage is mixed with concentrates.

The above advantages must be weighed against the cost of pelleting the feed.

Grinding. Grinding is especially desirable for the extremely hard seeds such as grain sorghum or millet. These feeds may also be pelleted after grinding.

Unless they are also pelleted, shelled corn, oats, and barley are less desirable when ground than when rolled and crimped. Ear corn may be fed successfully if ground.

Rolling and crimping. Rolling is a method of flattening out the grain by passing it through heavy rollers. Crimping is done by a machine that cracks the grain coarsely and then flattens it out. These methods are recommended for the preparation of corn, barley, and oats that are to be fed to the older cattle, if the feed has not been pelleted.

Pastures for Feeders and Fattening Cattle. Good pastures are essential for maximum growth and fattening of cattle on grass. Like breeding cattle, feeders make greater gains on legume-grass pasture than on straight grasses. The pasture mixtures discussed in Chapter 6 are applicable for feeders and fattening cattle.

Factors Influencing Gains on Grass. What kind and weight of cattle should be turned on grass is a question facing many cattle feeders. Several factors, such as age, weight, and condition affect the gains cattle will make on grass.

Age and weight. Big, thin cattle have more frame on which to

put fat and a greater capacity for grass consumption. They can
be expected to improve fastest in condition. Yearlings would rank
second in total pounds gain, and calves would be last. However,
in proportion to starting weight, calves will make greater gains
per hundred pounds original weight than older cattle.

Condition. Cattle that have been wintered well, and are in high
condition, will need grain while on grass if they are to continue to
gain. It is not economical to turn cattle carrying too good a condition on grass without including grain in the ration. Such cattle
will lose weight rather than gain. Cattle that are intended for
grass during the pasture season to be further grown out and fattened the following fall and winter, should not be wintered to gain
more than one and a half pounds per day. Most cattlemen plan
one to one and a quarter pounds as the maximum wintering gain.

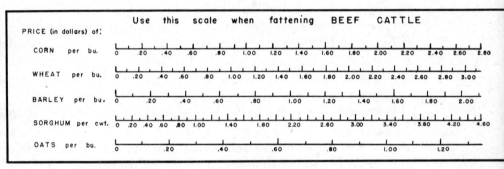

FIGURE 119. *Feed substitution scale. (Scales copyrighted, 1953, by Leonard W.
Schruben, Kansas State College, Manhattan, Kansas.)*

Concentrated Rations for Cattle on Grass. The kind and
amount of concentrates fed cattle on grass depend upon the gains
expected, the amount of pasture and the grains available, and the
time cattle are to be marketed. Cattle can be expected to make
greater total gains if fed grains on pasture than cattle receiving
pasture only. However, when concentrates are fed, less gain due
to grass alone will result. It may be more economical not to feed
grain to cattle that are on pasture when the grass is abundant and
the feeder expects to finish them in a dry lot at the end of the
pasture season.

Cattle receiving concentrates while on pasture may be fed the
same grain mixtures, except for roughage, as those in dry lots.
The roughage will be provided by grass. If the pasture is from

FIGURE 120. *These cattle are being fattened on grass and grain. They will be hand-fed until they are brought up to full feed and then placed on self-feeders. (Courtesy The Farm Journal-Country Gentleman.)*

20 to 50 per cent legumes, the amount of protein supplement may be reduced to one-half the amount generally recommended for dry lot rations in which legumes as hay or silage is fed.

When pastures are not adequate to supply sufficient forage, the pasture may be supplemented with either hay or silage.

Hauling pasture to cattle. Green lot feeding of fattening cattle is practiced by some cattle feeders. The practice was described in Chapter 6. The advantages and disadvantages of green lot feeding of fattening cattle are the same as for the breeding herd.

Fattening Cattle on Grass. Cattle feeders who have a considerable amount of pastures available may wish to utilize this grass to replace roughage in the ration. When cattle are pastured they are usually bought in the fall and wintered at the rate of one to one and a half pounds of gain daily and turned on pasture when the grass has made sufficient growth in the spring. They are fed a concentrated ration while on grass. Some feeders finish them entirely while on grass, while others will put them in dry lots for a few weeks or months for the final finish. The kind of cattle, market conditions, and available feed largely determine the system followed.

Advantages and disadvantages of pasture fattening. Some advantages of fattening cattle on grass are:

1. Pasture gains are cheaper because less grain and protein is used in the fattening process.
2. The manure is dropped on the pasture (unless green lot feeding is practiced), saving labor in hauling the manure onto the fields.
3. Little or no roughage other than grass is required, reducing labor in feeding and preserving roughages.

Some disadvantages of feeding cattle on grass are:

1. Cattle take longer to reach a desirable finish.
2. They have a lower carcass yield and usually sell for less than the same quality cattle dry-lot fed.
3. Summer heat and flies may slow up gains.
4. Cattle to be fed on grass have to be purchased either in the spring when feeders are scarce or in the fall when they must be wintered, thus increasing the length of time the cattle must be kept.

Starting Cattle on Feed. When cattle are shipped in from a distance, they are tired and need rest. They should have plenty of water and comfortable quarters. Until the cattle become adjusted to their new home, no attempt should be made to start grain feeding. It is good practice to give the cattle all the dry hay (preferably a legume-and-grass mixed hay) they can eat for ten days before starting them on grain. If cattle are bought early in the fall they may go on pasture until fully recovered from the effects of shipping. A pasture that has been allowed to grow and in which the plants are partially mature provides an excellent feed supply for newly purchased feeders from the range areas. After the cattle have become completely adjusted to their new environment, those intended to be immediately placed on a fattening ration may be started on whatever concentrates the feeding program calls for.

If grains are to be the principle concentrates, yearlings may be started on from 2 to 3 pounds of corn, or its equivalent in other grains, per head and continued on this amount until all the cattle are eating grain. Many western cattle have never tasted grain and must learn to eat it. Placing grain over the roughage will help to get them started on the grain. Care must be exercised to prevent a few, that start to eat quickly, from overeating. The grain may be increased one pound per head daily until the cattle are consuming 2 pounds per 100 pounds live weight, which is generally considered a full feed. Cattle to be finished on high-roughage rations may be started on grain the same way—but only brought up to 4 to 6 pounds, or the amount called for in the feeding program. Whatever protein is to be fed should be started with the grain, one-half pound of linseed, soybean, or cottonseed meal, or any other accepted cattle protein may be used at the start of the fattening ration. The rate of increase will depend upon the kind of roughage used. From one to one and one-half pounds is usually sufficient when full-feeding legume hay or legume silage. When low-quality roughages are used in quantity, from three to three and a half pounds may be necessary. If a high protein equivalent supplement (such as one containing urea) is used, the amount of the supplement will need to be limited in accordance with the protein content. The common oil seed meals will range from 32 to 47 per cent protein. If the supplement is a 55 to 60 per cent protein or protein equivalent, the amount may be reduced from a third to a half.

To start calves, feed from 2 to 3 pounds of oats per head daily until all calves are eating. When all calves are eating, add one pound of shelled corn per head. Increase the corn by one-half pound daily until the calves are consuming 2 pounds of grain per 100 pounds live weight. The oats may be continued at from 2 to 3 pounds or gradually cut back and discontinued. Protein supplement may be fed the same as for yearlings.

When ground ear corn is fed to fattening cattle it should be remembered that the cob makes up about one-fourth of the total weight. Therefore, the amount of ground ear corn fed will be more than if shelled corn is used.

The experienced cattle feeder knows that the condition of the droppings is a good barometer that indicates whether the feed is being increased too rapidly or whether the cattle are going along satisfactorily. Cattle that are being pushed too fast, will show thin, vile-smelling droppings. When this condition exists, the cattle will soon go off feed unless the amount of feed is reduced quickly. The droppings should not be hard nor too thin and watery.

FEEDING EFFICIENCY FACTORS

Rate of Gain. Thin two-year-old cattle that are thrifty and healthy will make the greatest gains in the feed lot; yearlings and calves follow in this respect. This may be explained on the basis that big cattle consume more total feed that may be turned into beef and therefore make more rapid gains.

Economy of Gains. Calves will produce 100 pounds of gain on less feed than older cattle of the same quality, although the time required for the same gain will be greater. The gain in body weight of older cattle is due largely to fat, while much of the gain on calves is due to growth. The time required to put market finish on calves is greater than for older cattle. Calves digest their feed more thoroughly than do older cattle.

As cattle fatten, the amount of feed required per hundredweight gain becomes greater. Experiments show that cattle weighing around 600 pounds when started on a fattening ration require 10 units of feed for the first 100 pounds of gain, 13 units for the second 100 pounds, 14-15 units for the third, 17-18 for the fourth and 22 or more for the fifth 100 pounds of gain. The difference in market price for *highly finished* cattle as compared to *medium finish* is the important consideration in deciding how long to feed cattle.

TABLE 22

Cost of Gains in Cattle Feeding

Good to Choice Steers, Dry Lot, High Grain Ration, Corn Calculated at $1.10 and $1.50 per Bushel

Gain	400-lb. calf Corn		640-lb. yearling Corn		840-lb. 2-year-old Corn	
	$1.10	$1.50	$1.10	$1.50	$1.10	$1.50
1st 100 lbs.	9.57	13.05	11.55	15.75	11.77	16.05
2nd 100 lbs.	10.67	14.55	13.53	18.45	14.41	19.65
3rd 100 lbs.	11.99	16.35	15.73	21.45	18.48	25.20
4th 100 lbs.	13.64	18.60	19.25	26.25	25.74	35.10
5th 100 lbs.	17.16	23.40	24.64	33.60	(17.93)	(24.45)*
6th 100 lbs.	19.14	26.10				
7th 100 lbs.	24.09	32.85				

* For 50 lbs. gain.
Source: Iowa State College Extension Service. EC Inf. 70.

Self-Feeding Fattening Cattle. Cattle that have been brought up to a full feed of grain may be successfully put on self-feeders. Self-feeders are especially valuable when full-feeding cattle on

FIGURE 121. *Self-feeders may be successfully used as a labor-saving device in fattening cattle.*

pasture.   Self-feeders reduce labor, but they require that proteins and grains be thoroughly mixed.

FITTING THE CATTLE FEEDING PROGRAM TO LOCAL FARM CONDITIONS

Farms vary considerably in the amount and kind of crops they produce.   Grade A corn belt land will probably be used primarily for the production of corn.   Legumes and grasses will be grown only to the extent that they are required for maintaining soil fertility and to provide some roughage for cattle.   Pasture land will be limited.   Other farms less adapted to corn production may have a considerable acreage in pasture and hay land.   Weather conditions may alter a farmer's plans.   A late spring and a cold wet summer followed by an early frost may result in soft corn that will need to be ensiled if it is to be preserved.   Various types of farms and crop growing conditions require a different type of cattle feeding program.

Prices of feeder cattle and the slaughter cattle price outlook demand consideration in determining the weight, grade, and time of buying feeder cattle.   There are so many possible conditions that space will not permit a discussion of all of them.   However, we will consider a few situations.   By carefully studying these conditions, the student or inexperienced cattle feeder may be able to develop a cattle feeding program best adapted to his own conditions.

Situation 1.   *The cattle feeder has plenty of corn or other high quality feed grains on hand, and a reasonable amount of high quality legume hay and legume silage for roughage.   He has very little pasture.   The price outlook for slaughter cattle seems quite favorable for the next 8 to 10 months in comparison to feed prices.   Feeder cattle prices are high.*

With this situation it would seem that the profit must come from the gain.   The feed is of high quality, therefore choice calves or light yearlings weighing from 400 to 500 pounds would fit the situation.   The initial cost will be lower by buying light cattle.   The cattle should be finished to choice and if the price looks good, they should be carried to prime grade.

Situation 2.   *The cattle feeder has an abundance of pasture; grain is limited, but he has a considerable amount of fair quality roughage available. Feed prices are high. Slaughter cattle price outlook is uncertain, and feeder cattle are high.*

Here he could buy medium to good calves or light yearlings, winter them on roughage to gain a pound per day, turn them on pasture without grain, and at the end of the pasture season give them a short dry lot feeding period. They should make a grade of good slaughter steers and the gains should be cheap.

Situation 3. *The cattle feeder has a fair amount of pasture, a reasonable amount of feed grains, but very little cured roughage. Feeder cattle prices are medium to high. The outlook for slaughter cattle prices is fairly good.*

This situation seems to call for the purchase of 600-pound yearlings to be bought in the late fall. The available roughage will be used for wintering. Winter gains should not exceed one and a quarter pounds daily. Cattle will be turned out on pasture in the spring and fed concentrates. They will be brought up to full grain feeding on pasture, and marketed at the end of the pasture season. If equipment is available, chopped green forage may be hauled to the cattle.

Situation 4. *The cattle feeder has a farm with considerable pasture land. The pasture is only fair. He has a very limited corn acreage. Nearby is a seed corn plant where he can get corn cobs for the cost of hauling. Feeder prices are medium, but the outlook for slaughter cattle prices is very uncertain.*

Common to medium grade cattle weighing around 600 to 700 lbs. would seem to fit this situation. These cattle may be wintered on ground cobs, using some molasses or 2 to 3 pounds of corn daily plus a complete supplement. The ration may be continued when the cattle are turned out on pasture. The second fall they can be finished to a grade of *good* by ensiling the limited corn and using a full feed of silage, ground cobs, with 2 to 3 pounds of molasses and a complete protein supplement.

Situation 5. *Feeder cattle are cheap; feed is high priced, and the slaughter cattle outlook is good for the next 120 days. The cattle feeder has plenty of grain and good roughage but no pasture.*

If a profit is to be made under these conditions, it will have to come from the margin. Heavy cattle weighing 800 pounds or better and short-fed would seem best. The price of fat cattle looks good for the next four months. A long feeding period would be unwise. The cattle feeder should buy more cattle and put less gain on them. Heavy feeders will finish into the higher grades in less time. His only reason for fattening is to increase the price received per hundred pounds over the cost.

The foregoing are only a few of the total number of conditions that may exist on any given farm in any given year. Available labor, equipment, and capital must also be considered in fitting a cattle feeding program to any situation.

SUMMARY

Cattle feeding involves a considerable capital outlay and risk. Only those who carefully plan their feeding operations and understand thoroughly cattle feeding can expect to make a profit. While most cattle feeders purchase their cattle from the range area, some farmers who have a considerable amount of pasture land raise their own feeding cattle. Direct cattle feeding profits must come either from margin on original weight, profit on gain, or both.

Manure value and increased fertility of the land are important sources of indirect profits from the cattle feeding operation. The value of the manure depends largely upon how well the fertilizing elements in it are preserved.

Roughages should make up a large part of the cattle ration. Preserved roughages may be divided into two major classes: (1) those that are dried, known as dry roughages, and (2) silage. There may be further classification, such as high-quality and low-quality roughages. Good legume-and-grass hay or silage, and corn or sorghum silage are recognized as high-quality roughages; corncobs, dry corn stalks or corn stalk silage, and straw or coarse stemmy hay are considered low-quality roughages. The value of legume or grass silage depends largely upon how it is made. The use of preservatives or wilted green materials is usually necessary for a high-quality product.

Haylage is produced by storing hay under airtight conditions when the hay is about 40 per cent moisture. This produces a highly desirable feed, which is much lower in moisture than is silage.

All of the grains may be successfully fed to cattle. However, corn, sorghum, and barley are the most common feed grains used. Wheat may be fed, depending upon the price. Wheat is equal to corn in feeding value up to one-half the ration. Molasses may be substituted for corn.   Molasses in the liquid form has a feeding value of about 70 per cent of corn, on a pound for pound basis. Animal fats have been successfully substituted for part of the grain in cattle fattening rations.

Corn and sorghum stored as high-moisture grains (moisture above 15 per cent) under airtight conditions produce somewhat faster gains with less feed per hundred pounds gain than does dry grain.

Fattening cattle require a ration consisting of from 9.5 to 10 per cent protein.   The oil seed meals are the most common sources of protein supplements used in cattle feeding.   However, several other protein feeds such as corn gluten feed and meal may be used. Urea, a nitrogen product, may be successfully substituted for a part of the protein in the ration.   The amount that can be safely fed depends upon the age of the animal and the kind of ration fed. The maximum safe limit for an 800-pound or heavier animal is 0.3 pound daily.   The protein block provides an easy way to supply cattle on pasture with protein.

Several complete supplements have been developed for feeding cattle, especially when low-quality roughage is used.   These supplements include vitamins, minerals, and some high-energy feeds, such as molasses or corn, in addition to 30 to 50 per cent protein.

Minerals and vitamins A and D need to be provided in the ration for beef cattle.   When legume hay or a good-quality silage is fed, vitamin A will usually be supplied.   Sunshine will supply vitamin D if cattle are exposed to direct sunlight.

Antibiotics have increased gains on young cattle receiving a high roughage ration.   They have had less effect on gains where a high grain ration was fed.

When stilbestrol, a hormone-like substance, was included in the rations of fattening cattle, considerably faster gains were produced. The recommended level is not to exceed 10 mg. daily.   Stilbestrol may be fed orally or implanted in pellet form at the base of the ear. Stilbestrol should not be fed to breeding animals unless further research proves otherwise.

Pelleted rations showed some advantage over other methods of preparation, especially when the ration consisted of 50 per cent or more roughage.   Rolling or crimping of corn, oats, and barley is preferable to grinding or feeding whole when rations are for older cattle.

A large variety of both wintering and fattening rations may be developed from the large number of feeds used for cattle feeding. The kind of cattle, degree of finish, and feed prices will determine the kind of ration selected.

Cattle will make substantial gains on pasture. Big, thin cattle will make the greatest gain. Cattle turned on pasture without grain should not be in too high a condition if they are expected to gain in weight.

Grass may be substituted for dry roughage or silage in the fattening ration. The concentrates fed to cattle on good pasture will not need to be as high in protein as would be necessary in dry lot feeding. Grass usually cheapens gains but grass-fat cattle will usually not sell for quite as high a price.

Cattle should be started on feed slowly and gradually brought up to full feed. Caution must be exercised to prevent overeating during the start of a fattening ration.

Calves will gain on less feed per hundred pounds than will older cattle. As the weight increases more feed is required for each hundred pounds of gain.

The cattle feeder should carefully consider his own conditions and develop a cattle feeding program best adapted to his own needs.

QUESTIONS

1. Where are most of the cattle that go into the feed yards produced?
2. What are the sources of profit from feeding beef cattle? Explain.
3. Explain how one may reduce the losses of plant food from manure.
4. Discuss the comparative value of the various kinds of dry roughages.
5. Why is it essential to include some high energy feeds in the ration when low quality roughage is fed?
6. What is silage?
7. What advantages are there in making legume or grass silage?
8. What is haylage, and what advantage does it have?
9. When should preservatives be added to silage?
10. What kinds of materials make good preservatives?
11. When silage material carries an excessive amount of water, what materials make good preservatives?
12. What is the wilt method of making grass silage?

13. Compare the feeding value of high-moisture corn with that of low-moisture corn.
14. Compare the feeding values of the grains for fattening cattle.
15. What per cent protein should a fattening ration for cattle contain?
16. What advantages are there in feeding molasses?
17. How do the various oil seed meals, corn by-products, and dehydrated alfalfa meal compare as cattle supplements?
18. Under what conditions is it advisable to feed a complete supplement?
19. How may urea be used as a protein replacement?.
20. What are the limitations of feeding urea?
21. Discuss the need for minerals and vitamins in the rations for stockers and fattening cattle.
22. What is stilbestrol?
23. What advantages are there in feeding stilbestrol?
24. What is the recommended level for feeding stilbestrol?
25. How may stilbestrol be purchased?
26. What are the advantages and disadvantages of implanting stilbestrol, compared with those of feeding it?
27. What advantages are there in feeding antibiotics to cattle?
28. Make up several suggested rations for cattle intended to make choice or prime slaughter grades.
29. Give several rations suitable for lower grade feeders to be finished as commercial to good slaughter cattle.
30. Give some good rations for wintering feeders to make only a growth gain.
31. What kind of cattle gain best on grass?   Discuss.
32. What are the factors that effect the feed efficiency when cattle are fattened?
33. What advantages are there in fattening cattle on grass?
34. Discuss the various ways one could successfully start cattle on feed.
35. Discuss the type of cattle feeding program that would best fit your farm conditions at the present time.

REFERENCES

Annual Cattle Feeders' Day Report, 1957, 1958, 1959, 1960, Agricultural Experiment Station, Purdue University, Lafayette, Indiana.

Baker, Guy N., and Marvel L. Baker, *The Use of Various Pastures in Producing Finished Yearling Steers*, North Platte Substation Bulletin 47, 1952, University of Nebraska, Lincoln, Nebraska.

Beef Cattle Investigations in Texas, 1888-1950, Texas Agricultural Experiment Station, Bulletin 724, College Station, Texas.

Beef Cattle Feeding and Breeding Investigations, Agricultural Experiment Station, Circulars 272, 278, 298, 1951 to 1953, Kansas State College, Hays, Kansas.

Beeson, W. M., and T. W. Perry, *Supplementing Growing and Fattening Rations for Cattle*, Agricultural Experiment Station Mimeo. A. H. 123, 1953, Purdue University, Lafayette, Indiana.

────── *Chopped Forage vs. Pasture for Feeding Cattle*, Agricultural Experiment Station Mimeo. A. H. 122, 1953, Purdue University, Lafayette, Indiana.

────── *Improving the Formula of Supplement A With Alfalfa Meal*, Agricultural Experiment Station, Mimeo A. H. 101, 1953, Purdue University, Lafayette, Indiana.

────── *Antibiotics for Suckling Calves and Yearlings*, Agricultural Experiment Station, Mimeo A. H. 130, 1954, Purdue University, Lafayette, Indiana.

──────, Donald Webb and C. H. Nickel, *Nutritional Limitations of Grass Silage Made Without a Preservative*, Agricultural Experiment Station, Mimeo A 126, 1954, Purdue University, Lafayette, Indiana.

────── and M. T. Mohler, *Fattening Cattle on Corn Silage and Grass Silage*, Agricultural Experiment Station, Mimeo A. H. 105-106, 1953, Purdue University, Lafayette, Indiana.

──────, C. H. Nickel, and Donald Webb, *Supplementing Hay and Grass Silage for Growing Steers*, Agricultural Experiment Station, Mimeo A. H. 79, 1952, Purdue University, Lafayette, Indiana.

Brouse, E. M., *Wintering Calves in the Nebraska Sandhills*, Agricultural Experiment Station Bulletin 357, 1944, University of Nebraska, Lincoln, Nebraska.

Burroughs, Wise, *Beef Supplements with Dehydrated Alfalfa*, American Dehydrators Association, Kansas City 5, Missouri.

Burroughs, Wise, C. C. Culbertson, Edward Rief, Ward Repp, and W. E. Hammond, *Cattle Supplements Using Cornstalks, Corncobs and Hay in Fattening Rations for Yearling Steers*, A. H. Leaflet 182, 1952, Iowa State College, Ames, Iowa.

Burroughs, Wise, C. W. McDonald, J. M. Scholl, and Bob Zimmerman, *Grass Silage, Chopped Cornstalks and Various Supplemental Feeds for Wintering Yearling Steers*, Agricultural Experiment Station FSR-54-1951-52. Iowa State College, Ames, Iowa.

Burroughs, Wise, and C. C. Culbertson, *Adding Stilbestrol to Feeds for Growing and Fattening Beef Cattle*. Agricultural Experiment Station and Extension Service Pamphlet 215, 1954, Iowa State College, Ames, Iowa.

Cattle Feeding Experiments, Cattle Feeders Report 1954, Iowa State College, Ames, Iowa.

Corn and Sorghum Silage, E. C. 131, 1954, University of Nebraska, Lincoln, Nebraska.

Feeding and Breeding Test with Beef Cattle, Feeder's Day Report No. MP-34, 1954, Oklahoma A & M College, Stillwater, Oklahoma.

Feeding and Breeding Test with Sheep, Swine, and Beef Cattle, Progress Report 1952-53, Oklahoma A & M College, Stillwater, Oklahoma.

Grass Silage, E. C. 130, 1954, University of Nebraska, Lincoln, Nebraska.

High-Moisture Sorghum Grain for Finishing Cattle, Texas Agricultural Experiment Station, Cattle Series 154, 1959, Texas A & M, College Station, Texas.

Hoffman, E. N., Ralph Bogart, and M. J. Burris, *Corn, Barley and Bonemeal for Fattening Cattle Rations,* Station Bulletin 528, 1952, Oregon State College, Corvallis, Oregon.

Malone, Carl, *Guide to Profit for Cattle Feeders,* Agricultural Extension Pamphlet 127 (Revised), 1950, Iowa State College, Ames, Iowa.

Mayo, Henry, *Pastures for Growing and Fattening Cattle,* Agricultural Experiment Station Mimeo. A. H. 128, 1954, Purdue University, Lafayette, Indiana.

Quayle, W. L. and Leon H. Paules, *Fattening Cattle on Wyoming Feeds,* Agricultural Experiment Station Bulletin 308, 1951, University of Wyoming, Laramie, Wyoming.

Recommended Nutrient Allowances for Beef Cattle, A Report of the Committee on Animal Nutrition, No. IV (Revised), 1950, National Research Council, Washington, D. C.

Results of Cattle Feeding Experiments, A. H. 737, 1956; A. H. 746, 1957; A. H. 753, 1959; A. H. 779, 1959; A. H. 813, 1960; Iowa State University, Ames, Iowa.

Thirty-Fourth Annual Cattle Feeders' Day Report, 1952, Iowa State College, Ames, Iowa.

Twenty-Sixth Annual Cattle Feeders' Day Report, 1954, University of Illinois, Urbana, Illinois.

Beef Cattle Housing and Handling Equipment

Well-planned buildings, lots, feed bunks, and handling facilities are essential to a successful beef-cattle enterprise. When prices of beef cattle are favorable to the cattlemen it is wise to use a percentage of the profits for building, remodeling or repairing cattle equipment. It is also important that equipment be so planned that the total investment and cost of upkeep is in proportion to the size of the cattle enterprise. Buildings and equipment are both expensive to build and to maintain. The cattleman should plan to meet his needs but should not be overequipped. Materials that are durable and strong should be used in the construction of equipment. Repair costs as well as first cost should be given consideration when planning equipment.

Housing for Beef Cattle. Beef cattle are not especially sensitive to changes in weather conditions. Warm and expensively built barns are not needed except when the cattle program calls for cows to calve during severe cold weather.

Housing for the cow herd. The producing herd may be successfully wintered without any shelter even in the northern regions where winters are cold. However, a good windbreak will reduce the amount of feed necessary to winter the herd and provide additional comfort for the cattle. Trees, a high board fence, or a natural windbreak provided by a hill or a similar wind barrier will provide ample protection except under the most severe conditions.

Many cattlemen, especially in the Midwest, provide barns or sheds open on the south side and equipped with a hayrack for feeding and storage room for hay and bedding as wintering shelters for the cow herd. These shelters are often of pole type construction which is both economical and durable.

In the **northern areas, when the cattle** production plans calls for calving during the cold months, warm housing will need to be provided during the calving period. Warm sheds equipped with swinging gates or movable panels that may be used to make individual calving stalls are desirable. The cows may be placed in the stalls for a few days during the calving period. Later the calves may be kept in community pens and turned out with the cows morning and night to nurse until they are old enough to follow their mothers. Creeps should be constructed in the sheds where the calves may eat grain and hay and have protection from the cold.

FIGURE 122. *Warm and comfortable calving stalls are essential for early calving in the cold regions. (Courtesy American Hereford Association.)*

Housing for feeder cattle. Feeder cattle need little more than a windbreak. Many Midwest cattle feeders have carried on a profitable feeding program with only a high board fence or a good tree windbreak for protection. Cattle that are on full feed will seldom go inside sheds even in the coldest weather. Calves that are being

FIGURE 123. *(top) A combination-type cattle shed that may be used to shelter the cowherd and, by means of swinging gates and panels, converted to calving stalls and calf pens. (Courtesy Harry Groves.) (center) An open shed for protection of older cattle and a closed shed for calving and calf stalls. (Courtesy Geo. A. Hormel and Company.) (bottom) A pole-type shed. Hay is stored at the rear and fed by means of a portable manger.*

wintered on rations that provide a growth gain of only one to one and a half pounds daily will need more protection than fattening cattle. Under no conditions is it necessary to provide more than a shed open on the south side for fattening cattle or for those being wintered for later fattening.

FIGURE 124. *A high board fence will give adequate protection to fattening cattle even in the cold regions.* (*Courtesy Geo. A. Hormel Company.*)

Shades. Young growing cattle or cattle being fattened on grass will make more rapid gains during the hot part of the summer if they have access to shade. When natural shade such as trees is not available, artificial shades will prove profitable. Shades may be constructed from various materials. The most common method is to set posts in the ground and connect the tops of these posts with boards or poles. Wire may be stretched across the top and covered with straw or some similar type of material.

Feeding Equipment. Grain feed bunks may be of two different types depending upon which will best fit the cattle program. Stationary feed bunks may be constructed along one side of the cattle lot. This type may be constructed of concrete and placed close to the feed supply. If properly constructed they are very durable and maintenance costs are small.

FIGURE 125. *Shade is essential for best gains when cattle are on pasture.* (*Courtesy* Wallaces' Farmer and Iowa Homestead.)

Portable feed bunks have the advantage of being easily moved from one lot to the next or onto the pastures if desired. They are usually less durable than well-constructed permanent bunks. Plans for several types of grain feed bunks are available from the agricultural colleges. The requirements of a good feed bunk are correct shape, strength, tightness, and proper proportions. Dehorned ani-

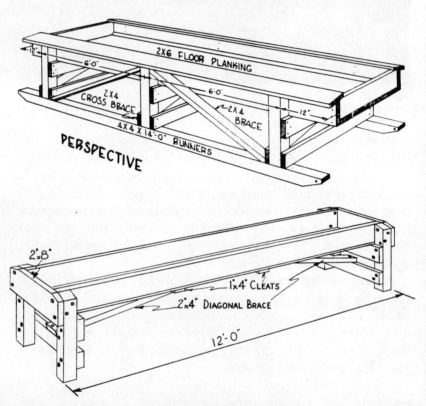

FIGURE 126. *Two types of portable feed bunks. One (top) is built on skids and may be easily moved by a tractor. (bottom) This is a well braced bunk that is durable. (Courtesy Oklahoma A&M.)*

mals will require about two and a half feet of feeder space and horned animals about three and a half feet. Calves 400 pounds and under need about 2 feet.

Automatic feeding equipment. Cattle feeding is becoming a highly specialized enterprise on many farms. Hundreds of head of cattle are being fed out annually. To reduce labor costs, many operators have installed power-driven augers that take the feed from the bins, or silage or chopped hay from the storage area, and distribute it into the feed bunks or self-feeders at the push of a button or the pull of an electric switch by the operator.

Since the various types of automatic systems are so numerous, no attempt to describe them in detail will be made.   However, information about different kinds and costs can be obtained from one or more of the many companies engaged in manufacturing and installing this equipment.

Whether to install automatic equipment or not should be determined by the cost and availability of labor, the size of the operation, and the financial condition of the owner.   If the labor saved will more than offset the interest on the investment and the upkeep and depreciation of the automatic equipment, it will probably be a wise investment.

FIGURE 127. *A portable manger for self-feeding hay from a stack. (Courtesy American Hereford Association.)*

FIGURE 128. *Fence line feed bunks made of concrete can be easily filled from a self-loading wagon, thereby saving time and labor. (Courtesy Keith Peterson.)*

Hay Mangers. Like grain feed bunks, hay mangers may be of the fixed type for feeding along one side of the feed lot or the portable type. Portable mangers may be of two types: those designed for feeding hay or silage directly from a stack or hay barn and those that are designed to be easily moved from lot to lot or onto the pasture. Figure 127 shows a manger constructed to be moved up to a hay or silage stack which will save considerable labor when feeding roughage. Figures 129, 130, and 131 show three types of movable mangers which may be used for feeding hay on pastures or easily moved from lot to lot.

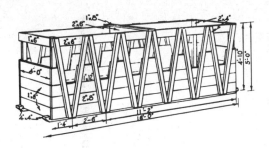

FIGURE 129. *A portable hay rack, suitable for twelve animals. It has a capacity of about two-third ton of long hay.* (*Courtesy Reuben Albaugh, C. F. Kelly, and H. L. Belton*, Beef Handling and Feeding Equipment, *University of California Circular 414.*)

FIGURE 130. *A portable hay rack mounted on wheels for easy moving.* (*Courtesy* Wallaces' Farmer and Iowa Homestead.)

FIGURE 131. *A mounted hay rack. Note the welded wire placed in order to prevent waste of hay.* (*Courtesy* Wallaces' Farmer and Iowa Homestead.)

FIGURE 132. *Chopping green forage and blowing it into a self-feeding wagon.* (*Courtesy Deere & Company.*)

FIGURE 133. *This portable calf creep is designed for cattle producers who wish to creep feed calves while they are still with their mothers. This type of creep is in reality a self-feeder with creep stalls on each side. The creep may be converted to a self-feeder for larger cattle by removing the creep divisions and cutting back the overhanging roof to give higher clearance. Greater height can also be obtained for larger cattle by anchoring the 4" x 6" runners to the tops of logs or old cross-ties. The creep may be covered with solid sheathing and composition roofing or with metal on top of horizontal nailing strips. The nailing strips should be 1" x 6" or 2" x 4" on two foot centers. The 4" x 6" runners should be treated with pressure preservative to give them longer life. A roof hatch in the top of the feeder may be preferred by some cattlemen. This would give greater capacity than when using end doors. (Courtesy Oklahoma A&M.)*

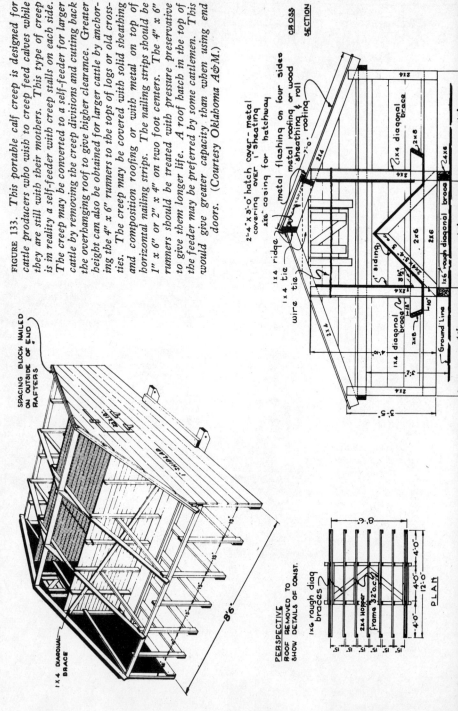

216

Creep Feeders. When calves are produced for sale either as feeder cattle or to be fed out and sold as fat cattle, creep feeding will increase the rate of gain (see Chapter 7). Movable creeps that may be placed on the pasture are desirable.

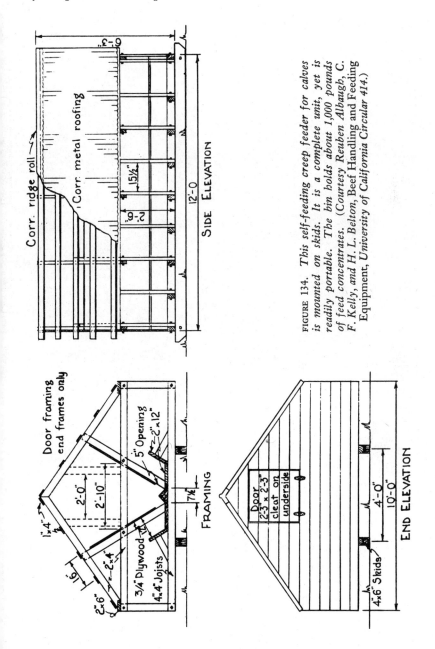

FIGURE 134. *This self-feeding creep feeder for calves is mounted on skids. It is a complete unit, yet is readily portable. The bin holds about 1,000 pounds of feed concentrates. (Courtesy Reuben Albaugh, C. F. Kelly, and H. L. Belton, Beef Handling and Feeding Equipment, University of California Circular 414.)*

Self-Feeders. Self-feeders reduce labor in feeding cattle. They are especially valuable for feeding concentrates to cattle that are on pasture.

FIGURE 135. *This molasses self-feeder was constructed around a surplus Navy pontoon tank, by Mr. Stanley Cahoon, Soledad, California.* (*Courtesy Reuben Albaugh, C. F. Kelly, and H. L. Belton,* Beef Handling and Feeding Equipment, *University of California Circular 414.*)

Mineral Feeders. Mineral feeders, built to protect the mineral mixture from rain or snow, should be placed in an area where it will be easy for the operator to fill them and where the cattle can get at the minerals conveniently. The best place to locate mineral feeders is usually near the watering facilities.

Loading Chutes. Every cattleman needs a loading chute. These chutes may be portable or of the fixed type. If it is a fixed-type chute, it should be located where large and small trucks and trailers can reach it conveniently any time of the year.

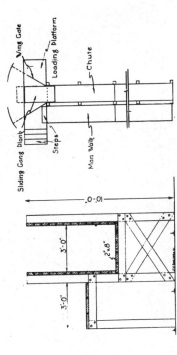

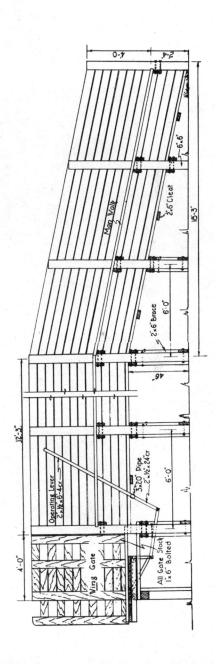

FIGURE 136. *An adjustable loading chute including a man walk. (Courtesy Reuben Albaugh, C. F. Kelly, and H. L. Belton, Beef Handling and Feeding Equipment, University of California Circular 414.)*

FIGURE 137. *A simple but safe loading chute constructed from old railroad ties and earth. (Courtesy Livestock Conservation, Inc.)*

FIGURE 138. *One type of portable loading chute. (Courtesy Livestock Conservation, Inc.)*

FIGURE 139. *Another kind of portable loading chute. (Courtesy Reuben Albaugh, C. F. Kelly, and H. L. Belton, Beef and Handling Equipment, University of California Circular 414.)*

Restraint Equipment. It is necessary to secure cattle for hoof trimming, dehorning, and other similar operations. Stocks and squeezes are used for these purposes.

220

Cattle stocks. Cattle stocks work well for purebred herds and small commercial herds that have to be handled and may be easily led or driven. When properly constructed they are durable and

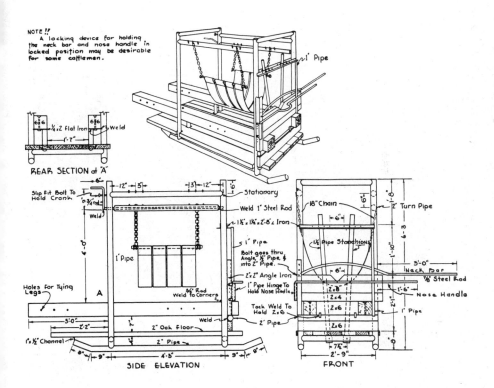

FIGURE 140. *The cattle-stock plan shown here was constructed by Mr. R. C. Borum and Sons, ranchers, Muskogee County, under the supervision of Mr. Ira J. Hollar, former County Agent. Cattle stocks are important equipment on farms and ranches where valuable breeding stock is handled. The use of such equipment in trimming hoofs and horns or in vaccinating or treating cattle reduces the liability of injury and requires fewer laborers in performing such operations. The welded pipe and angle iron construction make this piece of equipment adequately strong for handling most farm animals. For large 2,000-pound bulls the framework should be constructed of three- to four-inch pipe. For these large-size bulls, increase the width of the frame to 3'6" and the height to 7 feet. Some operators prefer to use only two canvas belts for the sling instead of the four as shown in this plan. The oak floor can be removed from the stock, which makes loading easier when the equipment is transported by truck from one location to another. The pipe skids make for easy moving about the farm. (Courtesy Oklahoma A&M.)*

thoroughly restrain the animal. They may be equipped with a canvas sling for placing under the animal to prevent it from lying down.

FIGURE 141. *An animal confined in a cattle stock.* (*Courtesy American Aberdeen-Angus Breeders Association.*)

Branding chute and cattle squeeze. A cattle squeeze is more convenient than stocks for restraining cattle that are not easily driven or led. The squeeze may be set up at the end of a branding chute and cattle may be driven through the chute and into the squeeze, where they may be caught and restrained.   The branding chute is very convenient for sorting cattle.   A two-way gate may be set up at the end of the chute and only one animal can pass through the chute at a time.   The gate may be swung back and forth directing cattle into pens on either side.

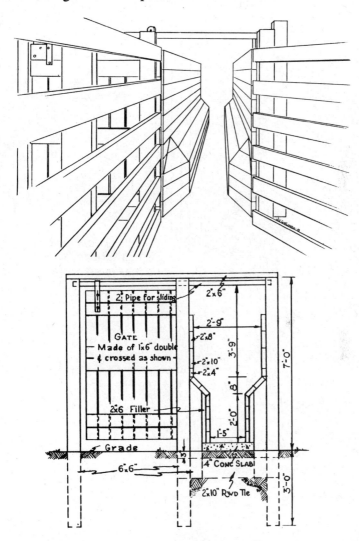

FIGURE 142.   (*top*) *Branding chute, looking down the entrance end. Note flared ends near the bottom to guide cattle into the chute and prevent bruising. A squeeze can be set up at the far end. (bottom) Construction details of the chute shown. Treat bottom of posts with preservative; give concrete floor a rough finish. (Courtesy Reuben Albaugh, C. F. Kelly, and H. L. Belton,* Beef Handling and Feeding Equipment, *University of California Circular 414.*)

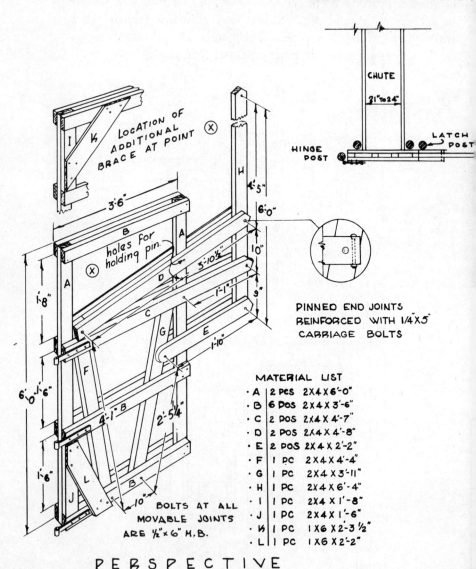

CHUTE

21" TO 24"

HINGE POST

LATCH POST

I

LOCATION OF ADDITIONAL BRACE AT POINT Ⓧ

3'-6"

holes for holding pin.

Ⓧ

H

4'-5"

6'-0"

10"

3'-10½"

9"

1'-1"

1'-10"

1'-8"

6'-0" 1'-6"

4'-1" B

2'-5¼"

1'-6"

10"

PINNED END JOINTS
REINFORCED WITH 1/4"X5"
CARRIAGE BOLTS

BOLTS AT ALL
MOVABLE JOINTS
ARE ½"x 6" M.B.

MATERIAL LIST

· A	2 PCS	2X4 X 6'-0"
· B	6 POS	2X4 X 3'-6"
· C	2 POS	2X4 X 4'-7"
· D	2 POS	2X4 X 4'-8"
· E	2 POS	2X4 X 2'-2"
· F	1 PC	2X4 X 4'-4"
· G	1 PC	2X4 X 3'-11"
· H	1 PC	2X4 X 6'-4"
· I	1 PC	2X4 X 1'-8"
· J	1 PC	2X4 X 1'-6"
· K	1 PC	1 X6 X 2'-3½"
· L	1 PC	1 X6 X 2'-2"

PERSPECTIVE

FIGURE 143. *A good head gate is one of the important parts of the corral and handling equipment. The plan shown here has been widely used by farmers and ranches in Oklahoma. The gate is located at the end of the chute and is mounted on posts by means of hinges and lug bolts. The middle hinge lug should be pointed downward so cattle will not lift the gate off the lugs. (Courtesy Oklahoma A&M.)*

Cattle Yards and Lots. Well-planned corrals and lots make handling of stock easier and saves labor. Paved lots are ideal especially in the more humid regions. Paved lots keep cattle out of

FIGURE 144. *A good corral for handling cattle, including all the necessary equipment arranged for convenience. This corral may be adapted for large or small size ranches or farms, by reducing or increasing the dimensions. (Courtesy Reuben Albaugh, C. F. Kelly, and H. L. Belton,* Beef Handling and Feeding Equipment, *University of California Circular 414.)*

FIGURE 145. *A detailed drawing of the corral shown in Figure 144. (Courtesy Reuben Albaugh, C. F. Kelly, and H. L. Belton,* Beef Handling and Feeding Equipment, *University of California Circular 414.)*

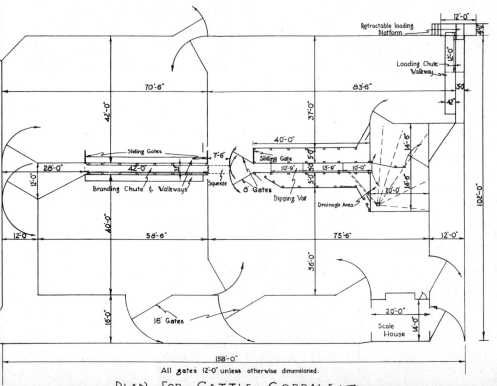

All gates 12'-0" unless otherwise dimensioned.

PLAN FOR CATTLE CORRALS

the mud, make it easier to work with them, and saves manure. Paved lots are easy to clean.   If the 'lots are not paved they should be located on well drained areas.

FIGURE 146. *Lots should either be paved or located on a well-drained area. (Courtesy of Harry Groves.)*

Fences.   Feed lot fences need to be strong.   A good fence can be made by combining plank and woven wire, with posts set not more than ten feet apart.   While it is more expensive, a plank fence made by bolting 2-inch planks to wooden posts makes a very durable fence.   Cattle confined to small lots subject fences to considerable punishment.

FIGURE 147. *A well-constructed cattle lot fence. (Courtesy of Harry Groves.)*

Feed Storage Equipment.   The kind of feed storage equipment needed will depend upon the kind of feed to be used.   Where silage is the principal roughage, a trench silo will provide temporary but cheap storage facilities.   Trench silos are constructed by digging a trench into the side of a sloping area where there will be drainage. The sides should be wider at the top to prevent crumbling of the walls.   Trench silos may be made more permanent by concreting the sides.   Legume or grass silage may be stacked on top of the ground.   If the stack is well packed, little spoilage results.   The upright silo is more permanent but also more expensive.

Hay may be stacked outside on an area where drainage is good. If it is properly covered, it will keep well.   In the more humid areas hay that is to be fed late in the season should be protected. Hay barns that shed water are all that are necessary for keeping the hay.   To conserve labor the roughage should be stored close to the feed yard.

Grains other than ear corn should be placed in well-constructed tight bins where moisture will not cause spoilage.   Ear corn does

FIGURE 148. *Cattle feeding is a large operation on many farms. To save labor, many cattle feeders are installing automatic equipment. The complete ration is mixed automatically and augered into the feed bunks. These are two types of automatic feed lots.*

not spoil easily if placed under a roof that will shed water and on a floor that is off the ground a few inches. Ear corn storage cribs should be ventilated on the sides. This is accomplished by using a slated side type construction or any substantial material that will allow for the movement of air through the corn. Grain bins and cribs should be located near the feed lot to make for greatest ease in feeding.

FIGURE 149. *A chopped hay self-feeder. Cones constructed inside keep hay divided, allowing it to feed down. Gates on the bottom may be opened so cattle can get at the hay. (Courtesy Iowa State College.)*

TABLE 23

SILAGE, HAY AND BEDDING STORAGE SPACE REQUIREMENTS

Material	Wt. Per Cu. Ft.	Cu. Ft. Per Ton
Hay (Loose)	4.0 to 4.5 lbs.	440 to 512
Hay (Baled)	15.0 to 20.0 lbs.	100 to 133
Hay (Chopped)	10.0 to 12.0 lbs.	165 to 200
Straw (Loose)	4.0 lbs.	500
Straw (Baled)	12.0 lbs.	167
Silage (Silos up to 30′ deep)	40.0 lbs.	50
Silage (Silos of more than 30′)	50.0 lbs.	50

Mechanized Feeding Systems. One who is anticipating the building or remodeling of a cattle feeding plant will profit by making a study of various labor saving systems that have been devised by many cattle feeders. By using properly constructed bins, mechanical augers and feed conveyors, it is possible to mix feed and deliver it into the bunks for the cattle with very little hand labor.

Since labor is always an expensive part of any farm or feeding enterprise, labor saving equipment that will reduce the number of man hours necessary for carrying on any farming program should be considered. Lack of capital may prevent the operator from developing the plant completely at one time. However, a complete plan that is adapted to the conditions should be made and each building or piece of equipment added should fit in with the general plan.

SUMMARY

Well-planned equipment is essential to the successful handling of beef cattle. Housing need not be elaborate or expensive for beef cattle unless cows calve during cold weather.

Feeding equipment may consist of either fixed or portable grain bunks and hayracks or both. Portable equipment is convenient when forage or concentrates are fed to cattle that are on pasture.

Loading chutes and restraining equipment are an essential part of the cattleman's equipment.

Lots and corrals should be either paved or located on well-drained land. Lots should be planned for the convenient sorting, loading, and handling of cattle.

Feed storage should be located close to the cattle yards for ease of feeding and the saving of labor. Mechanized feeding systems will reduce labor and should be considered before building or remodeling a cattle feeding plant.

QUESTIONS

1. Describe the kind of protection needed for beef cattle on your farm or on the average farm in your community where beef cattle are kept.
2. Make a list of equipment needed for the handling of beef cattle on your farm.
3. Make a sketch of a plan for beef cattle yards or corrals that would meet the needs of the average cattleman in your area.
4. What advantages do paved lots have?

5. What feed storage equipment is needed by the average cattleman in your area?
6. Where should feed storage facilities be located?   Why?
7. Make a plan for a mechanized cattle feeding plant.

REFERENCES

Albaugh, Reuben, C. F. Kelly, and H. L. Belton, *Beef Handling and Feeding Equipment*, Agricultural Experiment and Extension Service Circular 414, 1952, University of California, Berkeley, California.

Beef Cattle Housing in the North Central Region of the United States, By the Committee on Housing of Beef Cattle and Sheep, Agricultural Experiment Station Bulletin 382, 1946, South Dakota State College, Brookings, South Dakota.

Plans for Cattle Feeders and Equipment, Extension Service Circular 540, Oklahoma A & M College, Stillwater, Oklahoma.

Keeping Cattle Healthy

Cattle diseases, parasites, and other ailments may be divided into four groups: (1) external parasites, (2) internal parasites, (3) infectious diseases, and (4) noninfectious ailments. The average cattleman is not a veterinarian. Therefore, his chief preventive measures in maintaining a healthy herd are good sanitation, the proper use of sprays and disinfectants, and the vaccination of his herd against those diseases for which vaccines have been perfected, when recommended by a reliable veterinarian.

Remember the old adage that "an ounce of prevention is worth a pound of cure"—and is a lot cheaper. Extreme caution may seem to be time-consuming and expensive, but many diseases, once in the herd, can force a man out of the cattle business. Most infections and diseases that cattle are subject to are brought into the herd as a result of poor management practices. Parasites and diseases usually breed best under filthy conditions. Many diseases spread from infected animals to healthy ones.

A PROGRAM OF DISEASE AND PARASITE PREVENTION

The following steps are important if a disease- and parasite-free herd is to be maintained.

1. Bring only clean animals into the herd. Many serious diseases, such as brucellosis, can be detected through a test for the disease. A veterinarian may save serious losses if he is called to examine animals before they go into the herd.
2. Drain lots so that they will remain dry and free of stagnant water. Paved lots will aid in keeping cattle out of the mud and filth.

231

3. Isolate all animals that are known to have contagious infections. Animals that have been purchased or otherwise added to the herd should be isolated until it is reasonably certain that they are free of disease.

4. Have the breeding herd tested at least once a year for brucellosis, tuberculosis, and other diseases for which tests have been developed.

5. Vaccinate for diseases common in the community if a successful vaccine exists.

6. Disinfect housing and equipment regularly.

7. Treat open wounds and the navel of newborn calves with a reliable disinfectant.

8. Provide plenty of exercise for the breeding herd.

9. Spray or dust for external parasites, such as flies, and eliminate manure piles and other filth accumulations where flies breed.

10. If cows calve in places other than clean pastures, be sure the area is well bedded and disinfected.

11. Avoid cold floors and drafty housing quarters for young calves dropped during cold weather.

EXTERNAL PARASITES

The Screw Worm. These pests are more prevalent in the southern and southwestern states. In these areas they are one of the most important causes of cattle losses.

Life history. The screw worm fly is bluish green in color, with orange shading below the eyes. The three prominent dark stripes along its back distinguish it from similar insects. The flies lay their eggs in masses along the edges of open wounds. The eggs hatch into tiny maggots that burrow into the flesh, where they feed from four to seven days.

When the worms have reached their full growth, they drop to the ground and burrow into the soil. A few days later they emerge from the pupa or dormant stage as adult flies. The entire life cycle may be completed within 21 days under favorable conditions.

Prevention and control. The U.S. Department of Agriculture has developed several smears that will kill the worms or prevent them from infecting wounds. The newest of these smears is known as "Smear EQ 335." The ingredients consist of the following: lindane, 3%; mineral oil, 40-44%; pine oil, 35%; emulsifier,

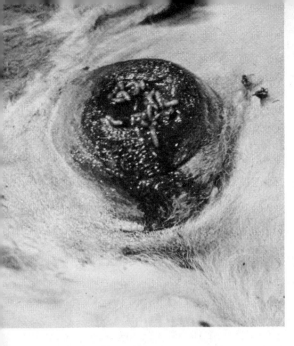

8-12%; and silica aerogel, 8-12%. This mixture should be applied to the surface of all open wounds, and deep into the wound.

CO-Ral used as described for grub control is also effective in the control of screw worms.

Dehorning, castrating, and other operations should be performed during the winter season, when the screw worm is less active.

Grubs. Cattle grubs or heel flies seldom cause death in cattle, but the loss resulting from the uncomfortable effect they produce upon the animals is greater than is generally realized by herd owners. Milk production may be severely reduced and the growth rate of young animals slowed down.

Life history. The heel fly lays its eggs on the lower parts of the animal during the spring and early summer. The eggs hatch and the tiny grubs bore through the skin and migrate through the animal's body, feeding on the tissues for about nine months. They appear as lumps along the back from early winter until spring. The mature grubs perforate the skin and come out through the openings in the hide, drop to the ground, and soon develop into adult flies. These flies seldom travel more than a mile, so if a cooperative effort is made they can be controlled in any area.

There are two species of cattle grubs, one known as the *common cattle grub* and the other as the *Northern cattle grub*. The life cycles of the two are similar except that the duration is longer for the Northern grub.

233

Prevention and control. The newest and one of the most effective sprays for grub control is a product known by the trade name of CO-Ral. This material not only controls grubs but also gives effective control for most of the external parasites that affect beef cattle. The spray is made by dissolving 4 pounds of 25 per cent CO-Ral wettable powder plus ½ pound of detergent in 25 gallons of water. Use 3 to 4 quarts of this mixture for each animal and spray thoroughly. Apply shortly after the heel-fly activity has ceased but at least 60 days before the animals are to be slaughtered.

A product known as Et-57, or by such trade names as Trolene, Ectoral, and others, is very effective as a control for grubs when given as a bolus shortly after the heel-fly activity has ceased. The dosage is 5 grams of Et-57 for each hundred pounds of body weight. Treatment must not be used within 60 days of slaughter.

Since the end of heel-fly activity varies with the area, the time for treatment with either CO-Ral or Et-57 will also vary. Consult

FIGURE 151. *Cattle badly infested with grubs. Note the lumps along the back. (Courtesy Livestock Conservation, Inc.)*

the Vocational Agricultural Instructor, the County Extension Director, or your veterinarian as to the correct time to use these products.

Rotenone, applied as a dust or spray, will destroy the grubs in the backs of cattle after the grubs have appeared. The spray is made by using 7½ pounds of 5 per cent rotenone wettable powder plus 2 pounds of detergent per 100 gallons of water. Use one gallon per animal and wet the backs thoroughly. One to 1.5 per cent rotenone dust is effective if rubbed onto the backs. However, the disadvantage of rotenone is that the grubs have already done most of the damage before they are destroyed.

Since CO-Ral is absorbed into the body through the hide, both CO-Ral and Et-57 destroy the grubs as soon as they enter the body tissue.

Cattle Lice. These pests are most abundant during the winter. Cattle infested with lice rub along fences and feed bunks in an effort to relieve the irritation. The hair appears dry and dead. There will be bare places on the shoulders, neck, topline, and flanks where

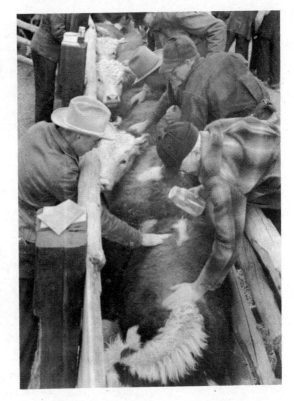

FIGURE 152. *Dusting for cattle grubs. (Courtesy Tony Fellhauer, University of Wyoming.)*

the hair has been rubbed off. Milk production may decline and young animals may slow up in their development.

Prevention and control. Spraying with CO-Ral or rotenone (see grub control) is very effective for the control of lice. Lindane, used at the rate of 2 pounds of 25 per cent wettable powder plus 2 pounds of detergent per 100 gallons of water and sprayed thoroughly on the animals, is also very effective. Spray must not be applied within 60 days of slaughter. A spray made by using 57 per cent malathion emulsifiable concentrate and 2 pounds of detergent per 100 gallons of water is also very effective for the control of lice. Malathion must not be applied within 30 days of slaughter.

Cable-type treaters, which consist of a cable or chain wrapped several times with burlap or some absorbent-type material, will control lice. Treaters are hung loosely between posts or with one end fastened near the ground and the other end three to four feet up, in a manner that allows the cattle to rub their necks and backs on them. The wrappings are soaked with a 2 per cent oil solution of malathion or a 5 per cent oil solution of methoxychlor.

FIGURE 153. *Who knows how much loss lice cause on animals like these? Lice can be prevented by sprays at the right time. (Courtesy Livestock Conservation, Inc.)*

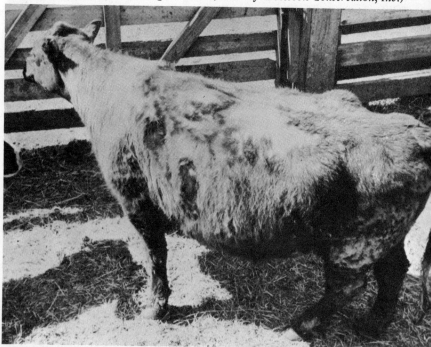

GENERAL RECOMMENDATIONS FOR FLY AND MOSQUITO CONTROL

Buildings and Fences. The first step in effective fly control is to eliminate all possible breeding places. Keep barns and lots free from manure and as dry as possible. Repair leaky water tanks and hydrants to prevent mud puddles. Keep weeds and grass cut around buildings. Spray the inside of buildings once every three weeks with a malathion spray consisting of 2 gallons of 50 per cent emulsifiable malathion and 2 gallons of white Karo syrup per 100 gallons of water. For the syrup, 20 pounds of sugar may be effectively substituted. The material is effective for 10 to 20 days inside buildings and from 5 to 10 days outside. A .5 to 1 per cent Diazinon solution or a 1 to 2 per cent Korlan solution may also be used. Board fences and the lower parts of barns and cattle sheds, where flies and mosquitos rest, should be sprayed with the same materials once every one to two weeks, depending upon the amount of rainfall. Low shrubs and trees should be sprayed every week or two with a 1 per cent water emulsion malathion spray.

Beef Cattle. Beef cattle should be sprayed every two to three weeks with a 5 per cent solution of malathion, methoxychlor, or toxaphene. These sprays should be discontinued 30 days before animals are to be slaughtered. CO-Ral as used for grubs will be effective from 10 to14 days as a fly spray, but must be discontinued within 60 days of slaughter.

FIGURE 154. *Using a power spray to control flies. (Baily photo. Courtesy* Successful Farming.)

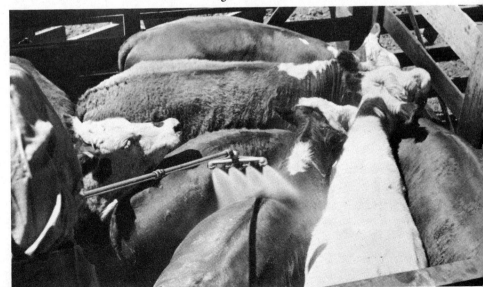

Horn Flies. These are the first flies to appear in the spring and continue as cattle pests the entire summer. They are small black flies often seen resting in large numbers around the base of the horns. They suck the blood from around the back, shoulders, and withers, causing considerable loss of gain, and reduction of milk.

Prevention and control. See general recommendations for fly control.

Stable Flies. These flies remain on the cattle only while feeding on the blood of the animal. When not feeding, they will be found resting on fences and other objects outside the barn. They are more commonly found around the barn lots than in the pastures. This is because they depend upon manure, rotting straw, and other similar materials in which to breed.

Prevention and control. See general fly-control recommendations.

Horse Flies, Deer Flies, and Mosquitoes. Although these species of insects differ considerably in their life cycle and habits, the control measures are essentially the same. They breed around swampy areas and water holes, and rest in trees, bushes, or other tall growing plants when not feeding.

Prevention and control. See general fly control.

FIGURE 155. *A commercial-type back scratcher and automatic sprayer.*

Ticks. There are several species of ticks that affect cattle, one of which may carry the disease known as Texas fever, which in the past resulted in heavy losses in the South. However, as a result of the work of the U.S. Department of Agriculture and the state experiment stations, Texas fever has all but been eliminated from the United States.

Prevention and control. A lindane spray consisting of 8 pounds of 25 per cent lindane wettable powder and 2 pounds of a wetting agent per 100 gallons of water is an effective control measure for ticks. Lindane should not be used within 60 days of slaughter. Calves under three months of age should not be sprayed with lindane. CO-Ral as used for grubs will control ticks. A spray made by using 2 quarts of 60 per cent toxaphene plus 2 pounds of detergent per 100 gallons of water and applied once every three weeks for as long as necessary is also recommended. The toxaphene formula should contain 6.325 pounds of toxaphene and 12.5 per cent emulsifier per gallon.

Mites. Cattle mites produce what is known as sarcoptic mange or cattle scab. The mite spends its entire life cycle on the body

239

of the animal, piercing the skin and feeding on the lymph, producing a thickened, tough, wrinkled skin.

Prevention and control. The same lindane spray as that recommended for ticks sprayed at 300 to 400 pounds of pressure is very effective in the control of mites.

FIGURE 157. *Cow leaving portable sprayer.* (*Courtesy Livestock Sprayer Manufacturing Co.*)

INTERNAL PARASITES

There are several different types of stomach and intestinal worms that affect cattle, but the common stomach worm is the greatest menace.

Common Stomach Worm. Worms, similar to those found in sheep, may infest young cattle, particularly calves under six months of age. Adult cattle are seldom affected. Heavily infected animals lose weight and become thin and weak. The hair becomes rough, and the membranes of the mouth are pale. A soft swelling, known as *bottle jaw*, may develop under the jaw.

Prevention and control. Sanitation is the most important means of prevention. Worm eggs pass in the droppings and hatch into tiny worms, which are picked up by other animals. Placing water and feed where it will not be contaminated by droppings and rotating pastures frequently are effective control measures. In areas where stomach worms are a problem, particularly in the South, confining calves to pens on pasture and moving the pens frequently has helped to control worm infestation. A recommended practice is to start the calves at the bottom of a slope and gradually move them up the hill as they graze each area.

Infested animals may be given a fluid drench, containing 20 grams of phenothiazine powder per 100 pounds of body weight. The maximum dose should not exceed 60 grams regardless of the animal's weight.

Doses should be repeated every 20 days where heavy infestation occurs. The drench may be given with a syringe placed in the side of the mouth and discharged near the base of the tongue. Usually after the first dose, low level feeding of 2 grams per day per animal of phenothiazine powder will keep them free of worms. To accomplish this, the drug may be mixed with the mineral or supplement. A mixture of 1 part phenothiazine powder to 9 parts salt and mineral mixture may be fed.

Coccidiosis. This disease is the result of poor management and unsanitary conditions. It is caused by the entrance of protozoa into the digestive systems of young calves through contaminated feed and water.

Symptoms. Common symptoms are loss of appetite, bloody diarrhea, and weakness.

Prevention and control. Sanitation, the drainage of pastures and yards, rotation of pastures, and general good management are the best preventive measures. Veterinarians may successfully treat infected animals in the early stages of the disease with sulfa and other drugs.

Anaplasmosis. Anaplasmosis is caused by a protozoan parasite that destroys the red blood corpuscles. It is thought that various insects such as fleas, ticks, and mosquitoes are responsible for transmitting the disease from one animal to the other.

Symptoms. High fever, anemia, loss of weight and appetite are the common symptoms. The disease may be present in either the chronic or acute form. In the acute form the temperature will run from 103° to 107°F. for two to three days then drop to normal. Breathing is difficult and urination is frequent and sometimes bloody. In the acute form death often occurs within five days after the first symptoms are noted.   In the chronic form animals often recover but may be carriers of the disease.

Prevention and control.   No cure has been perfected for the disease.   The U.S. Department of Agriculture has perfected a test that will aid in detecting animals that are carriers of the disease. The elimination of such animals from the herd is the best control measure.

INFECTIOUS DISEASES

There are many infectious diseases of cattle, but only those that cause the greatest economic losses will be discussed in this book.

Brucellosis or Bang's Disease.   This is number one in importance not only because of the economic losses resulting from the disease, but also because undulant fever, which also affects human beings, may be contracted from animals affected with it.

Symptoms.   Infected animals may abort or give birth to a dead or weak calf; this is the most commonly observed symptom of brucellosis.   On the other hand, the birth may be normal, but the cow may fail to clean or expel the afterbirth.   Animals that are infected often have higher than normal temperatures at calving time.   Milk production is reduced.   Heavily infected herds may have 50 per cent or more aborted or dead calves among heifers.   Great care must be taken by persons coming in contact with animals infected with brucellosis to avoid contracting undulant fever.   The disease may be contracted from the consumption of nonpasteurized milk produced by infected animals, and great danger exists in handling newborn calves or aborted fetuses from infected herds.

Prevention and control.   Brucellosis finds its way into a herd through any of the following ways: (1) the purchase of infected or exposed animals, (2) contact with a neighbor's herd over a line fence, (3) exposure at livestock shows where an infected animal may be on exhibit, (4) livestock trucks that go from farm to farm handling animals and that have not been properly cleaned and disinfected, (5) public livestock auctions where proper sanitation is not practiced, (6) aborted calves that are dragged on the place by carnivorous animals.

Brucellosis may be detected by having a veterinarian blood-test the herd.   If the disease is found to exist, there are two recommended plans for its eradication:

1. Test all the cows and heifers, removing any reactors from the herd and vaccinating all calves between the ages of six and eight months that are not infected.

2. Test and keep all reactors separate from the herd and vaccinate the calves. Since cows will generally produce normal calves after the second calving, reactors may be kept, but should not be in the same area with heifers since they are carriers of the disease. The plan should be to eliminate the reactors as quickly as it is economically possible.

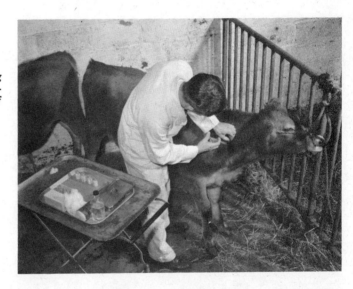

FIGURE 158. *Vaccinating for brucellosis.* (*Courtesy U.S.D.A. Bureau of Animal Industry.*)

FIGURE 159. *Cow and aborted calf.* (*Courtesy U.S.D.A. Bureau of Animal Industry.*)

Since brucellosis may crop up in any herd at any time, it is advisable for the cow herd owner to start a program of calfhood vaccination as a preventive measure.

Tuberculosis.   This is a serious disease of cattle, but because of the state and federal eradication programs, it is steadily declining in the United States.

Symptoms.   Many times animals will show no outward sign of the disease.   There may be a gradual loss of weight, swelling of the joints, and labored breathing.   The part of the animal affected has much to do with the outward symptoms.

Prevention and control.   Tests have been perfected for determining the presence of tuberculosis in the herd.   Periodic testing and elimination of reactors constitutes a reliable control program.

Blackleg.   This is one of the most infectious diseases of young cattle and generally proves fatal.

Symptoms.   Blackleg is usually accompanied by high fever, loss of appetite, and labored breathing.   Rapidly developing tumors under the skin that make a crackling sound when subjected to pressure (owing to gas) are one of the clearest indications of the disease.

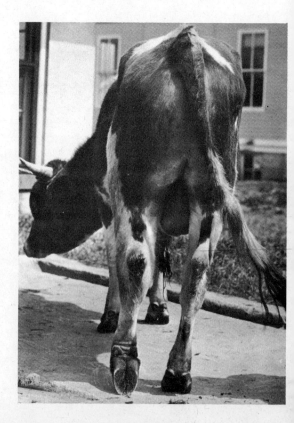

FIGURE 160. *Calf with blackleg. Note the swelling in the leg. (Courtesy U.S.D.A. Bureau of Animal Industry.)*

Prevention and control. If blackleg infection is found in the area or in the herd, vaccination of animals not affected is the only prevention. Affected animals will not generally respond to vaccination, but if the disease is diagnosed during its early stages, penicillin treatment by a veterinarian may cure some animals. Carcasses of animals killed by blackleg should be completely destroyed by burning.

Anthrax. This is caused by an organism that may live in the soil for many years. For this reason, some areas have more outbreaks of the disease than others. Outbreaks usually occur during dry spells, when pastures are short and cattle tend to pick up soil while grazing. They may also occur following a flood, when the pastures are overflowed.

Symptoms. High temperatures and bloody discharges from natural body openings are symptoms. Sudden death without apparent cause follows.

Prevention and control. The prevention of anthrax lies mainly in following a vaccination program, especially in areas where outbreaks of the disease occur quite regularly. Vaccination provides immunity for the season but will not permanently immunize the animals. Infected animals may be cured by penicillin treatment if it is given during the early stages of the disease. If the cattleman suspects that anthrax infection is present, he should immediately call a veterinarian.

Shipping Fever. This is a blood disease affecting mostly young cattle. A weakening of resistance due to exposure when being shipped from one point to another often leads to infection by the germs that cause shipping fever.

Symptoms. High temperature, coughing, and watery discharges from the nostrils and eyes are common symptoms.

Prevention and control. Overexposure and drafty means of transportation should be avoided. The cattle should have plenty of water and should not be overcrowded. Infected animals should be separated from the rest of the herd. The cattle should be kept dry and in protected places for a few days after shipping. Vaccines are used but should be given ten days before shipping. Serum should be used if animals are to be shipped immediately or are exposed by coming in contact with animals suffering from the disease. Antibiotics, especially penicillin, may prove effective in the treatment and prevention of shipping fever.

FIGURE 161. *Calf with shipping fever.* (*Courtesy U.S.D.A. Bureau of Animal Industry.*)

Veterinarians are using sulphonomids and electrolytes in the water of newly shipped cattle as both a preventive and a treatment for shipping fever. Cattlemen are advised to contact their veterinarian as soon as the cattle arrive. Some veterinarians prescribe that the first water consumed by the cattle contain the above materials and that the treatment be continued for 5 to 7 days after shipment.

Rhinotracheitis or Red Nose. This is a serious disease in cattle. Although the actual death loss may not be large, cattle, especially fattening cattle, may lose from two to three hundred pounds of weight during the course of the disease. It is caused by a virus.

Symptoms. Rhinotracheitis is very hard for even a veterinarian to diagnose because the symptoms are much like those of shipping fever. Animals have difficulty in breathing and usually have a discharge from the eyes and from the nose (from where it is sometimes bloody). They cough, have an excessive flow of saliva, and have temperatures from 103 to 108 degrees.

Prevention and control. A number of vaccines are on the

246

market and veterinarians use them as both a preventive measure and a treatment. If the disease is suspected, a veterinarian should be called immediately in order to reduce losses.

Virus Diarrhea. This is a comparatively new disease in the United States. The loss in weight and the death rate will be high unless cattle are promptly treated.

Symptoms. Virus Diarrhea, in its early stages, can be confused with several other diseases, including Rhinotracheitis and shipping fever. The initial signs are nasal discharge and mouth sores. At first the feces are very hard, but later the animal will scour and mucus, and blood may appear in the feces.

Prevention and control. No positive prevention has been found. Veterinarians have had some success treating the disease with various drugs.

Foot Rot. This is an infection of the feet of cattle and is a serious disease in many beef herds. It usually occurs when cattle are confined for long periods in muddy lots. It is caused by a germ that invades the tissues of the foot from the soil. An injury resulting in a break in the skin of the foot provides a means by which the germs may enter.

Symptoms. Affected animals become sorefooted, and the infected foot swells and is foul-smelling. There may not be a visible sore at the start, but later the skin cracks open and a dirty yellowish pus is present.

Prevention and control. Keeping lots clean and well drained and barns free from manure or well bedded are good preventive measures. A box four inches deep filled with hydrated lime and placed where the cattle will be forced to walk through it will aid in preventing the disease. Infected animals may be treated by scraping the sore and saturating the foot with Lysol or a one per cent solution of copper sulphate. Veterinarians have successfully treated foot rot with sulfa and other drugs.

Pinkeye. This infection attacks animals of any age but seldom occurs during the cool season.

Symptoms. The first indication of pinkeye is a flow of tears and a tendency to keep the eyes closed. There will be a swelling of the eyelids and a general inflammation of the eye.

Prevention and control. Affected animals should be segregated. Blowing sulfa powders into the eyes is helpful in many cases. If left alone, most animals will recover.

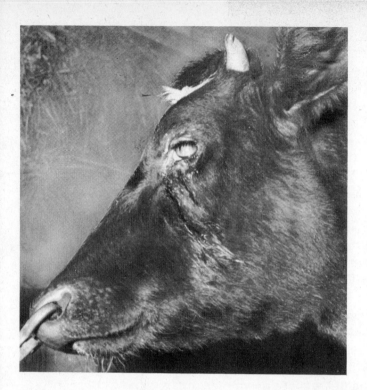

Mastitis. This is one of the worst diseases of dairy cattle but is less common in beef cattle. The disease is caused by several types of germs that find their way into the udder, often as a result of an injury.

Symptoms. There are two forms of mastitis, one known as the acute and the other as the chronic form. In the acute form the teat and quarter are swollen and painful. This form is often accompanied by fever and loss of appetite. The milk will be stringy and sometimes bloody. The chronic form is more mild and may go unnoticed until it flares up in the acute form. In chronic mastitis there may be no swelling. The milk, however, will generally show clots and watery consistency under close inspection. Usually only one quarter is involved at a time. Milk production drops and the udder may be ruined unless treatment is started during the early stages of the disease.

Prevention and control. Eliminating sources of udder injury, such as obstacles that may cause bruises or cuts, is important in mastitis prevention. Poorly bedded cement floors are invitations for udder injuries. Milking a few streams from each quarter will give the operator an opportunity to observe any stringiness or clots in the milk. The Brome-Thymol-Blue test, although not 100 per

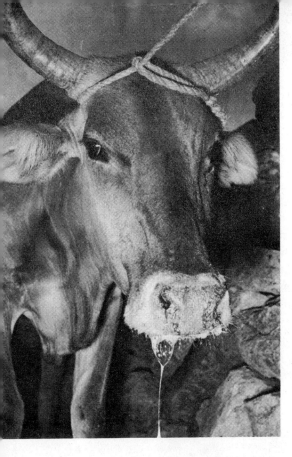

FIGURE 163. *Foot-and-mouth disease. (Courtesy U.S.D.A. Bureau of Animal Industry.)*

cent accurate, will give a good indication of the presence or absence of mastitis. To conduct the test, place a drop of Brome-Thymol-Blue on a blotter with an eye-dropper, using one drop in a separate spot for each quarter of the udder. Place a few drops of milk on the same spot. If the color changes to a bluish green, mastitis infection may be suspected. In mild cases, successful treatment may result by administering antibiotic ointment that may be obtained in a small tube fitted with a spout. The ointment is injected into the affected quarter through the teat canal. In the most serious cases or in cases where there is no response to this treatment, the cows should be placed under the care of a veterinarian.

Foot-and-Mouth Disease. Foot-and-mouth disease is highly infectious. The few outbreaks that have occurred in the United States have been quickly brought under control.

Symptoms. The disease is characterized by blisters that form on the tongue, the lips, the cheeks, and the skin around the claws of the feet and on the teats and udder. The blisters cause a heavy flow of saliva that hangs from the lips in strings. Infected animals smack their lips and, owing to tenderness of the feet, sway from one hind foot to the other.

Prevention and control. To control the disease, infected animals should be destroyed and the premises disinfected with a lye solution. A vaccine has been developed that is used in areas outside the United States. Authorities in the United States have not recommended vaccination, because it is not considered conducive to complete eradication. The policy followed in the United States has been to destroy infected animals, disinfect, and quarantine the area where the outbreak occurred until the disease has been eradicated. If foot-and-mouth disease is suspected, federal authorities should be notified, because quick control is essential.

Warts. The condition occurs on calves and is caused by a *virus* which spreads from one animal to another by contact.

Symptoms. The warts appear around the neck and head, often near the eyes.

Prevention and control. Wart-infected calves should be placed

FIGURE 164. *Calf with warts.*

away from other calves. Painting the warts with iodine once or twice during a two-day period, followed by application of castor oil, will often eliminate them. A vaccine has been developed that is very effective in controlling warts.

Calf Scours. This is one of the worst diseases of young calves.

It has been reported that from 10 to 15 per cent of deaths in calves is the result of calf scours.

Symptoms. Calf scours is characterized by a pasty white scour that usually affects calves under three weeks of age. The animals become weak and lose their appetite.

Prevention and control. The first step in prevention is good management. Calves should be kept in clean, well-bedded stalls when they are dropped during cold weather.

Antibiotics fed in small daily amounts, particularly aureomycin or terramycin, have been effective in the prevention of calf scours. A dose of 3 mg. of aureomycin per pound of body weight for the first three or four weeks and 1.5 mg. per pound of body weight from three weeks to three to six months of age is recommended as a preventive measure. Calves that have the disease should have concentrated doses administered under the direction of a veterinarian.

Ringworm. This is a contagious skin disease of cattle. Young stock is more susceptible to the disease than older cattle.

Symptoms. Oval scaly areas around the sides, neck, eyes, and back are signs of ringworms.

Prevention and control. Infected animals should be separated from the rest of the herd and treated by applying phemerol to the areas affected. Washing with soap and water and painting the infected area with a tincture of iodine will often control ringworms.

Leptospirosis. This is a disease threat to cattle that was first

FIGURE 165. *Typical ring worm infestation.* (*Baily photo. Courtesy* Successful Farming.)

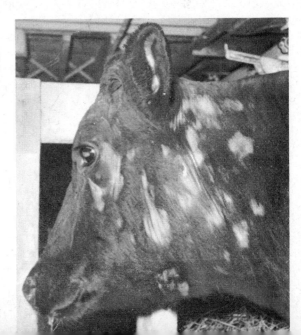

discovered in the United States in 1944. It is one of the most serious of diseases affecting cattle. The death rate averages about 5 per cent for those animals infected with the disease, but it may run up to 25 per cent for young stock. About 25 per cent of the cows infected abort.

Symptoms. Fever, depression, loss of appetite, and loss of production are common symptoms. The milk may take on a yellow color and become thickened in consistency. Sometimes it will be bloody. There may be blood in the urine.

Prevention and control. Great care should be taken to eliminate the possibility of bringing infected animals into the herd. Suspected animals should be given a blood test by a veterinarian. Antibiotics, especially penicillin, are effective in treating animals when treatment is started during the early stage of the disease. Vaccines have been perfected that are effective up to a year or more. In areas where the disease is common, the vaccination of the herd is recommended.

Pneumonia. This is a serious threat to young calves. The disease often occurs in calves weakened by scours. The highly infectious type may invade healthy calves and result in death unless treated in the early stage.

Symptoms. Labored, rapid breathing, coughing, high body temperature, nasal discharge, weakness, and loss of appetite are common symptoms.

Prevention and control. Clean well-bedded pens free from drafts and maintained at even temperatures will help prevent the disease from occurring. Infected calves may be successfully treated with the sulfa drugs and antibiotics administered under the supervision of a veterinarian.

Calf Diphtheria. This is an infectious disease which often attacks young suckling calves. Suckling calves housed inside are more susceptible than late calves on pasture. The disease may strike when the calf is only a few days old and if untreated will result in heavy losses.

Symptoms. The common symptoms are difficulty in breathing, eating, and drinking. Drooling and frequent attempts to swallow may be noted. Upon inspection of the mouth, yellowish patches of dead tissue may be found along the edges of the tongue adjacent to the molar teeth and in the throat.

Prevention and control. Regular cleaning and disinfecting of the housing quarters constitutes the best prevention. An infected animal should be isolated. Treatment consists of scraping away the dead tissue and painting the affected area with a tincture of iodine.

Navel Ill. This is an infection entering the body by way of the navel in newborn calves. The disease is usually associated with poor sanitation and is more prevalent among calves born in sheds and dry lots than calves dropped on pasture.

Symptoms. The common symptoms consist of fever, swollen joints, stiffness, lameness and inflammation of the navel.

Prevention and control. Sanitation and the immediate disinfecting of the navel at birth with tamed iodine or methylate are good preventive measures. Affected calves respond to sulfonamides and antibiotics administered under the direction of a veterinarian.

Lumpy Jaw and Wooden Tongue. These two diseases are an infection of the mouth, head, and tongue usually as the result of an injury.

Symptoms. The common symptoms are drooling, difficulty in eating, and a swelling of the tongue, jaw, and nasal bones. As the disease progresses there will be a discharge of pus accompanied by a foul odor.

Prevention and control. Prevention consists largely of sanitation and the elimination of feeds or objects that may result in mouth injuries. First stage cases may be successfully treated by painting the affected areas with a tincture of iodine. Advanced cases will need surgical treatment by a veterinarian.

Circling Disease or Listerellosis. This is a disease often affecting cattle. It more often occurs in the winter and spring. Affected animals seldom recover.

Symptoms. The disease affects the nervous system. The common symptoms are staggering, circling and other awkward movements. The course of the disease is short and death usually occurs within a few hours after the first symptoms are noted.

Prevention and control. Isolating infected animals and the administration of antibiotics are the only known means of prevention and control.

Johnes Disease. The disease usually occurs in cattle two to six years old. It is a chronic incurable infectious disease in some respects resembling tuberculosis. The disease is widespread and difficult to eradicate from a herd.

Symptoms. Rapid loss of flesh, intermittent profuse diarrhea and extreme emaciation or loss of flesh are the common symptoms. Appetite, attitude, and temperature remain normal.

Prevention and control. Manure is the primary source of contamination. The frequent removal of manure, sanitation, and the isolation of infected animals constitutes the best preventive measures. A test known as the Johnin test, similar to the tuberculin test, may be used for the detection of infected animals. Herd additions and all young animals should be tested in areas where the disease is prevalent.

Tetanus. This is a disease which often follows a wound infection and attacks the nervous system. It is more common in the South than in other areas. The disease may follow castration, dehorning, or other operations.

Symptoms. The first sign of the disease is usually a stiffness about the head. Difficulty in eating, chewing, and swallowing may be noted. The eyelid may be seen protruding over the surface of the eyeball. Later symptoms are violent spasm and lockjaw.

Prevention and control. The disease can usually be prevented by reducing the incidence of wounds and the prompt disinfecting of wounds with a tincture of iodine. Where the disease is prevalent yearly vaccination with toxoid will constitute an effective immunization.

Vibriosis. This disease may attack mature female cattle. It resembles brucellosis and can be differentiated only by a laboratory test.

Symptoms. Like brucellosis, abortions, low conception rate, retained placentas and weak calves are the common symptoms. Bulls may become affected and spread the disease to cows at the time of service.

Prevention and control. Sanitation and careful selection of disease-free bulls are the best preventive measures. The use of streptomycin under the direction of a veterinarian is a recommended treatment.

Blue Tongue. This is a comparatively new disease in the United States. Authorities must be notified immediately of its appearance. It is apparently transmitted through the bites of certain insects.

Symptoms. High fever, reddish blue color and ulceration of the mouth and tongue, foul odor, drooling, and a discharge from the eyes and nose accompany the disease. Other symptoms are swelling of the coronary band of the foot, lameness and rapid loss of condition.

Prevention and control. Vaccines are available for immunization and are recommended in areas where an outbreak of the disease occurs.

NONINFECTIOUS AILMENTS

X Disease. This is usually fatal. It has appeared in many areas. The cause of the disease, according to most authorities, is chlorinated naphthalene, which is present in some types of grease used on farm and feed-mixing machinery.

Symptoms. The disease has a rather slow course, often as long as three months, before death occurs. It generally begins with a loss of weight and watery discharges from the nose and eyes. Animals slobber at the mouth, and sores are often found in the mouth.

Prevention and control. No known treatment exists. Close inspection of animals for running eyes, slobbering, and sore mouths should be made before purchasing them. Keep the cattle away from any grease that may contain chlorinated naphthalene.

Bloat. This is a condition in which the rumen becomes filled with gas, which the animal is unable to expel. The condition may be caused by a growth or other obstruction in the esophagus, but is more often caused by feeds that ferment rapidly in the rumen, causing large amounts of gas to form. Feeding on legume pastures is one of the most common causes of bloat. Saponins (plant materials that produce a soapy lather) are thought to be the principal ingredient in legumes responsible for bloat.

Symptoms. The chief symptom is a great distention of the upper left side of the abdomen. Rapid breathing and uneasiness occur. If the animal is not relieved, it will stagger and fall. The pressure becomes great enough to prevent lung action, and suffocation is the final cause of death.

Prevention and control. If the gas pressure is not too great, walking the animal will induce belching and provide relief. Tying a rope or a stick in the mouth will often help. If immediate relief is required, a puncture of the rumen becomes necessary. The puncture should be made in the center of a triangle formed by the last rib, the hip bone, and the transverse processes of the backbone on the left side.

Pastures should not contain more than 50 per cent legumes. Giving the cattle a fill of dry hay before they go on pasture or making dry hay available to cattle on legume pastures will help to prevent bloat. Cattle that have water easily accessible are less apt to bloat than are those that drink only in the morning and in the evening when they come from the pasture.

Research work to find an effective method of controlling bloat is in progress. The most promising method at this time is the addition of water-dispersible oil to the drinking water and the sprinkling of crude soybean oil over fresh-cut alfalfa, to be consumed at the rate of one-quarter pound (about one-half pint) per animal daily. Antibiotics, (especially pencillin), administered at rather short intervals, have given some promise of bloat control.

Poisonous Plants. Many plants are poisonous to cattle. A large group of plants will develop what is known as *prussic acid*, especially under conditions that retard growth, such as extreme dry weather or frost. Among this group of plants are sudan grass and other plants belonging to the sorghum family. Johnson grass, chokecherry, black cherry, arrow grass, velvet grass, and Christmas-berry. Prussic acid is very poisonous and often proves fatal within a few minutes after consumption of the plant containing it.

Sweet clover hay or silage not properly preserved often proves toxic to cattle. Certain weeds, such as snakeroot, larkspur, loco-weed, water hemlock, milkweed, and cocklebur, will poison cattle if consumed in large enough quantities.

SUMMARY

The first steps in the prevention of disease and parasite infestation of the herd are sanitation, clean and well-drained lots, clean and regularly disinfected buildings, and precautions against the purchase of sick animals or animals that have been exposed to infections.

The most effective control measure for external parasites is the use of proper sprays and dusts. CO-Ral and Trolene are very effective for the control of grubs. Other external parasites may be controlled by spraying with malathion, lindane, CO-Ral, and other sprays. Applying Smear EQ 335 on all wounds will prevent screw-worm and blow-fly infestation. The common stomach worm may be controlled with phenothiazine.

Brucellosis is best eradicated by a testing and vaccinating program, whereas tuberculosis is controlled by testing and eliminating reactors. Blackleg and anthrax can both be prevented by vaccination.

Foot rot may be successfully treated by using disinfectants like lime, Lysol, or copper sulphate. If the case is advanced, a veterinarian should be called.

Mastitis can often be detected by the Brome-Thymol-Blue test. Antibiotics injected into the udder through the teat canal will help in many cases.

Warts may be treated with iodine followed by applications of castor oil. A special vaccine is also effective. Ringworms are best treated by applying phemerol or iodine to the affected area.

Bloat is caused by the formation of gas that the animal is unable to expel. It is often caused by certain feeds, such as young legume pasture. Treatment that will induce belching should be used. If such methods fail, making a slit through the animals's side into the rumen will allow the gas to escape.

Poisonous plants cause death losses among cattle. Knowing the poisonous plants and preventing their consumption is the only means of prevention.

QUESTIONS

1. List the steps of a good disease and parasite prevention program.
2. Give the control program for brucellosis and explain the circumstances under which you would recommend each control measure.
3. Name the common external parasites of cattle and give the methods of control of each.
4. How would you control the common stomach worm?
5. What diseases can be successfully controlled by vaccines?
6. Give the home treatments for warts and ringworms.
7. How would you control calf scours?

REFERENCES

Gunderson, Harold, *Controlling Livestock Pests*, Agricultural Extension Service, Pamphlet 132, 1953, Iowa State College, Ames, Iowa.

Raun, Earle S., *Controlling Insect Pests of Cattle*, Agricultural Extension Service, Pamphlet 181, 1952, Iowa State College, Ames, Iowa.

Snapp, Roscoe R., and A. L. Neuman, *Beef Cattle* (Fifth Edition), John Wiley and Sons, Inc., New York, 1960.

Buying and Selling Beef Cattle

The farmer, rancher, or feeder who has produced or fattened cattle for the market is very much concerned about the price he will receive for his product. The market price, at the time of sale, is largely responsible in determining whether the enterprise is profitable. Prices received for cattle and other farm products are largely determined by the old economic laws of *supply* and *demand*.

Supply. As it relates to cattle, supply may be defined as the amount or number of cattle available for sale at any given period. Several factors affect cattle numbers. Among these factors are: (1) feed cost and kind and amount of available feeds, and (2) price trends.

Feed cost and available feeds. Feed cost and amount available have an important bearing upon the numbers of cattle bought by feeders for the feed lot for fattening purposes. When the price of feed grains and supplements is high in relation to the price of fat cattle, there is a reluctance on the part of feeders to buy cattle. If this situation should continue for two or more years the numbers of finished cattle will very likely be sharply reduced. If the reverse is true—plenty of feed at low prices in relation to fat cattle prices—more cattle will find their way into the feed lots and within a period of two to three years the supply of finished beef will have increased.

The rancher or cattle producer is less affected by feed prices than the feeder. His feed consists largely of grass and his only market for that grass is through cattle. During periods of drought he may find it necessary to buy large amounts of hay and possibly some grain to maintain his herd. If the cost of these purchased feeds is excessive, he will be inclined to reduce the size of his breeding herd. Those breeding animals will go to market, which will result in a temporarily increased supply. Since the breeding herd is reduced there will be less cows to produce calves, which will result in a reduction in numbers a few years later.

Price and market trends. During periods of good cattle prices, farmers and ranchers are inclined to expand their operations to the very maximum permitted by the size of their farms or ranches and the equipment and labor available. It is also true that individuals who have never been in the beef cattle business are constantly attracted to the enterprise. All of which results in larger numbers of cattle. During times of unfavorable cattle prices the inexperienced producer is crowded out by economic necessity. Many of these who jumped in when things looked good become discouraged and drop out, while the old, established cattlemen tend to reduce the size of their operation. All of which means increased cattle numbers on the market during the liquidation period only to be followed by less numbers later because of fewer breeding animals. When the proportion of cows and heifers appearing in federally inspected slaughter houses rises considerably above recent levels, the numbers of all cattle on farms and ranches may be expected to turn down. It is also true that when the numbers of female animals appearing in the slaughter cattle market is less than the recent level, increased numbers of cattle will follow.

Studies reveal that when the numbers of cows and heifers on the slaughter cattle market equal 50 per cent or more of the total cattle, reduction of cattle numbers is probable. If the cow and heifer slaughter is less than 44 per cent of the total, increased numbers of cattle on farms and ranches will follow. If the cow and heifer slaughter remains between 44 and 50 per cent, the number of cattle on the farms and ranches may be expected to remain about the same.

Information on the number and kinds of cattle sold for slaughter during any given period is available through the United States Government marketing service, the State Department of Agriculture marketing services, the daily newspaper reports and other sources. The cow and heifer slaughter is probably one of the best keys to the future cattle supply situation.

Demand. This term may be defined as the desire of the consumer or buyer to purchase a given product and to possess the purchasing power to realize this desire. The most important factors that affect demand are: (1) purchasing power, (2) advertising and attractive packaging, (3) competition from similar products, (4) season and weather, (5) value of by-products, and (6) feeds available and their prices.

Purchasing power. The buying power of the consumer is probably the number one consideration in determining demand for cattle and other products. People like meat and especially beef. When their incomes will permit, they will buy beef. If employment is high and wages are good, the housewife will include more beef in her grocery order. It is also true that with high income the demand for high quality beef and the better cuts are more in demand. When people can afford them they prefer steaks and prime rib roast to the less desirable cuts. Under good economic conditions the spread between prime or choice beef and the lower grades becomes greater.

During periods of heavy unemployment and low incomes the housewife turns from the more expensive cuts and quality of beef to the less expensive cuts or to food which may substitute for beef. This results in a lowered demand for the product and a narrower spread between the grades.

Advertising and packaging. Attractive displays and advertising will do much to increase the desire of consumers to purchase a product. The best selling points of beef are its nutritional value and excellent flavor. Beef, when properly prepared, is a nearly perfect food. It furnishes proteins, vitamins, minerals, fats and carbohydrates, all of which are essential to good health.

Competition from other meat products. Pork, lamb, poultry, fish and eggs are all competitors of beef. If these substitutes are available at attractive prices, the consumer will buy less beef, thereby decreasing the over-all demand for cattle. The cattleman must pay close attention to the prices of these highly competitive products, as this knowledge will help him to determine the future price of cattle.

Season. People eat more meat during cold weather. Meat consumption of all kinds usually drops in summer, especially if the weather is unusually warm. This is probably due to a decrease in appetites and a reluctance on the part of the housewife to prepare hot meals.

Value of by-products. There are many important by-products resulting from the slaughter of beef cattle. Casings, tallow, hides, some drugs, livestock feed and many other products that are not consumed in the form of meat add to the value of the beef animal.

By-products make up 10 to 20 per cent of the total value of slaughter cattle. Prices received by meat packers for the various by-products influence the amount bid by the meat packing industry for live cattle.

Available feeds and feed prices. Available feeds and feed prices have more influence on the demand for feeder cattle by cattle feeders than upon the demand for slaughter cattle. In the fall, following a bountiful harvest of high quality feed grains, cattle feeders become interested in securing feeder cattle. When feed grains are plentiful and the price ratio of feed and beef is favorable to cattle feeding there will be increased buying of feeders for the feed yards. This increased demand will probably extend over several months. The first signs will appear in early August and continue well past the first of the year.

Occasionally the corn belt will experience a late spring, followed by a cold wet summer and early frost. Such a season will very likely result in immature, soft corn that will not keep longer than the first winter following harvest. Soft corn has little market value except as livestock feed. Under these conditions farmers scramble for cattle to fill the feed lot and consume the soft corn before spring and spoilage occur. This situation often results in a great demand for feeder cattle early in the fall with a considerable lessening of demand in late fall and winter. The producer of feeder cattle should carefully study the feed situation in the corn belt as a key to probable demand for his cattle.

The law of supply and demand, then, may be summarized as follows. When the supply is greater than the demand for a product the price of that product will probably decline. This is especially true of beef cattle since meat is a perishable product and cannot be kept fresh for very long periods. The consumer prefers fresh beef. When the packer's coolers are filled, he must move the meat before he can purchase more. To decrease his purchases he lowers his bid, or he may go out of the market altogether until such time as he has facilities available to handle more meat. It also follows that if the demand for beef or any product is greater than the available supply prices will strengthen.

Because beef is a highly perishable product and must move quickly, we have day by day and week by week fluctuations in the cattle market. The numbers of cattle offered for sale also vary from day to day and season to season. A steady demand plus a stable supply equal to that demand is the only way prices can be maintained at a constant figure. However, because of the large number of factors influencing both demand and supply, it is not probable that price fluctuations in beef prices will ever be eliminated.

FIGURE 166. *Prices of beef fluctuate depending upon the relationship of supply to demand. When the two are balanced, prices will be stable. If one becomes greater than the other we have price fluctuations. (Courtesy Swift and Co.)*

MARKETING FEEDER CATTLE

The producer of feeder cattle depends largely upon the farmers in the grain producing areas for his market. While the meat packing industry offers some competition, especially for cattle carrying a good grass finish, the larger percentage of feeder cattle are sold into the grain producing areas for further finishing before they go to the slaughter cattle market. It is equally true that farmers who make a business of fattening cattle are dependent upon producers for the cattle to fill their feed yards. The methods whereby the producer and feeder get together are important to both.

Direct Buying and Selling. In recent years there has been an increase in the number of sales made by ranchers directly to the feeder. Such sales are generally made on the ranch. Feeders make the purchases either by contract in advance of delivery date or take the cattle immediately after sale. Studies made by a committee representing eleven western states and reported in the Wyoming Agricultural Experiment Station Bulletin 317, showed that approximately 20 per cent of the cattle sales were made directly to farmers and ranchers.

Contract sales. When cattle are contracted for, an agreement is made between the buyer and the seller. The important provisions in contract sales are:

1. *Price.* This involves the amount paid down to seal the bargain and the balance paid at the time the cattle are removed from the farm or the ranch.

2. *Time and place of delivery.* If the ranch is equipped with scales and loading facilities, the cattle may be taken directly from the range by the buyer, otherwise the seller usually agrees to deliver the cattle to a certain weighing and loading point.

3. *The per cent of shrinkage to be allowed.* When cattle are moved for any distance or handled extensively, a certain amount of body weight is lost, largely the result of feed and water the animal eliminates that is not being replaced by regular feeding and watering. The amount of shrinkage depends upon the time in transit, weather conditions, the length of time cattle are allowed to rest, feed and drink before weighing and the age and weight of the cattle.

FIGURE 167. *The cattle have been moved from the range to a rural concentration point for weighing and sorting before shipment into the cornbelt fattening yards. (Courtesy Union Pacific Railroad.)*

No figure can be given that will be accurate enough to determine shrinkage in all cases, but 3 per cent is commonly used for feeder cattle.

For example, if a buyer purchased 600-pound cattle directly from a ranch where they had ample feed and water and they were weighed without undue handling or delay, he would be paying for approximately 18 pounds of feed and water contained in the digestive system of the animals. On the other hand, if these cattle were moved 50 or more miles and weighed without feed and water, these 18 pounds would probably have been lost in transit. Obviously the buyer could afford to pay more per pound for the cattle after shrinkage than before. If it is agreed to pay a certain price per hundred at the ranch, but it is necessary to transport the cattle several miles before weighing, a shrinkage percentage ranging from 1 to 5 per cent (depending upon the distance moved and time in transit) may be agreed upon. The practice of adding to or deducting from actual weight is referred to as *pencil shrinkage*, the exact amount depending upon the agreement between the buyer and the seller. According to the Wyoming Agricultural Experiment Station Bulletin 317, 39 per cent of all sales of cattle direct to farmers or ranchers were made with agreed shrinkage allowances and 61 per cent without any allowance for shrinkage.

Direct selling with immediate delivery. Immediate delivery or acceptance of the cattle involves no type of contract other than the price per hundredweight and allowable shrinkage. Settlement is made then and there and the ownership of the cattle is transferred from seller to buyer within a short time.

Advantage of Direct Selling. The chief advantage of direct dealing is that it eliminates the middleman and the profit he would necessarily have to make for handling the cattle. Contract sales are usually made for the following reasons: (1) it insures the buyer the cattle he wants when he wants them, (2) usually both buyer and seller feel they have made a good price bargain, (3) both know in advance what the price will be, and (4) both know when delivery will be made.

Selling Through a Dealer. Cattle dealers are individuals or companies that make a business of buying cattle for the feeders. The dealers either buy on a commission basis or depend for their profit on reselling the cattle at a higher figure than the cost. Sometimes packing companies purchase cattle for their customers at little or no profit as a service.   The packer thereby helps to promote cattle feeding in his area and increases the possibility of having a greater number of slaughter cattle available for purchase.   Many times small operators can get their cattle cheaper through a dealer than if they spent the time and money necessary to inspect and buy their own cattle.

Order buyers.   An order buyer is a cattle dealer who specializes in buying cattle of a particular age, weight, grade, and sex to meet the needs of his customers.   For example, a feeder may approach an order buyer and give him an order to buy 40 choice steer calves weighing about 400 pounds each.   The feeder designates the price he is willing to pay and the buyer tries to locate the cattle.   The order buyer then either charges a commission or a flat fee for his services.   Since order buyers make it their business to know the market conditions and where the cattle are he can very quickly inform the feeder of the prospects he has of filling his order.   Dealers purchase from 20 to nearly 60 per cent of the cattle from the eleven western states.

Auction Sales.   Auction sales are a common method of transferring cattle from producer to feeder.   Most auctions are private or company owned.   The selling service is paid for by a commission (which is usually paid by the seller) and is based on a percentage of the selling price.

FIGURE 168.   *The auction sale has become an important means for selling feeder cattle.*

Terminal Markets.   Large terminal feeder cattle markets are located in many western and midwestern cities.   Producers who sell through these markets consign them to a commission firm that will sell on a commission basis.   A terminal market usually consists of a stockyards company which furnishes yards, scales, loading and unloading facilities, and feed and water for the stock.   For this service, the stockyards company charges a fee.   The amount varies, but it usually ranges from 75 cents to $1.25 per head for yardage.

FIGURE 169.   *This load of feeder cattle have been shipped to a central market where they will be sold by a commission firm.*   (*Courtesy* Wallaces' Farmer and Iowa Homestead.)

Cattle are fed hay at the rate of about 10 pounds per head.   The hay constitutes an additional charge which is usually higher than the cost of hay on the farm.   However, the price includes cost of delivery and placing it in the mangers for the cattle.   If the cattle are shipped to a commission firm, selling experts will handle and dispose of the cattle for the owner.   They sort mixed grades into uniform lots and see that the cattle bring the best possible price obtainable at the time.   The cost of yardage, feed, insurance, and selling charges is deducted, and the balance is paid to the owner.   Cattle shipped to a central market must be consigned to a commission firm. The large central markets have several commission firms operating at each market giving the seller a choice as to the firm he desires to bill his stock to. The fee charged by commission firms vary from market to market and upon the number of cattle in the consignments. The range in price is from $1 per head for consignments of over 15 head to $1.50 for single animals or small lots.

Some of the large feeder cattle markets are the areas of Kansas City, Missouri; Sioux City, Iowa; Omaha, Nebraska; Denver, Colorado; San Antonio, Texas; Oklahoma City, Oklahoma; South St. Paul, Minnesota; Wichita, Kansas; and St. Louis, Missouri.

Selecting a Method of Marketing. The important factor in selecting the method of marketing is the determining of which method will bring the greatest net income. The highest price per hundredweight may not always result in the greatest net profit. If the market is located a great distance from where the cattle were produced, transportation cost and shrinkage will be high. The selling price will have to be proportionately higher to offset these factors. Also there are other costs, such as commissions, yardage, and so forth. The wise operator, in attempting to determine what his cattle will bring at home, will get market information from other prospective markets and estimate shrinkage and other costs before finally deciding upon the method of marketing he will use.

Season. The majority of feeder cattle are sold during September, October, and November—i.e., the fall months that correspond with the end of the grass season in the northern plains states. Producers generally desire to cut down on their herds and avoid the necessity of making arrangements for the increased feed supplies for wintering the extra cattle. Because of the heavy movement of feeder cattle in the fall, market prices tend to be somewhat lower than at other seasons. From the buyers' standpoint, therefore, fall is a good time to buy. From the producers' point of view, even though prices may be expected to become higher during the remainder of the year, most of them feel that the cost of additional feed, plus the danger of loss from storms or loss from overcrowding in shelters, is too great to compensate for the rise in price. However, when cheap feed and adequate protection are available, cattle carried over until spring often pay good dividends.

Information that is Helpful in Determining When to Sell. When to sell cattle is a question every producer is asking. No one can consistently predict the time when the market will be highest. However, a grasp of the following facts will be helpful.

1. *The total number of cattle.* Numbers of cattle as compared to normal will affect the markets. When cattle numbers are high, increased marketings will result and downward pressure on the market can be expected.

2. *Conditions in the grain area.* The corn belt farmer is the principal buyer of feeder cattle. The number he buys will depend upon his feed supply. If crop conditions are good, the producer can expect a heavy demand for feeders. The reverse is true if the crop outlook is unfavorable.

3. *Slaughter cattle prices.* When slaughter cattle prices are high in proportion to feed costs it indirectly affects the price of feeder cattle. Cattle feeders are inclined to buy more cattle and pay higher prices if the outlook for fat cattle is good. Also, the packers will furnish more competition for range cattle that are in good flesh.

4. *Grass condition on the range.* When the range areas are well supplied with moisture, there will be lots of feed. Ranchers are inclined to keep their cattle until late, putting on as much weight as possible before selling. Under good grazing conditions early fall feeder markets are usually high, followed by an exceptional slump with the first general snowfall, at which time feeders pour into the market.

If a severe drought should occur over a large area of the range country it will usually force large numbers of cattle to market unseasonally. Such a condition will usually cause a rather sharp drop in feeder cattle prices.

5. *Employment conditions.* Farmers and ranchers are dependent upon the consumer for his final market. What the average American eats and how much, are the factors that determine prices of farm products. Since the largest group of people are the laboring class, their wages and the number employed are important. When the number of unemployed increases, beef and all farm products can be expected to move downward in price.

Sources of market information. Current market information based on the conditions just listed may be obtained from agricultural colleges, state and federal market information services, newspapers, magazines, radio and television reports, and private outlook information services.

While no one can always predict when the market conditions will be best, a careful study of the available information should enable the cattle producer to have a good batting average, resulting in a more profitable beef business.

MARKETING SLAUGHTER CATTLE

Classes and Grades. The successful marketing of slaughter cattle is determined by feeding for the proper grade, methods of marketing, and the time the producer sells. Slaughter cattle are classified and graded according to sex, age, weight, and grade. The following table shows the commonly used system of classifying and grading.

TABLE 24
CLASSIFICATION AND GRADES OF SLAUGHTER CATTLE

Sex	Age	Weight	Grade
Vealers: Bulls Heifers	Less than 3 months	Light Medium Heavy	Prime, choice, good, standard, utility, cull
Calves: Bulls Heifers	3 to 8 months	Light Medium Heavy	Prime, choice, good, standard, utility, cull
Steers	Yearlings	Light Medium Heavy	Prime, choice, good, standard, utility, cutter, canner
	2 years or older	Light Medium Heavy	Prime, choice, good, standard, commercial, utility, cutter, canner
Heifers	Yearlings	Light Medium Heavy	Prime, choice, good, standard, utility, cutter, canner
	2 to 3 years old	Light Medium Heavy	Prime, choice, good, standard, utility, cutter, canner
Cows	More than 3 years	All weights	Choice, good, standard, commercial, utility, cutter, canner
Bulls	Yearlings	All weights	Choice, good, commercial, utility, cutter, canner
	2 years old and older	Light Medium Heavy	Choice, good, commercial, utility, cutter, canner
Stags	All ages	All weights	Choice, good, commercial, utility, cutter, canner

The higher grades consist of cattle well-developed in the areas of valuable cuts (back, loin and hindquarters) and uniformly covered with a high degree of finish. Choice and prime cattle usually are long-time grainfed cattle. They not only cut a high yielding carcass, but it is also one with a clear white firm fat that is well distributed around and through the muscle or lean meat. Young cattle (yearlings and two-year-olds) produce the more popular sized cuts and are more tender and flavorful than older cattle. In contrast to older and lower grade animals, young prime cattle usually are sold at premium prices. The carcass yield is important in determining grades. Young prime cattle will dress from 62 to 67 per cent; choice, from 60 to 64 per cent; good, from 58 to 60 per cent; standard, from 52 to 58 per cent; and cutters and canners will average around 42 per cent.

Prime. This grade is reserved for young cattle under approximately 36 months of age. They are of beef breeding, highly finished with a uniform covering of fat over the body. They must be well developed in the areas of valuable cuts (back loin and round), low set, compact, and short necked.

Choice. Choice cattle may be up to 42 months of age. They are mostly of beef breeding. They need not carry as high a degree of finish as prime cattle. The area of valuable cuts need not be as well developed as is required for prime cattle.

Good and standard. These grades consist of cattle that lack the well-developed confirmation and finish required for the choice and prime grades. The maximum age limit is approximately 48 months.

Commercial. The requirements for this grade are about the same as for the standard grade. There is no age limit and the grade is used mostly for cows, bulls, and stags.

Utility and cutter. Cattle in these grades are rangy, upstanding, angular, and thinly fleshed. The proportion of meat to bone is very small. They are usually narrow over the back and loin and light in the hindquarters.

Canners. Canners are usually old cattle that are extremely thin. The bony framework is very evident. The joints are large and the amount of meat is very low.

Score Card. Buyers and feeders with considerable experience can determine grades of cattle quite accurately on the hoof. For beginners, a study of the score card for fat cattle may be of some help in determining possible grade. The score card will help the inexperienced cattleman to properly evaluate the various parts of the animal. However, grading accuracy can be learned only by associating with cattle buyers who know grades. Anyone who plans to go into the cattle business might find it profitable to spend some time at a large central market and observe the experienced cattle buyers at work.

SCORE CARD FOR FAT BEEF CATTLE *

Scale of Points	Standard
A. GENERAL APPEARANCE—38 per cent	
1. Weight according to age, estimated ____ pounds; actual, ____ pounds	10
2. Form—broad, deep, low-set, smooth, compact, cylindrical, straight top and underline, stylish	10
3. Quality—loose, pliable skin of medium thickness, dense, clean, medium-sized bone; fine, soft hair	8
4. Condition—deep, even covering of firm, mellow, flesh, free from patches, ties, lumps, and rolls; full cod and flank, indicating finish	10
B. HEAD AND NECK—6 per cent	
5. Muzzle broad; mouth large; nostrils large and open	1
6. Eyes, large, clear, placid	1
7. Face short, jaws strong	1
8. Forehead broad, full; ears medium sized, fine texture	1
9. Neck short, thick, blending smoothly with shoulders; throat clean with light dewlap	2
C. FORE QUARTERS—8 per cent	
10. Shoulder vein, full	2
11. Shoulders smoothly covered, compact, snug, neat	3
12. Brisket trim, neat; breast wide and full	2
13. Legs wide apart, straight, short; arm full, shank fine	1
D. BODY—30 per cent	
14. Chest full, deep, wide; girth large; crops full	4
15. Ribs long, arched, thickly and smoothly fleshed	8
16. Back broad, straight, thickly and smoothly fleshed	8
17. Loin thick, broad, evenly covered	8
18. Flank full, even with underline	2
E. HINDQUARTERS—18 per cent	
19. Hips smooth, evenly covered	2
20. Rump long, wide, level; tail head smooth; pin bones wide apart, not prominent	5
21. Thighs deep, full	5
22. Twist deep, plump	5
23. Legs wide apart, straight, short; shanks fine, smooth	1
TOTAL	100

* Adapted from U.S.D.A. Score Card.

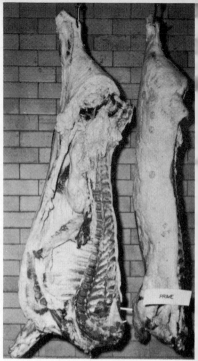

FIGURE 170. *This is a prime slaughter steer and the carcass from the same steer. Note the uniform covering of fat, the plump well-developed round, the width of loin, and general uniformity. (Courtesy Rath Packing Co.)*

Length of Feeding Period. The length of the feeding period will depend largely upon the grade of feeders the individual has on feed. High-grade slaughter animals are produced from well-bred feeder cattle and by long-time feeding. It is a mistake to feed

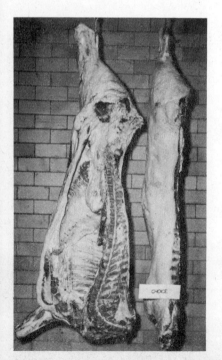

FIGURE 171. *This choice slaughter steer furnished a very desirable carcass. However, as compared to the prime carcass, it shows less finish, lacks the width and uniformity, and is not as well developed in the round as the prime carcass. (Courtesy Rath Packing Co.)*

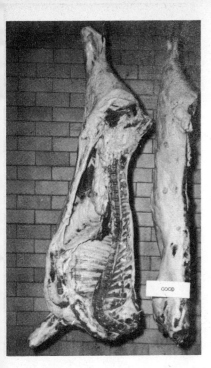

FIGURE 172. *This steer graded good. Although the carcass is quite desirable, it definitely lacks finish and proper development in the back, loin, and round. (Courtesy Rath Packing Co.)*

cattle beyond their grade. Low grade feeders tend to become bunchy and patchy with excess fat. Unless the finish is uniform, extra fat will not improve the grade. The ability to finish uniformly is a matter of breeding. It is essential that the grade of **feeders** purchased will correspond to the grade desired in the

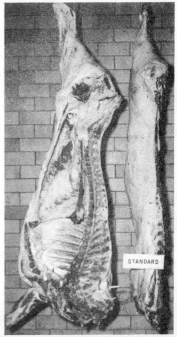

FIGURE 173. *This standard slaughter steer is too low in finish and too poorly developed in the regions of the valuable cuts for high-quality beef. (Courtesy Rath Packing Co.)*

273

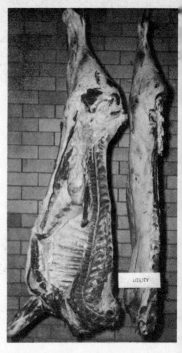

FIGURE 174. *This utility-grade slaughter steer would not provide tender highly palatable steaks. A few fair quality roasts may be provided from the loin and round. The rest of the carcass could best be utilized as boiling beef, hamburger, or processed meats. (Courtesy Rath Packing Co.)*

finished cattle. Common grade feeders cannot be expected to grade higher than *good* grade when finished, whereas *good to choice* grades should finish as *choice* and *prime* beef.

Types of Marketing Procedure. The cattle feeder may (1) sell cattle directly to the packer or a packer buyer who generally works on a salary paid by the packer he represents, or (2) ship to a central market and consign to a commission firm, or (3) sell to a private buyer who buys from the feeder and either sells directly to the packer or ships them to a central market.

Selling to the packer or packer buyer. Many cattle are trucked or shipped directly to the packer. Usually, on the day they arrive, they are weighed and paid for at the current price being paid for their grade. Most packing companies have buyers in the field who will bid on the cattle at the farm; such bids may be qualified by adding a shrinkage stipulation.

Selling on grade and yield. During recent years there has been some interest on the part of farmers to sell their cattle to the packers on what has become known as the *grade and yield.* Under this method of sale the live weight of the cattle has nothing to do with the price that is paid. After the cattle are slaughtered the pounds of meat and grade the cattle yield are the determining factors in establishing the price. For example, suppose a farmer sells a 1,000-

274

pound steer and the steer hangs up a 560-pound carcass of good beef.   Now, let us suppose that the value given to this grade of beef is $.50 per pound; then 560 pounds times $.50 equals $280.00 or the amount the farmer received.   This is equivalent to $.28 per pound of live weight.   Should the animal grade higher or lower than *good*, the price is adjusted upward or downward depending upon the grade.   If the dressing percentage is higher or lower than that given in the example (56%) then there will be more or less weight in the dressed carcass and the farmer will be paid accordingly.

Advantages of selling on grade and yield.   The advantages of

FIGURE 175.   (*upper*) *A load of choice slaughter cattle at a central market.   (Courtesy American Aberdeen-Angus Breeders Association.)   (lower) A load of prime Angus slaughter steers.   (Courtesy Rath Packing Co.)*

FIGURE 176. *A view of the stockyards at a large cattle market.* (*Courtesy Fred Fredrick.*)

selling on a grade and yield basis are: (1) The farmer who produced a quality product is paid accordingly. (2) Shrinkage does not have to be considered since shrinkage is due largely to the loss of feed and water in the digestive tract during transit. This would not be considered in the dressed carcass weight since it is waste material and not an edible part of the animal.

Selling through a commission firm. When slaughter cattle are shipped to a central market either by rail or truck they are billed to a commission firm. The process of yarding and marketing of fat cattle are essentially the same as that described for the marketing of feeder cattle—i.e., through a central market. The chief difference lies primarily in who buys the cattle. In the large central markets that deal essentially with slaughter cattle, the packer is the chief purchaser. There are several packing plants located near the stockyards at the central markets. They rely principally on the cattle shipped to that market for their supply. In addition to the packing plants located at the market, other plants may send buyers to purchase animals of a certain weight and grade for which they have a demand. These buyers are known as *order buyers.*

Occasionally cattle that have not been finished enough to make the grade they are capable of making, may be bought by feeders who will ship them on to their farms for further feeding. These

FIGURE 177. *A commission firm representative and a cattle buyer negotiating for a group of cattle at one of the large cattle markets.* (*Courtesy Fred Fredrick.*)

feeders usually believe that by putting more finish on the cattle, they will bring enough higher price to net them a profit.

There is also a class of buyers known as *speculators* who buy cattle for the purpose of holding them for a higher market. The speculator may feed the cattle to a higher finish or resell them in a few days depending upon which way he thinks he can profit most.

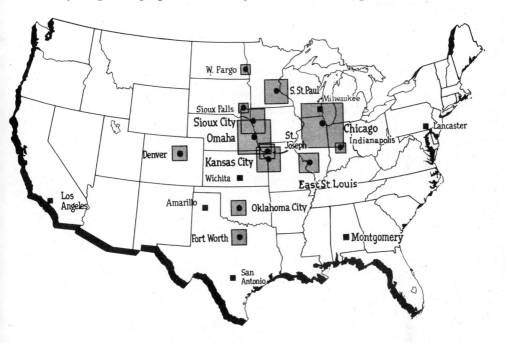

FIGURE 178. *The twenty leading markets are located in or near the heavy cattle-producing areas. In 1959, over 16 million cattle were received at 59 public markets. About 50 per cent of these cattle were received at the leading markets of Chicago, Omaha, Sioux City, South St. Paul, Kansas City, and St. Joseph. (Courtesy Swift and Company.)*

Selling to private buyers. Many communities have private stock buyers who buy cattle and other livestock and send them on to the packers. Such buyers offer an outlet for small lots of animals because they generally have yard facilities where they can bunch animals according to age, sex, and grade before shipping or trucking them on to market.

Cooperative Marketing. Various types of cooperative marketing facilities have developed during recent years. Cooperative commission companies have been the principal type of cooperative that has affected beef cattle marketing. The commission companies operate much like private concerns except that the profits are paid to the members in the form of patronage dividends.

DETERMINING WHEN TO SELL SLAUGHTER CATTLE

Seasonal Price Trends.   The marketing of slaughter cattle follows a rather definite seasonal pattern, if a period of years is used to determine the pattern.   However, so many factors may affect the marketing for any one year that the long-time trends cannot always be relied upon as a means of hitting the top market in any one given year.   However, for the cattleman who continues in the feeding business over a period of years, a study of these long-time trends may prove profitable.

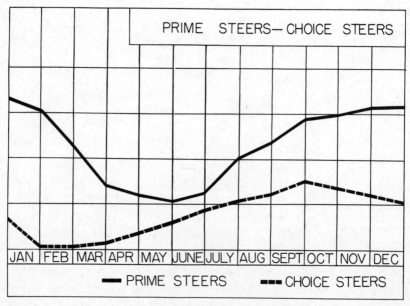

FIGURE 179.   *This chart shows the average seasonal price trend for slaughter cattle of higher quality.*

When to Sell Choice and Prime Steers.   Choice and prime steers will usually bring the most money during September, October, November, and January.   High quality cattle are usually lowest in the spring and increase from 10 to 20 per cent to the high point during the fall or early winter.

One desiring to market the higher grades of steers should buy choice steer calves or yearlings in the fall when the selection is good and finish them ready for market the following fall or early winter.

When to Sell Heifers. Heifers must be moved more quickly than steers because if they are kept long enough to develop cowlike conformation, they will be discounted. Heifer calves bought in the fall should be brought up to full feed as quickly as possible, finished for their grade, and sold during the late spring and early summer months. Yearling heifers should be turned as quickly as possible since many of them may have been bred before being purchased by the feeder.

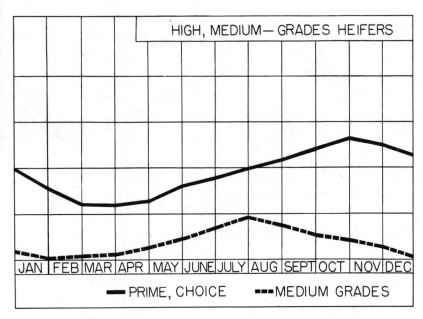

FIGURE 180. *This chart shows the average seasonal price trend for the high and medium grades of heifers.*

When to Sell Middle Grade Steers. May, June, and July are the months when the prices for middle grade steers (*high commercial to good*) are generally the best. These grades of cattle may be finished primarily on pasture and preserved roughages.

When to Sell Low Grade Cattle. The low grade cattle, culled beef cows, dairy cows, bulls, and poor quality steers will usually sell best during the spring months of April, May, and June. Most farmers hesitate to sell any kind of cattle that may be put out on grass at the beginning of the grass season. For this reason there are not many low grade cattle going to market in the spring. By early summer large numbers of southern grass fed cattle go to market, lowering the price for these kinds of cattle.

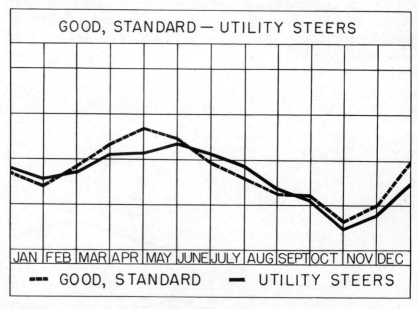

FIGURE 181. *The middle and low grades of slaughter steers usually bring the best price during the months of April, May, and June.*

Other Factors that Affect Cattle Prices. Like the marketing of feeder cattle, certain types of information (that may be secured from the same agencies previously listed under feeder cattle marketing) will help to determine when to sell slaughter cattle.

National income and employment. In the final analysis, the consumers determine the price of beef by the amount of money they are willing to spend for this product. When incomes and numbers of people employed are high, a larger amount of money will be spent for food. Such conditions contribute to strong beef prices.

A study of the following charts will show how closely the prices paid for beef on the hoof follows the prices the packer receives for the wholesale cuts of beef which he sells to the retailer or butcher

FIGURE 182. *This chart shows the comparative prices of live and dressed choice steers over a three-year period. (Courtesy Swift and Co.)*

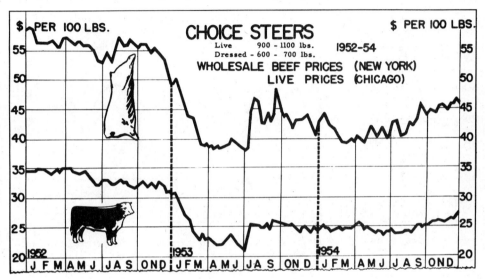

FIGURE 183. *This chart shows the comparative prices of live and dressed beef for grade good slaughter steers over a three-year period. (Courtesy Swift and Co.)*

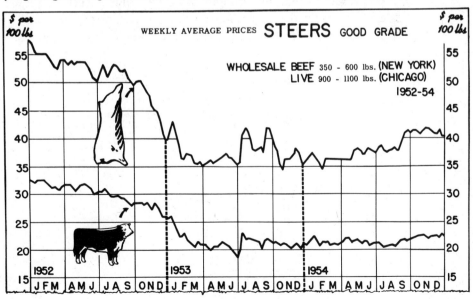

shops.   The local butcher depends upon the prices he can get from his customers to determine the amount he can afford to pay the packer for the wholesale cuts of beef.

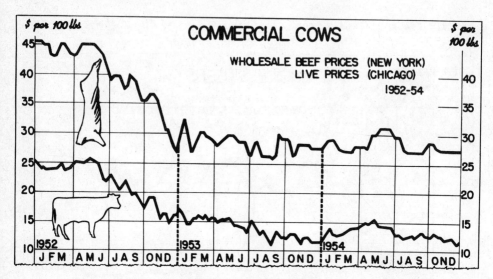

FIGURE 184.   *A comparison of the dressed and live prices of commercial grade cows over a three-year period.   (Courtesy Swift and Co.)*

Number of cattle fed.   The number of cattle in the feed lots is important in determining possible price and time to sell.   If the cattle numbers on feed are above normal, lower prices in general can be expected while short numbers are favorable to strong prices.

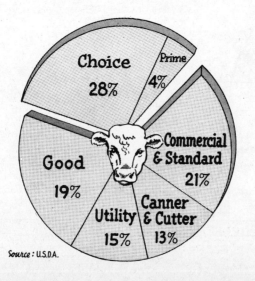

FIGURE 185. *Slaughter cattle production by grades. (Courtesy Swift and Company.)*

Feed situation. The amount and kind of feed available over the general cattle feeding areas are important considerations in selecting a time to sell. When the feed grain crops have been abundant and quality is good, the tendency is for long feeding periods. The peak marketing periods especially for the higher grades of cattle may be delayed, and the price drop may come later than usual. If the corn belt has a soft corn crop, there will be a rush for feeder cattle to consume the corn. Since soft corn will not keep when warm weather arrives, it is important to buy enough cattle to consume the feed quickly. Under such conditions the heavy movement of cattle will very likely be earlier than normal with a price break coming early.

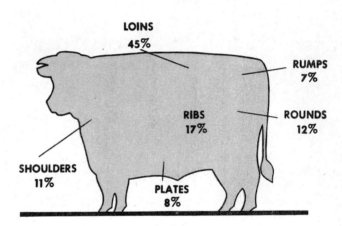

FIGURE 186. *The highest per cent of bruises occur in the regions of the most valuable cuts. (Courtesy Swift and Co.)*

LOSSES DUE TO DAMAGED CARCASSES

Losses running into the millions of dollars are sustained by the livestock industry as a result of damaged carcasses. Most of this damage could be prevented. Producers are not aware of the personal losses caused by bruises, because such injuries can only be determined after slaughter. Usually the producer has his check by the time the animal is slaughtered and thinks this loss is the packer's. However, packers have learned through experience the per cent of such losses, and these losses are reflected in the prices bid for live animals. Most bruised carcasses result from horn damage, careless handling, overcrowding, prodding with clubs, and

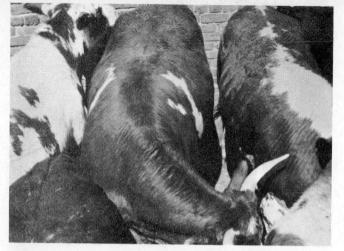

FIGURE 187. *Animals whether in the feed lot, loafing pen, or on the way to market suffer severe loss and damage when there is as few as one horned animal present. Horns should be removed while the animal is very young. (Courtesy Livestock Conservation, Inc.)*

FIGURE 188. *Feed lot obstacles are often the cause of bruises. (Courtesy Livestock Conservation, Inc.)*

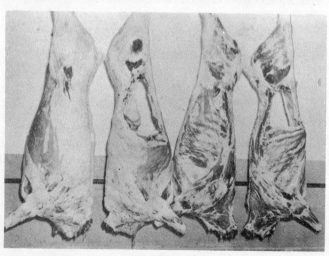

FIGURE 189. *Losses, such as these, cost the livestock industry millions of dollars each year. Most of this loss could be prevented by dehorning and more careful handling of livestock. (Courtesy Livestock Conservation, Inc.)*

284

feed lot obstacles. Bruised areas in the carcass must be trimmed out. The areas of the carcass removed cannot be sold for human consumption. It usually goes into the manufacture of livestock feed where it is worth less money. Most of the bruises occurring on beef animals are in the regions of the most valuable cuts, loins, rumps, rounds, and ribs.

BEEF FROM PRODUCER TO CONSUMER

Many consumers believe that the entire price they pay for a pound of steak or other beef cuts goes to the producer. Many farmers and ranchers do not fully appreciate that the consumer must pay more for a pound of beef than the price received by the producer.

FIGURE 190. *Two-thirds of the cattle are produced west of the Mississippi while two-thirds of the people of the United States live east of the Mississippi. (Courtesy Swift and Co.)*

Freight. A large percentage of the cattle for consumer consumption is produced on the western range and in the corn belt. A quick glance at the map of the United States will reveal that the range and much of the corn belt lie west of the Mississippi River.

Two-thirds of the population in the United States live east of this great river. All of which means that most of the cattle must be shipped hundreds of miles before they reach the consumer's table as beef. The cost of moving this beef as live animals to the packer and as beef to the consumer constitutes an additional increase in price.

Cattle Are Not All Steak. Cattle are not all steak. In fact, they are not all beef. The amount of edible meat produced by the average beef animal the packer receives is equal to only about 55 per cent of its live weight. The balance is by-products and waste.

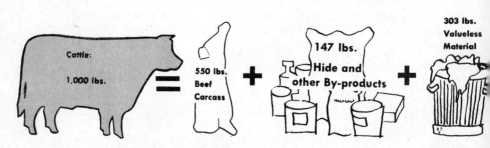

FIGURE 191. *Cattle are not all steak. This drawing shows the average amount of edible beef, by-products, and valueless material from a 1,000-pound steer. (Courtesy Swift and Co.)*

A 100 pounds of choice carcass of beef will produce approximately 17 pounds of higher quality steaks that come from the loin, 24 pounds of the round or slow-cooking steaks, 9 pounds of standing rib roast, 26 pounds of pot roasts and hamburger, 12 pounds of boiling and stew meat, 4 pounds of flank steak or stew, 4 pounds of shank stew and soup meat, and 4 pounds of suet. Some of the more undesirable cuts may have to be priced only slightly above the cost if they are to be sold. Therefore, the high quality cuts such as the steak and standing rib roasts will need to bring much higher prices to pay for the cost of processing and marketing.

Processing and Distributing Beef. Most of the beef animals produced by farmers and ranchers find their way into the packing plants. Here they are slaughtered and inspected by federal or state inspectors to determine their fitness for human consumption. The packer may sell the carcasses in halves (known as beef side) or cut the carcass into the wholesale cuts and sell them directly to the local retailer or to branch houses. Branch houses are selling agencies located in the larger towns and cities. They have refrigerating facilities, expert meat cutters, and handlers. The branch houses receive daily or weekly shipments of meat in refrigerated cars or trucks. The retailer goes to the branch houses and bargains for the sides of beef or wholesale cuts according to their local customer demand.

Thus, we see there is considerable handling of the beef animal from the time it leaves the farm or ranch until it becomes a part of a consumer's meal, all of which adds to the cost of the product.

FIGURE 192. *This photo shows the location of the wholesale cuts of beef and the average percentage of each. (Abernathy photo. Courtesy American Aberdeen-Angus Breeders Association.)*

SUMMARY

Prices received by farmers and ranchers for their beef animals are largely determined by supply and demand. When the supply is larger than the demand for any product, the price of that product goes down. It is also true that when the demand is greater than the supply, prices go up.

Feed cost and price trends largely influence supply while purchasing power, advertising and packaging, competition from other meat products, season, value of by-products, available feeds, and feed prices affect demand.

Feeder cattle may be marketed by direct selling either on contract for future delivery or immediate transfer from buyer to seller. Other methods of selling feeder cattle are through auctions, dealers, and central markets.

The shipping cost, shrinkage, and prices are important considerations in determining the methods of marketing.

Most feeder cattle are marketed in the fall which corresponds to the end of the grass season in much of the range area and the harvesting of crops in the corn belt.

Information that is helpful in deciding when to market feeder cattle consists of a knowledge of the numbers of cattle available at a given time, feed conditions, prices of slaughter cattle, and the employment situation. This information may be obtained from agricultural colleges, state and federal market information services, newspapers, magazines, radio and television reports, and private outlook information services.

Slaughter cattle are classified according to sex, age, weight, and grade. They may be sold directly to a packer or a packer buyer on a live weight or grade and yield basis. Other methods of selling are through a commission company at a central market or directly to a private buyer.

Seasonal price trends for the various grades, national income and employment conditions, available supply, and the feed situation constitute information helpful to the successful marketing of slaughter cattle.

Damage to valuable parts of the carcass resulting from unwise handling of the live animals costs the cattle industry thousands of dollars each year. Most of this loss could be averted.

Beef travels hundreds of miles from producer to consumer. Freight, processing, and retailing costs all add up to the consumer's paying considerably more for beef than the farmers receive for their products.

QUESTIONS

1. Explain what is meant by the law of supply and demand.
2. What are the factors that affect supply? Demand?
3. How do the numbers of female animals appearing in the slaughter cattle market give us a guide to future numbers of cattle that will be produced? Explain.

4. List the different methods by which feeder cattle may be marketed and describe each method.

5. What is meant by contract sales?

6. What is shrinkage? How does the shrinkage affect the prices received?

7. What are the important factors in selecting a method of marketing feeder cattle?

8. During what season are the majority of feeder cattle sold? Why?

9. What information is helpful in determining when to sell and how may it be secured?

10. What are the classes and grades of slaughter cattle?

11. How may slaughter cattle be marketed? Explain.

12. What information is needed to successfully market slaughter cattle?

13. Explain the price trends for different grades of cattle.

14. Discuss the losses due to damaged carcasses and how they may be averted.

15. Explain the steps that beef must take from producer to consumer.

16. What per cent of the live weight of the animal is edible meat? By-products? Waste?

17. What are the wholesale cuts of beef?

REFERENCES

Hamilton, Eugene, *Seasonal Market Variations and Their Importance to the Iowa Farmer*, Agricultural Experiment Station and Extension Service, Bulletin P 5, Iowa State College, Ames, Iowa.

Malone, Carl. C., *Making Your Farm Pay*, Iowa State College Press, Ames, Iowa, 1951.

Marketing Feeder Cattle and Sheep in the North Central Region, Agricultural Experiment Station, Bulletin 410, University of Nebraska, Lincoln, Nebraska.

Potter, E. L., *The Marketing of Oregon Livestock*, Agricultural Experiment Station, Bulletin 514, Oregon State College, Cornvallis, Oregon.

Stevens, I. M., R. T. Burdick, H. G. Mason, and H. P. Gazaway, *Marketing Western Feeder Cattle*, Agricultural Experiment Station, Bulletin 317, University of Wyoming, Laramie, Wyoming.

Reproduction, Inheritance, and Breeding
Systems in Beef Cattle

Much of the improvement in the conformation, type, and production of beef cattle has come about through the use of carefully planned breeding programs. Cattlemen have found that the pedigree and ancestry of an animal are very important in selecting breeding stock. Animals are usually selected according to the breeding program being followed. A cow or bull may fit in excellently with one breeding program and be a misfit in another. The breeding of livestock requires careful planning based upon basic principles of reproduction and inheritance.

We present in this chapter a brief explanation of (1) reproduction, (2) the reproductive organs of male and female cattle, (3) the laws of inheritance that affect reproduction, and (4) systems of breeding beef cattle.

REPRODUCTION

Reproduction is the process by which new individuals are produced in plant and animal life. The process begins when the female germ cell is fertilized by the male germ cell. The female cell is called the ovum, or egg, and the male cell is called the sperm. This fertilization process follows closely the breeding of the female by the male.

The egg or ovum contains the hereditary materials of the dam, and the sperm contains the materials of inheritance contributed by the sire. The contributions of the sire and dam, as far as inheritance is concerned, are equal. The fertilization of the egg, however, takes place within the body of the mother and the offspring is nourished and protected until birth by the mother.

Female Reproductive Organs.   As shown in Figure 194, the reproductive system of the cow consists of the ovaries, the oviducts, the uterus, the vagina, and the vulva.

Ovaries.   These two glandular organs are located in the sublumbar region and produce eggs.   Each ovary contains many follicles, in which the eggs are produced.   As the eggs mature, they are dropped into the oviduct.   The process is called ovulation and takes place during or shortly after the heat period.

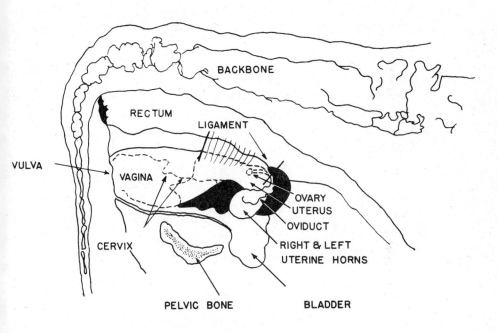

FIGURE 193. *The reproductive organs of the cow.* (*Drawing by Francis G. Telshaw.*)

Oviducts.   These tubes lead from the ovaries to the horns of the uterus.   The fertilization of the egg usually takes place near the upper end of the oviduct.

Uterus.   This is a hollow organ containing two horns, which are connected to the oviducts.   The fertilized egg moves from the oviduct into the uterus and becomes attached to the wall.   The fertilized egg develops in the uterus.

Cervix. This is the neck of the uterus and separates it from the vagina.

Vagina. This tube connects the vulva and the cervix.

Vulva. Both the urinary and reproductive organs of the female terminate in the vulva.

Male Reproductive Organs. The reproductive system of the male consists of (1) the testicles, (2) the sperm ducts, (3) the seminal vesicles, (4) the prostate, (5) the Cowper's glands, (6) the urethra, and (7) the penis.

Testicles. Sperm cells are produced in the two testicles, which are suspended in the scrotum.

Sperm ducts. These tubes connect the testicles with the urethra. Sperms pass through and may be stored at the upper end of these tubes.

Seminal vesicles. These glands open to the urethra and secrete a fluid.

Prostate. The prostate gland is located near the bladder and the urethra. It also produces a secretion that becomes a part of the seminal fluid.

Cowper's glands. These glands secrete a fluid that precedes the passage of the sperm cells down the urethra.

Urethra. This long tube extends from the bladder to the penis and carries both urine and semen.

Penis. This organ deposits the sperm cells within the female reproductive system.

Conception. Reproduction begins with the heat period in the female or the time when she will be receptive to the bull. As explained in Chapter 6, the heat period varies with individual animals but in cows usually occurs on an average of every 21 days. The first heat period usually occurs when heifers are about one year old. However, good feeding and good management hasten sexual maturity, whereas poor feeding and poor management tend to retard it. From 6 to 20 hours after the heat period, the female germ cell or egg is released from the ovaries. If the female is bred and a sperm (male germ cell) comes in contact with the egg, fertilization takes place and the female becomes pregnant. It takes from 4 to 9 hours for the sperms to travel from the vagina to the oviducts, where fertilization normally takes place. Therefore, a cow bred near the end of her heat period is more apt to conceive than if she is bred early in the heat period.

Fetal Membranes. These consist of three separate structures which surround the fetus or unborn calf. One contains many blood vessels which lead into the placenta and unite the mother and her unborn calf. Another membrane contains a fluid which protects the fetus from injury. At the time of birth of the calf this fluid is released and lubricates the vagina, making it easier for the cow to expel the calf. The third membrane serves as a holding place for urine from the fetal bladder. The three membranes constitute the afterbirth.

Placenta. This vascular structure is that portion of the fetal membrane that unites the mother and the fetus. The blood vessels of each lie close together, which permits the interchange of food materials through their extremely thin walls.

Navel Cord. This cord connects the fetus and the placenta and serves as a passage way for blood to and from the fetus. It also contains a tube leading from the fetal bladder.

Multiple Pregnancy. Cattle usually produce one offspring at a time. However, twins, triplets, and once in a great while, quadruplets occur. Multiple pregnancy is due to more than one female egg cell being fertilized or to a division of the fertilized cell. When a bull and a heifer calf are born twins, the heifer is often sterile. It is believed that this sterility is due to the hormones of the male being dominant to those of the female, which results in imperfect development of the female reproductive system. When this occurs, the heifer is known as a *free-martin.*

LAWS OF INHERITANCE

Chromosomes and Genes. Each germ cell (sperm and egg) contains chromosomes, which in turn carry genes. The genes determine the characteristics to be found in the individual. The color of hair, the conformation of the body, the type, and other characteristics are determined by the genes in the germ cells.

The number of chromosomes in the nucleus of a cell is constant. They occur in pairs. In swine there are 19 pairs, whereas in sheep, cattle, and horses there are 30 pairs. The members of each pair carry genes that affect the same characters of physical conditions of the animal, but they may not affect them in the same way. For example, in breeding cattle, factor A on chromosome 1 may affect color of hair by producing red color, whereas factor A on the other chromosome of the pair may produce white color. If neither color is dominant, the progeny will possess both colors. Red, however, is usually dominant over white.

Dominant and Recessive Characters. When a pure polled bull is mated to a horned cow, the offspring is polled. Certain characteristics are dominant, whereas others are recessive. When dominant and recessive characters are brought together, the progeny will possess the dominant characteristics, but will produce in the next generation some animals that will show the dominant characters whereas others will possess the appearance of the recessive.

Black color in cattle is dominant to red. When an Angus cow is mated to a Hereford bull, the calf produced will be black with a white face. Darker colors are usually dominant to lighter colors. The red in Red Poll cattle is dominant to the fawn in Jersey and Guernsey breeds.

When a polled beef animal such as the Angus is mated to a horned animal such as the Hereford, the first generation or first cross will be polled. However, the crossbred offspring will carry the recessive factor for horns and if a crossbred from this parentage is mated to a similar crossbred, an average of one animal in four will be horned. The following diagram will show how the ratio develops.

D   D = Angus (pure polled which is dominant)

⋈

d   d = Hereford (pure horned which is recessive)

First generation, Dd—All animals polled, but carry the recessive factor for horns.

D   d = Male of first generation cross of Angus with Hereford

⋈

D   d = Female of first generation cross of Angus with Hereford

Ratio of offspring:

    1 DD—Pure polled
    2 Dd—Polled but carry recessive factor for horns
    1 dd—Horned (no factor for polled present)

Chromosome Segregation. The normal reproductive cell in cattle contains 30 pairs of chromosomes, yet when two cells are brought together there still are only 30 pairs of chromosomes. This is because a reduction process takes place in the process of germ cell production, reducing the number of chromosomes by one-half. Only one chromosome of each pair is included in the germ cell. The bringing together of the two germ cells through fertilization restores the normal number of chromosomes.

Hybrid. An animal is considered a hybrid for any one character when it possesses one dominant and one recessive gene. When a hybrid is crossed with another hybrid, about 75 per cent of the progeny show dominance, but only about one-third of the group are pure dominant for the one character. The other two-thirds have the appearance of the dominant but are hybrid. Those that show recessive characteristics are pure recessives.

Hybrid Vigor. The crossing of two superior animals of different breeds usually results in increased growth rate, increased efficiency of fertilization, improvement of body conformation, and increased production. Crossbreeding in hogs, cattle, sheep, and chickens has been done for years, but not until rather recently has it been done on a truly scientific basis.

Heterosis, or hybrid vigor, is the term applied to the increase in vigor and performance resulting when two animals of unrelated breeds are crossed. The increase in vigor may be explained in the terms of the genetic principles discussed in previous paragraphs. The genes producing vigor are dominant to those producing a lack of vigor. By crossing breeds, a larger number of dominant genes are brought together in the progeny than are involved in breeding animals of the same breed. It is thought, also, that animals of the various breeds differ in the factors that contribute toward vigor. A greater number of vigor-producing factors are involved when breeds are crossed than when matings are made of animals of the same breed. The problem in crossbreeding is to determine the crosses that produce the most hybrid vigor.

Grading and Purebreeding. These two systems of breeding involve the mating of animals of the same breed. Upgrading involves the mating of purebred sires and grade females of the same breed. Purebreeding involves the mating of purebred sires and purebred females of the same breed. In both cases animals to be mated are selected according to their body conformation, vigor, growth rate, and production record. Purebred animals are quite *homozygous,* i.e., the genes are usually alike. The hybrid condition referred to previously does not exist. The animals tend to reproduce progeny like themselves—like begets like.

Inbreeding and Linebreeding. Inbreeding is the mating of closely related animals, such as (1) brother to sister, (2) son to dam, and (3) sire to daughter. It is done primarily to intensify the degree of homozygosity, or the similarity of the genes in the reproductive cells of the animals. The crossing of inbred lines of two or more breeds results in hybrid vigor greater than that produced when two or more noninbred lines are crossed.

Linebreeding is similar to inbreeding but involves the breeding of animals less closely related. The mating of cousins and of grandsire with granddaughters are examples of linebreeding. It is done to conserve and perpetuate the good traits of certain outstanding breeding animals. It tends to produce an homozygous genetic condition.

INHERITANCE OF REPRODUCTION FACTORS

A large number of factors affect growth and conformation, and we assume that they are inherited. We have only circumstantial evidence on which to base most of our assumptions. We have completed only limited scientific research in this field. It is very difficult to separate the various gene factors, and it is difficult also to separate the inherited from the environmental factors.

The following factors are assumed to be related to production and growth ability: (1) size of animal, (2) capacity for feed, (3) udder size, (4) udder quality, (5) persistency of production, (6) type, (7) vigor and vitality, and (8) disease resistance.

Proven Sires. Proven sires are bulls that have proven their ability to sire fast growing calves of desirable conformation. It is believed that most of the characteristics possessed by beef cattle are inherited. Feeding and environmental conditions may limit the animal's ability to develop to the full extent of its inherited ability. Therefore when comparing the calves sired by one bull with those sired by another, it is important that the feeding and management conditions be the same for both groups.

SYSTEMS OF BREEDING BEEF CATTLE

The same methods are used in breeding beef cattle that are used in breeding other types of livestock, but there is more uniformity in the methods used. Breeding programs for swine and poultry quite often include two or more breeds. Most breeding programs involving beef cattle are one-breed programs. The most common breeding programs in beef production are (1) upgrading, (2) outcrossing, (3) linebreeding, (4) crossbreeding, and (5) inbreeding.

Upgrading. Some breeders develop their herds by using purebred bulls of a certain breed on their original cow herds. By successive use of purebred bulls, a high-grade herd can be produced. An example of this method is the one used by a farmer who had a mixed herd of cows that he bred to a Shorthorn bull. The heifers produced carried 50 per cent Shorthorn breeding and 50 per cent of the breeding of the dams. These heifers were mated to another Shorthorn bull. The heifers produced from these matings carried 75 per cent Shorthorn breeding. The continued use of purebred Shorthorn bulls on the heifers from previous matings resulted in a herd of cattle that closely resembled purebred Shorthorn cattle. The fifth generation of cattle resulting from the use of this system carried 96.875 per cent of the inheritance of the Shorthorn breed.

The greatest increases in production by use of this method occur as a result of the first and second crosses. Many excellent herds have been developed by its use.

However, regardless of the number of generations during which this system is used, it is never possible to register these cattle as purebred Shorthorns, although some associations permit the registration of grades that meet certain minimum standards.

Outcrossing. This system is used by many cattlemen. It involves the mating of bulls from distantly related strains with cow herds of the same breed. Followers of this system believe that outcrossing brings together the factors in the two strains that produce high production and the desired type. The success of the system depends upon how well the two strains "nick" or complement each other when they are brought together. This system may be used either with grades or purebreds of the same breed.

Linebreeding. A considerable amount of linebreeding has been done by breeders of purebreds. This system involves the mating of two individuals that trace in pedigree to the same individual or line of breeding. Many of our top producers have been developed in this way.

The system makes it possible to concentrate on the qualities of a superior ancestor. Linebreeding reduces the number of common ancestors but avoids the decrease in fertility and vigor associated with inbreeding.

The following example of a pedigree shows how line breeding may be accomplished. In this case we will assume that Black Night 467345 was an outstanding sire and that the breeder desired to maintain a large percentage of his breeding in the herd. A study of the pedigree will reveal that this bull appears four times, twice on the sire's side and twice on the dam's side of the pedigree.

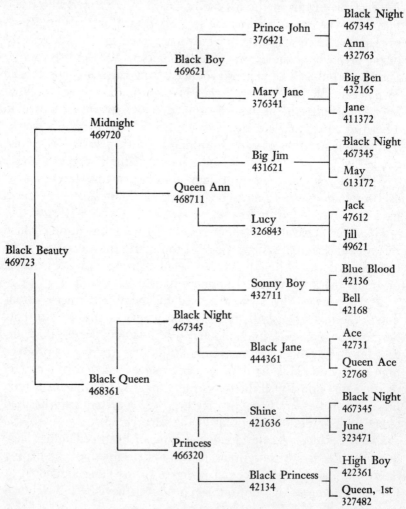

Black Beauty 469723 would be referred to as line bred to Black Night 467345. Black Beauty carries 43¾ per cent relationship to Black Night. You will note that Black Night was mated to his own **granddaughter** to produce **Black Queen**, the dam of **Black Beauty.**

It is not always necessary to have inbreeding as close as this to carry out a linebreeding program.

If the breeder is to improve his herd by linebreeding to a certain animal or strain, it is important that the valued ancestor be a highly desirable animal from a conformation and growth standpoint and that he has transmitted these qualities to his offspring.

Crossbreeding. This system, as described before, involves the mating of individuals of separate breeds. The animals may be either grade or purebred. The system has been used by cattlemen in upgrading their herds and by farmers who wished to produce feeder cattle from dairy cows. In the latter case, beef bulls are mated to dairy cows. Heifers resulting from this cross are inferior to their dams in milk and butterfat production and consequently are usually sold as beef animals.

Some cattlemen have crossed breeds in an effort to produce cows that produce faster growing calves than the original cows.

Brahman crosses. The Brahman breed has proven itself in the South as a beef breed well adapted to a hot climate and poor pastures. Brahmans have been crossed on nearly all of the European breeds, Angus, Shorthorn, Hereford, and Charolais. Several new breeds have been developed from these crosses (see Chapter 2).

FIGURE 194. *It takes a combination of a well-bred dam and a well-bred sire to produce a calf like this. (Courtesy American Aberdeen-Angus Breeders Association.)*

Many cattlemen in the South follow a regular crossbreeding program in which the Brahman breed is used as one of the parents.

Disadvantages of crossbreeding. The cattleman who crossbreeds his herd loses control of the factors that affect uniformity of size, color, and other characteristics of calves. It is not possible to make selections of crossbred animals on the basis of outward appearance or production records because they are hybrid and the productiveness of the progeny is difficult to predict.

Most of the value of crossbreeding is in the first cross. Later crosses add less to the productiveness of the herd. It is not always desirable for the average cattleman in the north central region to develop a herd of crossbred cattle, although it may be very desirable to consider crossbreeding in the southern states.

Inbreeding. This system involves the mating of closely related animals, such as sire and daughter or brother and sister. The system can be used successfully only by breeders with superior stock who wish to test the genetic makeup of certain animals, or who wish to develop a uniform herd around the characteristics of a few individuals. It is not a system that can be used effectively by the inexperienced cattleman or by the average farmer.

In general, inbreeding beyond 25 per cent is not recommended. Decreased fertility, a lack of vigor, and poor growth rate often result, and the conformation of the offspring is sometimes less desirable.

SUMMARY

The reproductive cell of the female is called an ovum. The male cell is called a sperm. Each parent contributes equally in the reproduction process.

The ovum is produced in a follicle of the ovary and is dropped into the oviduct. It is fertilized by a sperm in the upper end of the oviduct. From there it moves to the uterus, where it becomes attached to the wall and develops.

The sperm is produced in the testicle of the bull and moves through the sperm ducts to the urethra and the penis. The seminal vesicles, prostate, and Cowper's glands add secretions to the seminal fluid.

The heat period occurs about every 21 days and ovulation takes place from 6 to 20 hours after the cow has gone out of heat. Breeding should be timed so that the sperm is in the oviduct when the ovulation occurs. It normally takes the sperm from 4 to 9 hours to reach the ovum after being introduced.

The chromosomes in the reproductive cells carry genes, which determine the characteristics to be transmitted to the progeny. Chromosomes occur in pairs, with one of each pair in the male cell uniting with one of each pair in the female cell to produce the new individual. The reproductive cell in cattle has 30 pairs. The two members of a pair of chromosomes carry genes that affect the same physical conditions of the animal, but they may not affect them in the same way.

Some factors of inheritance are dominant, whereas others are recessive. A hybrid condition exists when the germ cell has one dominant and one recessive gene. When hybrids are crossed, 25 per cent of the progeny are pure dominant, 50 per cent are hybrid, and 25 per cent are recessive. Only the pure recessives will show the characteristics of the recessive.

Dark colors are usually dominant to lighter colors in cattle and the factor producing polled cattle is dominant to the factor producing horns.

The crossing of two superior animals of different breeds usually results in increased growth rate, increased efficiency of fertilization, improvement in body conformation, and increased production. These increases are usually referred to as hybrid vigor or heterosis. A proven sire is one that has offspring with fast growing ability and desirable body conformation. A minimum of five offspring comparisons are necessary in proving a bull.

It is assumed that the following factors are related to production ability: size of animal, capacity for feed, udder size, udder quality, growth, persistency of production, type, vigor, and disease resistance. Research is not available to prove the relationships of all these factors to production.

The most common systems in breeding beef cattle are upgrading and outcrossing. Upgrading involves the successive use of purebred bulls of a certain breed on the original cow herd and on its progeny. Outcrossing necessitates the mating of bulls from distantly related strains with cow herds of the same breed. The success of the system depends upon how well the two strains "nick" when they are brought together.

Linebreeding is practiced by breeders of purebred beef cattle who wish to concentrate on the qualities of superior ancestors. It involves the mating of cousins or more distantly related animals.

The crossing of beef breeds has not been a common practice. It is difficult to predict the type and production of the progeny of crossbred animals. The crossing of the European breeds has been successfully practiced in the South to produce beef animals with heat and insect resistance. The greatest increase in production in cross-breeding results from the first cross. Further crosses have little influence upon production increases.

The mating of closely related animals, such as brother and sister, is called inbreeding. Successful use of this system is dependent upon the excellence of the genetic makeup of the animals involved and the experience of the breeder. Inbreeding beyond 25 per cent is likely to cause decreased fertility, a lack of vigor, and poor production.

QUESTIONS

1. What are the reproductive organs of the female and what are their functions?
2. Name the reproductive organs of the male and indicate the function of each.
3. What is meant by ovulation and when does it take place in relation to the heat period?
4. What is the difference between a gene and a chromosome?
5. Explain the process of making and of fertilizing germ cells.
6. What contributes most to inheritance, the ovum or the sperm? Explain.
7. Explain the functions of the fetal membranes.
8. Explain the functions of the navel cord.
9. When should a cow be bred to best assure conception?
10. Explain hybrid vigor in terms of the gene composition of the chromosomes.
11. What differences exist in the gene composition of the chromosomes in purebred and crossbred animals?
12. Explain the difference between inbreeding and linebreeding.
13. What qualifications must be met in proving a beef bull?
14. What inherited factors are assumed to be related to the reproductive ability of a beef animal?
15. Which is the better system of breeding beef animals, upgrading or outcrossing? Explain.
16. Under what conditions should crossbreeding be done in beef breeding?

REFERENCES

Anderson, Arthur L., *Introductory Animal Husbandry*, The Macmillan Company, New York, 1952.

Ensminger, M. E., *Animal Science*, The Interstate Printers and Publishers, Danville, Illinois, 1959.

Lush, Jay L., *Animal Breeding Plans*, Collegiate Press, Inc., Ames, Iowa, 1937.

Rice, V. A., F. N. Andrews, and E. J. Warwick, *Better Livestock Breeding*, McGraw-Hill Book Company, Inc., New York, 1953.

Winters, Lawrence, *An Introduction to Breeding Farm Animals*, John Wiley and Sons, Inc., New York, 1942.

Fitting and Showing Beef Cattle

Large numbers of future farmers, 4-H members, breeders and cattle feeders show beef animals at the hundreds of county, state, national and international shows and fairs each year.

Why Show Beef Cattle.   Beef cattle shows offer an opportunity for breeders, feeders, and junior livestock producers to show to the public the fruits of their labors.   There probably is no better place for a prospective breeder to learn what is considered most desirable in type of cattle grown than at the beef cattle shows.   For those who have established a well-bred herd, shows offer an opportunity to advertise their herds and aids them in making profitable sales. Many farmers and ranchers who own commercial herds attend livestock shows for the purpose of locating and buying breeding animals with which to improve their herds.   Other breeders are constantly on the lookout for high quality purebreds to replace breeding animals they can no longer use.

Most exhibitors strive to win the blue and championship ribbons. Not all can be first but they can exhibit animals that are a credit to them and the cattle industry.

Animals in the show herd should be selected carefully for type and conformation and then fitted and groomed to show to the best possible advantage.

The factors to consider in selecting animals has been discussed in previous chapters.   In this chapter we will deal with the art of fitting and showing beef animals.

SHOW CLASSIFICATIONS

Beginners quite often have difficulty understanding the show classifications.   Beef animals, like other types of livestock, are classified according to age and sex.   The classes may vary somewhat from show to show, so it is important that the premium list be carefully read.   In general, beef cattle shows consist of individual classes for breeding males and females of different ages and group classes consisting of either females, males, or mixed sex groups.   In addition to the breeding classes, many shows have fat or market classes for both individual and groups of animals.   Market classes are judged largely upon their market qualities.   Following are classes commonly found in the premium lists of the larger shows held during the fall months of August, September, and October.

Individual Classes for Breeding Animals.   Under this designation the following classes are shown.

Two-year-olds.   This class is usually provided for both heifers and bulls.   To be eligible to show in the two-year-old class, an animal must have been calved between May 1 and August 31 two years prior to the show.   For example, if the show was held in September of 1955, animals eligible to show will have been born during the indicated months in 1953.

Senior yearlings.   Senior yearling bulls and heifers are those

FIGURE 195.   *American Aberdeen-Angus being shown in an outdoor show ring at Lexington, Kentucky.   (Courtesy American Aberdeen-Angus Breeders Association.)*

calved between September 1 and December 31 two years prior to the year in which the show is held.

Junior yearlings.   Junior yearling bulls and heifers are those calved between January 1 and April 30 one year prior to the year in which the show is held.

Summer yearlings.   Summer yearlings are animals calved between May 1 and August 31 one year prior to the year in which the show is held.

Senior bulls and heifer calves.   Senior calves are those calved between September 1 and December 31 one year prior to the year in which the show is held.

Junior bull and heifer calves.   Junior calves are those calved between January 1 and April 30 of the same year in which the show is held.

Other individual classes.   Other classes may provide for the showing of three- and four-year-old animals or those more than four years old, sometimes referred to as *aged bulls or cows.*

Group Classes.   This is another classification and following are the classes shown.

Get of sire.   Get of sire usually consists of four animals any age all by one sire, both sexes represented and all owned by the exhibitor.

Junior get of sire.   A junior get of sire often consists of three animals, both sexes represented from either the junior, senior, or both calf classes.

Other group classes.   Other groups sometimes listed include (1) a pair of yearling bulls or heifers and (2) a pair of bull or heifer calves from the individual classes.

FIGURE 196. *A Shorthorn get of sire group in the show ring.* (*Courtesy* Wallaces' Farmer and Iowa Homestead.)

Market Classes. Fat or market classes vary considerably with different shows. Some prefer to classify them according to age while others classify according to weight. Groups may consist of two, three, five or a carload or truckload which may vary from 10 to 20 animals depending upon the show. In some shows only steers are eligible to show in the fat or market classes while others make no distinction between heifers and steers. One desiring to show at any of the fat cattle shows should familiarize himself with the classes provided.

FITTING ANIMALS FOR SHOW

Breeding beef animals are generally put into a high degree of flesh before showing. While the excessive finish is undesirable for the best reproduction performance, it does tend to bring out the qualities of the animal. Many show animals especially bulls and open heifers have to be gradually reduced in flesh after the show before they are ready for breeding purposes.

It is especially important that animals exhibited in the fat classes carry a high degree of finish if they are to compete successfully.

The show herd should be selected early. It takes time to put on the finish required. Many animals fail to win the higher awards simply because they have not been properly fitted for the show.

Starting Show Animals on Feed. There is not much difference in the methods used for starting show animals on feed than that described for starting fattening cattle. Animals that have not had grain in their ration may be started on one pound per day for the first three days. The amount should be increased at the rate of a quarter to half a pound daily until the cattle are on full feed about a month later. At the beginning they may be given a full feed of hay. Grass hay is preferred by many fitters as it has less laxative effects than the legumes. How long the cattle are permitted a full feed of hay will depend upon how well they are finishing out for the show. If the gains are too slow, more grain will be consumed if the hay is limited to from 3 to 5 pounds daily. In the case of market animals it is necessary to limit the amount of hay in order to reduce the size of the paunch and eliminate the wasty middle that develops when animals consume large quantities of roughages.

Variety of Feed and Balanced Rations are Essential. There is less danger of animals that have been heavily fed over a long period

of time going off feed or becoming "stale" if the ration consists of a
variety of feeds.   It is also essential that the ration be well balanced.
Cattle on a well-balanced ration not only gain faster, but they are
healthier and will exhibit the sleek hair coat and general alertness
characteristic of good healthy animals.

Cattlemen vary considerably in the kind of fitting rations they
prefer.   Following are some rations used for fitting show cattle.

1. Rolled barley   20 lbs.
   Rolled oats   20 lbs.
   Ground corn   20 lbs.
   Rolled wheat   10 lbs.
   Wheat bran   10 lbs.
   Dried molasses beet pulp   10 lbs.
   Linseed oil meal   8 lbs.
   Soybean oil meal   2 lbs.

2. Rolled barley   14 lbs.
   Crimped oats   25 lbs.
   Cracked corn   40 lbs.
   Wheat bran   10 lbs.
   Linseed pellets   7 lbs.
   Alfalfa pellets   4 lbs.

3. Ground corn   50 lbs.
   Ground barley   40 lbs.
   Cottonseed meal   2 lbs.
   Soybean meal   3 lbs.
   Linseed meal   5 lbs.

4. Ground sorghum grain   50 lbs.
   Ground barley   30 lbs.
   Ground wheat   12 lbs.
   40% protein supplement   8 lbs.

5. Ground corn & cob meal   60 lbs.
   Ground barley   30 lbs.
   40% protein supplement   10 lbs.

6. Ground corn   70 lbs.
   Ground oats   20 lbs.
   40% protein supplement   10 lbs.

7. Ground corn   40 lbs.
   Ground oats   20 lbs.
   Ground barley   20 lbs.
   45-50% dry molasses feed   10 lbs.
   35% protein supplement   10 lbs.

8. Ground wheat   20 lbs.
   Ground sorghum grain   40 lbs.
   Ground corn   20 lbs.
   Ground barley   10 lbs.
   40% protein supplement   10 lbs.

NOTE: Cattle should be given free access to a mineral mixture consisting of equal parts of mineralized
salt and bone meal.

FIGURE 197. *A carload of fat cattle on exhibit.* (*Courtesy American Hereford Association.*)

Some breeders prefer cooked barley for fitting rations. Cooked barley is a highly palatable feed and some believe it produces a more mellow finish. Cooked barley may be prepared by adding 2 to 3 gallons of water to each 8 to 10 pounds of barley and cooking the material until the kernels are soft. Eight to ten pounds of cooked barley may be added to any one of the rations listed.

The inexperienced fitter may have more success with the bulky type rations such as No. 5. Gains will probably be less rapid but there is not as much danger of the cattle going off feed.

TRAINING AND GROOMING THE ANIMAL TO SHOW

An animal that has been properly selected and fitted to the correct degree of condition must be properly prepared for the show if it is to stand up well under competition. The good showman is able to handle the animal in such a way as to emphasize the strong points and to some extent cover up the weaknesses of his exhibit. Under no circumstances should a showman resort to unfair or unscrupulous practices to win. Such practices cause him to lose the respect and confidence of his competitors and all livestock men. It is also poor sportsmanship and very little personal satisfaction is gained by winning unfairly. However, there is no wrong in the proper training and the exterior grooming of an animal to make it look its best on show day. Poorly groomed and trained animals may make such a poor appearance that animals with less desirable type characteristics, but well shown and groomed, will be placed further ahead.

Training. It takes considerable time and patience to properly train an animal. The training should start several months ahead of the show date. The first step is to teach the animal not to be afraid of people. This may be accomplished by petting, brushing, and gentle handling. Next teach the animal to stand tied. A good

FIGURE 198. *Proper training is essential if an animal is to show to the best advantage.* (*Courtesy Sunbeam Corporation.*)

strong rope halter may be used for this purpose. Care should be taken not to let it become entangled in the tie rope and become injured in any way. After the animal has become used to the halter and to being tied, the next step is lessons in leading. Under no circumstances should it ever be allowed to break loose and get away from the handler.   If this happens it will continue to try to get away and the period required to teach it to lead will be considerably increased.   An animal too large to hold should be tied behind a tractor or some vehicle until it has thoroughly learned that any attempt to break loose is useless.   After hand leading starts the operator should always walk on the left side of the animal with the halter strap coiled in his right hand.   The handler should walk forward not backward, as the dairymen prefer to do.   For early training a rope halter may be used but the animal should become accustomed to a leather show halter well in advance of the fair.

After the animal has been broken to lead, the next step is to train the animal to stand properly.   A beef animal will strike its best pose when all four feet are placed squarely under it, the head held on a level with the back and the back straight.   While posing the showman should stand facing the animal, holding the halter strap in his left hand.   A stick about four feet long with a small nail driven in the end is useful in getting the hind feet into proper position; the showman's foot is best for obtaining correct placement of the front feet.   For the best effect the front feet should be on ground slightly

FIGURE 199.   *This animal presents a pleasing appearance from a side view. Note the feet squarely placed, straight top line, and proper position of the head. (Courtesy American Aberdeen-Angus Breeders Association.)*

higher than that for the hind feet. If the animal tends to stand sway-backed, it can be induced to bring the back up on a straight line by pinching it on the rump about midway back from the hips. Should the animal stand hunched up, the back may be brought down to a straight line by pinching the animal about the middle of the back.

FIGURE 200. *This animal is standing in the proper position to show advantageously from a front view. (Courtesy American Aberdeen-Angus Breeders Association.)*

FIGURE 201. *An excellent position to give good view from the rear of the well-proportioned Angus. (Courtesy American Aberdeen-Angus Breeders Association.)*

FIGURE 202. *An attractive show halter improves the show ring appearance of any beef animal. (Courtesy American Aberdeen-Angus Breeders Association.)*

Trimming the Feet. The feet should be trimmed regularly if the animal is to stand and walk properly. It is a good idea to examine the feet of the animal periodically and trim them if necessary. The feet of show animals should be trimmed the last time at least a month before the show date to avoid lameness and to give the animals an opportunity to adjust to changes in the length and evenness of the hoof. On young animals the hoof may be trimmed by using pruning shears or a hand chisel.

It is possible to shorten the hoof by cutting the edges with nippers or by cutting the tip of the toe with a hammer and chisel as the animal is standing on a solid wooden base. Care should be taken that the foot is not injured. Avoid cutting deeply, which may result in bleeding. The sole of the foot should be pared down with a chisel, hoof knife, or a rasp so that the animal will stand squarely on the feet. Usually a little more of the sole is taken off the inside of the toe than on the outside.

Trimming the outside toes closely may help to correct the condition that exists when the hocks are too close together. Long toes may cause the animal to appear sickle-hocked.

The hoofs of show cattle should be scraped until smooth before the show. A piece of broken glass works well for this purpose. They should be further smoothed up by using steel wool or 2/0 emery cloth. Just prior to the show a good polishing with a mix-

◄A

C
▼

▲
B

FIGURE 203. A. *Using a specially designed hoof trimmer to cut away the large portion of the hoof to be removed. (Courtesy Kents Feeds.)*
B. *An ordinary wood chisel may be used. (Courtesy Kents Feeds.)*
C. *Rasping the hoof to smooth it after using hoof trimmer or chisel. (Courtesy Iowa State University.)*
D. *Cutting away the dew claws. (Courtesy Sunbeam Corporation.)*

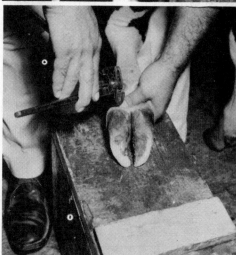

▲
D

ture of olive oil and pumice stone or Tripoli will improve their appearance.

Horn Training and Polishing. A well-polished pair of properly trained horns adds much to the appearance of the horned breeds of beef cattle. Quality and refinement are expressed in a good set of horns, whereas coarseness is expressed by poorly trained horns.

Considerable difference exists between the horned breeds as to what is desired in the way the horn curves. For example, horns of the Herefords curve downward, whereas the Shorthorn's horns should curve slightly forward and inward. To get the proper downward curve commercial horn weights, which are obtainable in different sizes, may be fastened to the end of the horns. Commercial trainers may also be purchased. They are designed to fasten on the ends of both horns and by regulating the tension the horns may be pulled inward if desired. The horns must be trained as they grow. Therefore, when about 2 to 3 inches long, the training of the horns should begin if they are not developing the desired curves. Prior to the show date the horns should be scraped and polished. For this purpose the same materials described for polishing the hoofs may be used.

Grooming. The daily brushing of show animals will remove the dirt, stimulate circulation in the hide, thus keeping it soft and pliable, and bring out the natural oils in the hair, giving the animal a sleek shiny hair coat. Short-haired animals should be brushed with the lay of the hair while long-haired animals should first be brushed with the lay of the hair and then upward in the opposite direction to make it loose and fluffy. A currycomb need be used only for the removal of dirt particles which will not come out by brushing. Care should be taken when using the currycomb not to scratch or injure the hide.

Blanketing the last few weeks before the show will help to keep the animal clean, keep the flies off, and put the hair in a glossy condition. Regular blankets that may be purchased commercially look nice and add to the appearance of the show herd while at the show. For home use they may be made from burlap or similar materials.

Washing. Frequent washing will remove dirt particles that will not come out by brushing, help to produce a heavy growth of loose fluffy hair and keep the skin in a mellow and healthy condition. Animals being fitted for show should be washed weekly for at least a month before the show date. In preparing an animal for washing first brush it vigorously, removing all loose dirt particles and loose hair. It is best to use reasonably warm water and a good lather-forming soap for washing. Some herdsmen prefer a pine tar soap while others use a mixture of liquid soap and powdered soap. A good lather should be thoroughly worked into the hair coat and then all traces of soap washed away with clean water. Care should be taken not to get water in the ears, eyes, nostrils, and mouth.

Final Preparations for the Show. Grooming should be done in such a way as will best emphasize the qualities desirable in beef type and to de-emphasize any defects in body conformation that may

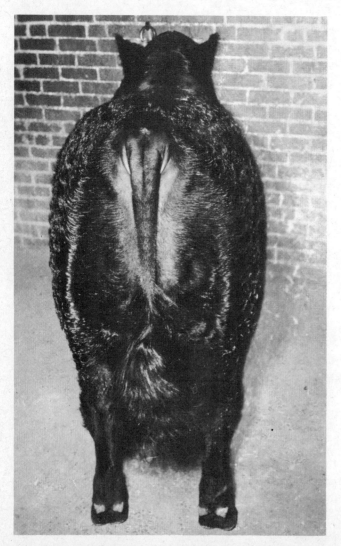

FIGURE 204. *The hind quarters and tail properly groomed to show width and depth of hind quarters. (Courtesy Sunbeam Corporation.)*

exist.   The skillful showman will groom his animal in such a way
that the animal will appear uniform in width, straight in its top and
under lines, and wide, deep and beefy.   He will accomplish this
largely by the way he brushes and curls the hair coat.

Curling the hair.   Cattle with long fluffy hair, such as the Hereford, Shorthorn, and Galloway, are often shown with the hair
curled in long parallel lines starting at the hindquarters and extend-

FIGURE 205.   *(top) Lining
the hind quarter of an
Angus. (bottom) Brush-
ing up the hair to form
the curl.   (Courtesy Sunbeam Corporation.)*

ing the full length of the animal.   The short-haired breeds are either brushed down smoothly or curled in the regions of the neck, the fore part of the shoulders, and the thighs.

Animals that are to be curled in preparation for showing should first be thoroughly cleaned by brushing and washing.   This should be done in time for them to dry before the curling procedure starts. About an hour before the show, thoroughly wet the animal with a solution made by adding one tablespoon of creosote dip to each gal-

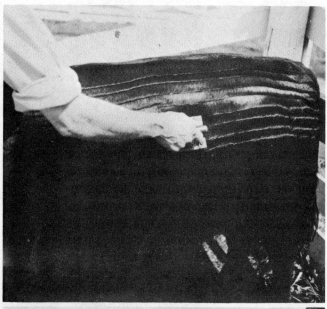

FIGURE 206.   (*top*) *Lining the entire side of the animal.   (bottom) Using an electrically operated brush to form the curl.   (Courtesy Sunbeam Corporation.)*

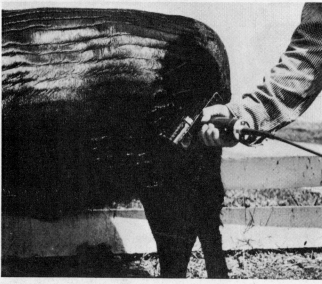

lon of water.   The solution may be applied by dipping a brush in the solution and sprinkling the animal.   After wetting, brush the hair smoothly against the animal in the direction that the hair naturally lies.   Then part the hair on a line running along the center of the back from neck to tail.   Comb the hair outward at right angles from the parting line to the extreme edge of the flat portions of the back to a point where the back starts to curve downward.   From a point directly below where the tail joins the body, downward to the twist, make a line and brush the hair sidewise.   This serves to emphasize both width of back and fullness of the hindquarters. Using a regular "liner" or an ordinary currycomb with the alternate rows of teeth pounded flat, mark off parallel lines along the entire body or along that portion that is to be curled.   Just as soon as the lines have been made, start brushing the hair upward using a stiff hand brush or an electrically operated brush.   Continue brushing until the hair is dry.   The experienced showman will fluff the hair more in hollows and low places to fill them out and make the animal appear uniform in its lines and covering.

Some showmen, especially Hereford men, prefer the wavy curl rather than the straight parallel curl.   This is accomplished by using the back side of a round currycomb and making the lines by drawing the comb downward in short wavy lines and then brushing them upward as described for the parallel curl.

If the hair should appear too dry or dead it may be livened up by rubbing lightly with a woolen or flannel cloth that has been dampened with a mixture consisting of equal parts of glycerine, rubbing alcohol and sweet oil.   It should be remembered that the animal should not enter the show ring wet or greasy in appearance.

A study of an international champion shown in Figure 207 reveals that all of the head except the ears (A) has been clipped, which is commonly done on polled breeds and sometimes on animals of the horned breeds that have been dehorned.   Long shaggy hair on the ears should be evened up but not necessarily clipped close.   The hair on the crest (B) is brushed to its apex on bulls and usually parted on females.

Part the hair over the shoulders (C) and brush out both ways from the center line.   The rump, loin, and back (D) can be dressed several ways, using the one that does most for the animal.   However, parting and brushing out, as already described, is usually best.

The hair on the back of the quarter (E) is brushed out from the tail to give width.   The hair on the sides of the hindquarters and the shoulders (I) should be lined and brushed upward or the entire side lined and brushed upward.   The tail (F) should be clipped above the switch and the switch (G) fluffed out.   The hair on the lower inside of the quarter (H) should be brushed up.

Another type of hair grooming is exhibited by the excellent Shorthorn shown in Figure 208.   The hair on the back has been parted and brushed up.   The hair on the hindquarters has been parted under the tail and brushed out while all the rest of the hair has been brushed upward without curling.

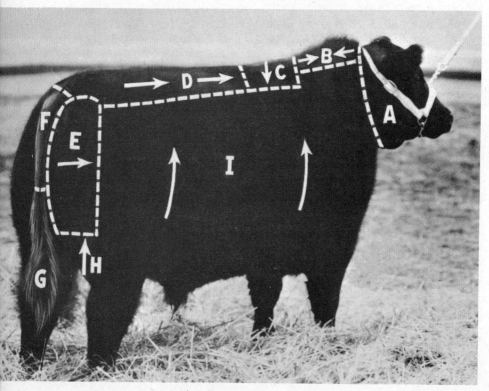

FIGURE 207.   *This photo shows how to brush the hair to show the animal to the best advantage.   (Courtesy Sunbeam Corporation.)*

Clipping.   As previously stated, it is common practice to clip the head on all polled breeds.   While no definite rule applies, it is common practice to clip from a point just back of the jawbone and about a half inch behind the ears.   The hair on the nose and the eyelashes is not clipped. Angus breeders seldom clip the ears. Other breeders of polled cattle often clip the outside of the ears leaving the inside untrimmed.

FIGURE 208. *This type of hair style is often used on Shorthorn cattle. (Courtesy American Shorthorn Breeders Association.)*

Breeders of horned breeds, unless they have been dehorned, do not often clip the head.

If the head is to be clipped it should be done a week before the show. The hair should have time to lose its stubby appearance before the show date.

It is common practice to clip the tails of all breeds of cattle. The tail should be clipped above the switch at a point where the fullness of the twist begins to taper off. The tail should be clipped to the tailhead and gradually blended so as not to leave roughness or ridges.

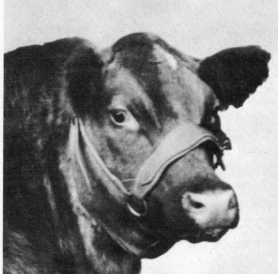

FIGURE 209. *Three breeds of beef cattle with heads clipped prior to showing: (top) an Angus, (center) a Shorthorn, and (bottom) a Hereford. (Courtesy Sunbeam Corporation.)*

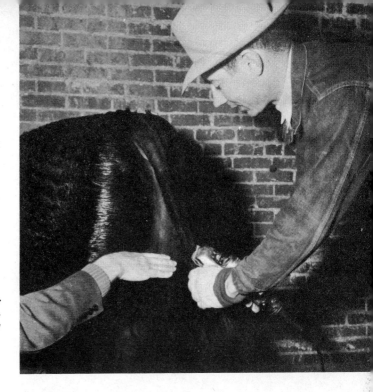

Fluffing out the switch. The tail switch, if properly fluffed out, will make the animal appear deeper and fuller in the twist. There are two common ways of accomplishing this. One is to hold the tail near the place where the long hairs forming the switch start and with the other hand comb the hairs upward and outward all around the tail. The second method is to wet the switch the night before the show and braid it into a large number of small braids (the more the better) and shortly before showtime comb out the braids.

Health Certificates. All show animals involved in interstate shipment are required to have a health certificate. Most fairs require health certificates as a prerequisite to unloading or within a very short time after the animals have been unloaded. The health certificate must be signed by a licensed veterinarian. Most cattle shows require that the certificate specify that within thirty days prior to entry and within ninety days prior to the date of the show the veterinarian has examined and found the animals that are to be exhibited free of brucellosis, tuberculosis, and other contagious types of infections.

Management at the Fair. As has already been stated, the principal reason breeders exhibit animals at the fairs is to advertise their herds.   This can best be done by keeping the animals well groomed and the stalls neat and clean.

Many fairs and shows regulate the size and kind of signs that may be used for advertising.   However, it is only good judgment to make use of the most attractive signs that may be used under the rules of the show.

Animals should be exercised each day.   During the warm seasons this may best be accomplished in late evening or early morning.

Sportsmanship.   In every show there must be a winner and a loser.   Good sportsmanship is essential.   Seldom has any judge ever placed a class of animals to the satisfaction of all concerned.   However, little is gained and much is lost by loud complaining over the placement of any class.   The poor loser or the bragging winner soon loses the respect of his fellow cattlemen.   It should always be remembered that cattlemen will support and give their competitors much help and assistance if they have their respect.

SUMMARY

The principal reason for showing cattle is to exhibit and advertise the herd.   Cattle for show purposes should be carefully selected as there is little gained from showing poor animals.   Not all can be winners but most cattlemen can show animals that are a credit to themselves and to the cattle industry.

Shows have various classifications based upon age and sex of the animals.   A prospective showman should secure a premium list and study the various classes at the shows where he intends to exhibit animals.

Proper fitting of animals is important for successfully competing in the shows.   The show herd should be selected early enough to permit proper fitting.   A large number of fitting rations have been used successfully.   It is important that the ration be well balanced and contain variety.

Proper training of the animals is essential if the animals are to be strong competitors.   This requires a great deal of work and patience on the part of the showman.   The animal should be easy to handle and trained to stand properly if it is to show its conformation to the best possible advantage.

Trimming of the feet will assist the animal in walking and standing properly.   The hoofs should be smoothed up by scraping and polishing.

The horns of the horned breeds should be properly trained according to what is considered desirable for the breed.   Horn weights and trainers may be used for this purpose.   Like the hoofs the horns should be smoothed and polished.

Grooming consists of brushing, washing, and curling the hair coat to the best possible advantage.   Clipping the head is usually practiced on the polled breeds and clipping the tail above the switch is common in all breeds.

Animals should be kept well groomed while at the fairs and the stalls should be kept clean.   Attractive signs allowed within the rules of the show will help to advertise the herd.

Good sportsmanship is essential.   Not all can be winners.

Health certificates are a prerequisite for exhibiting animals at most shows.   They must be signed by a licensed veterinarian.

QUESTIONS

1. How far in advance of the show date should the herd be selected? Why?
2. Explain the steps necessary to properly train the animal for show.
3. Explain how show animals should be started on feed.
4. Give several good fitting rations.
5. Explain the methods of trimming the feet.
6. How would you properly train horns?
7. What are the different methods of curling the hair for show purposes?
8. Explain the procedure in curling the hair.
9. Explain the procedure for clipping the head and tail.
10. How may the switch be fluffed out?

REFERENCES

Ensminger, M. E., *Beef Cattle Husbandry*, The Interstate Printers and Publishers, Danville, Illinois, 1952.

Snapp, Roscoe R., and A. L. Neuman, *Beef Cattle* (Fifth Edition), John Wiley and Sons, Inc., New York, 1960.

INDEX

INDEX

A

Aberdeen-Angus:
  crossbred:
    with Brahmans, 39-40
    with Herefords, 44-45
    with Shorthorns and Herefords, 45
  described, 23-24
  registration as purebreds, 51-52
  score card, 64-65
Abnormalities, 72-74
Abomasum, 90
Acreage control, 50
Additives, feed for cattle, 187-189
Advertising and packaging, 260
Age classifications, 77
Agriculture, Department of:
  control of screw worm, 232-233
  national beef breeding program, 71-72
  progeny tests, 69
Alfalfa, dehydrated meal, 181
American Brangus Breeders Association, 39-40
American desert region, 3
Amino acids, 92-93
Anaplasmosis, 241-242
Angus cattle (*See* Aberdeen-Angus cattle)
Animal fats, as feed, 179
Animal proteins, 98, 182
Anthrax, 245
Antibiotics:
  in feeding, 96
  for feeder cattle, 189
  for replacement heifers, 161-162
  for suckling calves, 159-160
Appalachian and Great Lakes region, 4
Arid lands, 3
  as grazing areas, 8-9
Associations, breed, 22-23
Auction sales, 17-18, 50, 265
Aureomycin, in creep ration, 159-160

B

Bacterial action in the rumen, 89, 90-91, 173
Bakewell, Robert, 20
Balanced ration, 98-99
Bang's disease, 242-244
Barley, as grain for feeder cattle, 178
Barrow, Richard, 35
Beef:
  per capita consumption, 1
  high quality, 11
  prices, 1, 18
Beef breeds (*See* Breeds)
Beef cattle:
  deformities, 72-74
  digestive system, 88-91
  edible meat, 286
  fitting and showing, 304-324
  nutrient requirements for, 99-102
  reproductive systems, 290-293
Beef cattle production:
  breed selection, 20-46, 49-51 (*See also* Breeds)
  breeding herd program, 112-139 (*See also* Breeding herd)
  classes of, 8-14
    combining two or more enterprises, 14
  disease prevention and control, 242-255
  feeder cattle program, 83-86 (*See also* Feeder cattle)
  losses from damaged carcasses, 283-285
  national beef breeding program, 71-72
  parasite prevention and control, 231-242
  planning program 15-18
    available feeds, 15-16, 49-50
    buildings and equipment, 16-17, 208-229
    capital requirements, 17, 50
    market conditions, 17-18, 50

Bulls:
  breeding of purebred, 13-14
  defined, 78
  as feeder cattle, 81
  feeding young bulls, 162-163
  mating:
    age at breeding, 134
    length of time with herd, 135
  progeny testing, 68-69
  proven sires, 69, 296
    national beef breeding program, 71-72
Burdizzo, 152
Buttram, Frank, 39
By-products, 286
  value of, 260-261

C

Calf scours, 250-251
Calves:
  Aberdeen-Angus, 23
  aiming toward 100 per cent crop, 70
  antibiotics in feeding, 96
  birth weight and growth rate, 68
  building needs, 17
  calf pens, 144
    sanitation, 144
  castration, 152-153
  creep-feeding, 157-160
    advantages, 158
    antibiotics, 159-160
    feeds, 158-159
    forages, 159
    preparations of grain, 160
    rations, 160
    starting calves to eat, 158
  defined, 77
  dehorning, 145-149
  delivery of, 136-137
  digestive processes, 91
  diphtheria, 252-253
  feeder cattle, 8
  feeding and management of, 141-164
  feeding replacement heifers, 161-163
  hand feeding, 94
  marking, 153-157
  navel ill, 253
  newborn, care of, 141-144
    quarters for, 143
  principal income source, 50
  progeny testing, 68-69
  putting market finish on, 199
    starting in feeding, 197
  slip, 153
  source of profit in breeding herd, 112
  weaning weight and milking ability

Calves (*Cont.*):
    of dams, 69-70
    young bulls, feeding, 162-163
Capital needs:
  in establishing breeding herd, 50-51
  in grass land, 10
  planning beef program, 17
  in purebred beef cattle production, 14
Carbohydrates, 92
  fiber and nitrogen-free extract, 98
  as measure of feed value, 106
Carcass quality, goals for, 70-71
Carotene (*See* Vitamins)
Castration, 152-153
Cattle dealers, 264-265
Cattle diseases (*See* Diseases, cattle)
Cattle feeders, 11-13
  acreage control, 16
  as market for purebreds, 22
Cattle feeding (*See also* Feeder cattle)
  fitting program to local conditions, 200-202
  profits from, 166-171
    gains, 168
    manure value, 168-171
    margin, 167-168
    securing cattle, 166
Cattle lice, 235-236
Cattle lots, 225-226
Cattle scab, 239-240
Cattle yards, 225-226
Central feeder cattle markets, 17-18, 50
Charbray cattle, 42-43
Charolais cattle, 33
  crossbred with Brahman, 42-43
Chewing the cud, 89
Choice cattle, 78-79
  selling, 278-279
Chromosomes, 293-294
  segregation, 294-295
Circling disease, 253
Classes of slaughter cattle, 269-270
Climate factor in beef program, 16-17
Clippers and saws in dehorning, 149-150
Closed formula feed tag, 108
Coccidiosis, 241
Collings brokers, 20
Colostrum, 142
Commercial grade of cattle, grain for, 84-85
Commercial mixed feeds, 108-109
Commission firm, 276-277
Common cattle grub, 233
Common grade of cattle, 80

Diseases, cattle (*Cont.*):
  infectious (*Cont.*):
    warts, 250
  noninfectious ailments:
    bloat, 118-119, 255-256
    X disease, 255
    prevention program, 231-232
    sanitation in calf pens, 144
    screw worm infestation, 152
    virus diarrhea, 247
    Texas fever, 239
Distiller's grains, 182
Distributing beef, 286-287
Dominant and recessive characters, 294
Dressing percentage, heifers, 84
Dry lands (*See* Arid lands)
Dry lot feeding, 16
  of breeding herd, 127-132
    amount of feed required, 131-132
    grazing winter pasture and crop residues, 129-130
    wintering rations, 130-131
    danger of deficiencies, 127
    Purdue Cow Supplement, 127-128
Dwarfism, 72-73

E

Ear notches, 154
Ear tags, 156
Elastrator, 153
Electric dehorners, 146
Environment as factor in breed selection, 22
Equipment:
  feeding, 211-218
  feed storage, 227-228
  fences, 226
  loading chutes, 219
  mechanized feeding systems, 212-213, 228-229
  planning beef program, 17
  restraint, 220-223
External parasites, 232-240
Eye diseases, 23

F

Fancy cattle, 78
Farms, profits from, and acreage control, 50
Fat cattle (*See* Slaughter cattle)
Fats, 92
  animal, as livestock feeds, 179
  as measure of food value, 106
Fattening ability (*See* Growth ability)
Fattening cattle (*See* Feeder cattle)

Feed:
  according to grade, 85
  antibiotics, 96
  availability of:
    as factor in beef program, 15-16, 261
    as factor in breed selection, 49-50
  balancing the ration, 98-99
  in cattle fattening, 8-11, 83-86, 171-186 (*See also* Feeder cattle)
    dry roughages, 171-173
    grains, 177-180
    minerals, 186
    proteins, 181-186
    silages, 173-177
    starting cattle on feed, 197-198
    vitamins, 186-187
  and cattle prices, 283
  cheap sources of protein, 92-93
  classification of, 97-98
    concentrates, 98
    legume roughages, 97-98
    non-legume roughages, 98
  commercial mixed, 108-109
  consideration in beef progam, 15
  corn stalk silage, 128-129, 176
  cost of and supply of beef, 258-259
  in dry lot feeding of cow herd, 127-132
  factors affecting quality of, 107-108
  fiber and nitrogen-free extract, 98
  food nutrients, 92-96 (*See also* Nutrients, food)
  and growth rate, 70
  hand feeding beef calves, 94
  for high quality slaughter beef, 83
  hormones added to, 96
  measuring value of, 102-107
    carbohydrates and fats, 106
    digestible nutrients, 102-105
    palatability, 106-107
    proteins, 106
    vitamins and minerals, 106
  nutrient requirements, beef cattle, *table*, 99-102
  pasture feeding for breeding herd, 114-127
    grasses, 119-120
    legumes, 118-119
    mixtures of legumes and grasses, 120-121
  preparation of, 193
  prices, 85
  in purebred production, 14
  rations for wintering beef cows, 130-131
  for replacement heifers, 161-162

336

Heterosis, 295
Hide brands, 153-154
High choice slaughter grade, 79
Highly finished cattle, 199
High-moisture grains, 180
Hormel & Company, 45
Hormones, implanting, 189
Hormones in feed, 96, 187
Horn brands, 156
Horn flies, 237
Horns:
 removing, 144-151 (See also
  Dehorning)
 training and polishing for shows, 315
Horse flies, 238-239
Housing for beef cattle, 208-210
Hybrid, 295
Hybrid vigor, 295

I

Illinois, University of, 44
Inbreeding, 296, 300
India, cattle from, 20-21, 35-36
Inferior grade of cattle, 80
Inheritance, laws of, 293-296
 chromosomes and genes, 293-294
 chromosome segregation, 294-295
 dominant and recessive characters,
  294
 grading and purebreeding, 295
 hybrid, 295
  heterosis, 295
 inbreeding and linebreeding, 296
Internal parasites, 240-242
Iowa State College, 128, 172-173, 185

J

Johnes disease, 253-254

K

Kansas State College:
 antibiotics, 189
 feeding growing heifers, 162
King Ranch, 37

L

Lasater, E. C., 41
Lasater, Tom, 41-42
Legumes:
 common pasture legumes, listed, 119

Legumes (Cont.):
 defined, 97-98
 hay, 127
 hays for feeder cattle, 171-172
 in pasture feeding, 118-119
  danger of bloat, 118
  when used with grasses, 119
 silage, 173-175
 sources of nutrients, 93, 96
Leptospirosis, 251-252
Lethal abnormalities, 73-74
Linebreeding, 296, 297-299
Linseed oil meal, 181
Listerellosis, 253
Loading chutes, 219
Long-yearlings, 77
Low grade cattle, selling for slaughter,
 280
Lumpy jaw, 253

M

Major minerals, 95
Male reproductive organs, 292
Manure:
 amount and value of, produced by
  fattening cattle, 170
 loss of value, 169
 preventing plant food losses, 169
 profit to cattle feeders, 12-13
 value of, as profit in cattle feeding,
  168-171
Margin (See also Profits):
 prices of feeder and slaughter cattle,
  85
 profits from, in cattle feeding,
  167-168
Market classes, cattle showing, 307
Market conditions:
 and establishing breeding herd, 50-51
 future outlook and selection of
  feeder cattle, 85-86
 planning beef program, 17-18
 sources of information, 268-269
 supply and demand, 258-262
Marketing:
 factors affecting price, 280-281
 feeder cattle, 262-269
 slaughter cattle, 269-283
  choice and prime steers, 278-279
  commission firms, 274, 276
  number in feed lots, 281
  order buyers, 276
  seasonal price trends, 278
  speculators, 277
Marking, 153-157
 ear notches, 154

Roughages:
  average composition of, 103-104
  bacterial action in the rumen,
    89, 90-91
  defined, 97-98
  dry, for feeder cattle, 171-173
  legume roughages, 93, 96
    defined, 97-98
  nonlegume roughages, 98
  in ruminant stomach, 88-91
  use of low quality, 84
  in wintering cow herd, 127-129
Rubber bands:
  in castration, 153
  in dehorning, 150-151
Rumen, 88-90
  bacterial action in, 89, 90-91
  of calves, 91
Ruminant stomach, 88-91
  abomasm, 90
  omasum, 90
  reticulum, 90
  rumen, 88-90
Rye:
  for feeder cattle, 178
  palatability of, 106

S

Salt, 110
  added to protein supplement, 116-117
  and pasture feeding, 115
Sanitation in calf pens, 144
Santa Gertrudis cattle, 37-38
Sarcoptic mange, 239-240
Score card:
  Aberdeen-Angus, 64-65
  Brahmans, 65-67
  for feeder cattle, 81-82
  Hereford breeding cattle, 62-63
  Shorthorn bull, 61-62
  slaughter cattle, 270-271
  unified, 60-61
Scotch Highland cattle, 34
  crossbred with Herefords, 45
Scours, 144, 159-160, 250-251
Screw worm, 232-233
Seasonal price trends, 278
Sex classifications of cattle, 77-78
Seeding, mixtures for pastures, 120-121
Self-feeders, 199-200
Shades, 211
Shipping fever, 245-246
Shorthorn cattle, 30
  bull score card, 61-62
  crossbred:
    with Brahman, 37-38

Shorthorn cattle *(Cont.)*:
  crossbred *(Cont.)*:
    with Herefords and Angus cattle,
      45
    with Herefords and Brahmans,
      41-42
  as milking breed, 29
  Polled Shorthorn cattle, 32
Short-yearlings, 77
Shows, beef cattle, 304
  classifications, 304-307
  fitting animals, 307-309
  sportsmanship, 324
Show cattle:
  castrating, 152
  dehorning, 146
  feed for, 307-309
  grooming, 315-323
    clipping, 320-321
    curling the hair, 317-319
    fluffing out the switch, 323
    washing, 315-316
  health certificates, 323
  management at fair, 323-324
  marking, 154-155
  training, 309-315
    horns, 315
  trimming feet, 313-315
Shrinkage, 274
Silage:
  average composition of, 105
  defined, 173
  for fattening cattle, 173-177
  legumes, 127
  moisture content, 174, 177, 180
  supplement to pasture feeding, 114
  use of preservative, 174-175
  wilted silage, 176
Silo, trench, 227
Simple stomach, 88
Sires, herd (*See* Herd sires)
Size, as factor in stock selection, 52-53
Slaughter cattle (*See also* Feeder
    cattle):
  breed selection, 20
  damaged carcasses, 283-285
  feeding according to grade, 271-273
  grades of, 79-80, 269-270
  marketing, 269-283
    through commission firm, 274-276
    cooperative marketing, 277-278
    for further finishing, 276-277
    on grade and yield, 274
    to private buyers, 277
    selling to packer or packer buyer,
      274
    when to sell, 278-280
  prices of, and selling feeder cattle,
    268